D0991212

SCHIZOPHRENICS IN THE COMMUNITY

SOCIOLOGY SERIES

John F. Cuber, *Editor*
Alfred C. Clarke, *Associate Editor*

SCHIZOPHRENICS IN THE COMMUNITY

AN EXPERIMENTAL STUDY IN THE PREVENTION OF HOSPITALIZATION

Benjamin Pasamanick, M.D., *Illinois Department of Mental Health*
Frank R. Scarpitti, Ph.D., *Rutgers University*
Simon Dinitz, Ph.D., *Ohio State University*

With the collaboration of
Joseph Albini, Ph.D., *Wayne State University*
Mark Lefton, Ph.D., *Western Reserve University*

NEW YORK
APPLETON-CENTURY-CROFTS
Division of Meredith Publishing Company

6106-1

Library of Congress Card Number: 66-25455

PRINTED IN THE UNITED STATES OF AMERICA

E69400

FOREWORD

Occasionally a research investigation brings forth positive findings which shorten the distance between the question and the answer.

The findings of such a study—*Schizophrenics in the Community: An Experimental Study in the Prevention of Hospitalization*—are reported in this volume. Their implications emphasize the relationship between the point of the arrow and the feathers of its shaft. The feathers give the arrowhead direction into the target.

For the national mental health program, the target is the establishment of a community-based mental health services program providing a continuity of care in treating the mentally ill.

This study of an experimental home care program for the treatment of schizophrenics provides specific scientific evidence that many schizophrenics—"the feared, the shunned, the isolated"—need not be hospitalized if they are adequately treated in their home communities.

Additionally, the implications of the findings offer indisputable support for the validity of the concept of the community mental health center, its constellation of community based mental health services and the involvement of entire communities in the national mental health program.

The study substantiates the need for community services—as contrasted to 24-hour hospital care, whether in a state mental hospital or a community general hospital. Results indicate that hospitalization, by and of itself, cannot achieve results as efficacious as can a program of services that includes a variety of treatment modalities adapted to the individual patient's immediate need.

Schizophrenics in the Community was a carefully controlled study undertaken by the Research Division of the Columbus Psychiatric Institute and supported by the National Institute of Mental Health. The walls of the mental health research laboratory have widened to include the world and the methodology of this study vividly illustrates that fact. The investigators were concerned with the schizophrenic patients at home and in the hospital, with the effects of drug medication and medication by placebo, with the effects of the patients on their families and of the families on the patients. They also worked closely with the public health nurses whose support of both the patients and their families played such a significant role in the success of home care treatment. The investigation encompassed all phases of the patients' environments.

The authors of the study state categorically that, "In the absence of considerable deterioration, an acute episode, or grossly exaggerated symptoms, no special reason exists for keeping schizophrenic patients hospitalized."

This, when more than one-half of the mental patients currently occupying hospital beds are schizophrenic, is a statement of extraordinary significance. It not only gives scientific basis for hope to the schizophrenic himself that his existence can be more free and less disordered; it also has implications that portend the success of the community-based mental health program, the eventual reduction of the cost of patient care, and a possible breakthrough in solving the problem of providing sufficient mental health manpower to deliver high quality care to anyone who requests or needs it. The results imply, further, that similar modalities of treatment may be efficacious when applied to the elderly patient enclosed in the symptoms of senility and to the patient who has been diagnosed as mentally retarded.

As the Director of the National Institute of Mental Health, personally and professionally involved in the development, utilization, and acceptance of community mental health centers across the United States, I highly recommend the report of this study to your attention. Unfortunately, the investigators have not found a cure for schizophrenia, but they have found a key to its control and treatment—outside the hospital and inside the home.

Stanley F. Yolles, M.D.
Director
National Institute of Mental Health

PREFACE

In his landmark message to Congress on "Mental Illness and Mental Retardation," on Feb. 5, 1963, the late President Kennedy strongly urged a change in existing practices in the care of the mentally ill. The message decried the neglect in the treatment and prevention of psychiatric disorders and the corresponding inadequacies of present facilities, the shortages of trained staff, the dehumanizing effects of massive institutions, and the custodial nature of many mental hospitals. Despite the huge expenditure of 1.8 billion dollars in direct public outlays for services to the mentally ill, 45 percent of the patients in state mental hospitals have been in continuous residence for 10 years or more; the average length of hospitalization for schizophrenia is still 11 years.

Optimistically, and with a view to stimulating concerted action by federal, state, local, and private agencies, the late President said:

> I propose a national mental health program to assist in the inauguration of a wholly new emphasis and approach to care for the mentally ill. This approach relies primarily upon the new knowledge and new drugs acquired and developed in recent years which make it possible for most of the mentally ill to be successfully and quickly treated in their own communities and returned to a useful place in society.
>
> These breakthroughs have rendered obsolete the traditional methods of treatment which imposed upon the mentally ill a social quarantine, a prolonged or permanent confinement in huge, unhappy mental hospitals where they were out of sight and forgotten.

In order to prevent the alienation of patients from family, friends, and community by prolonged confinement in mental hospitals, this new approach would involve the creation of comprehensive community mental health centers. These centers would serve to focus community resources and interest in all aspects of mental health care. Specific functions would include diagnostic and evaluation services, emergency care units, in- and outpatient treatment, day and night care facilities, foster home placements, and mental health information and education programs.

Whether or not the comprehensive community mental health center will replace the mental hospital in the foreseeable future or, even as projected, reduce the present 530,000 mental hospital population by half within a decade, is subject to some dispute. The ability and willingness of families to tolerate deviant or asocial family members in the highly complex urban environment remains problematic. Apart from family considerations, the entire conception of this community mental health center program rests largely on the prolonged utilization of the newer drug therapies to alleviate the acute symptoms of mental illness so that patients may continue to live at home and perform the ordinary and necessary activities of daily life.[1]

Although there have been some demonstrations and even a few operational projects in Europe and in the United States, no controlled test of the efficacy of home care treatment as a substitute for hospitalization for acute and chronic schizophrenia has been reported. This monograph describes the first such attempt. It details the origin, antecedents, design, implementation, results, and implications of an experimental research program in the prevention of hospitalization of schizophrenic patients at the time of or very shortly after their admission to a typical state mental hospital serving a metropolitan area. It also describes the same program as applied to an ambulatory schizophrenic population in the same community. For both the state hospital and the ambulatory schizophrenics the home care treatment program consisted primarily of psychiatric and public health nursing care and appropriate drug medication.

In all, 152 state hospital schizophrenic patients were involved in the study. All met the age, residence, diagnosis, and family criteria for study inclusion. Of this total number, 57 were randomly assigned to a drug home care group, 41 to a placebo (inert or nonactive drug) group, and 54 to a hospital control group. There were also 29 ambulatory

[1] Benjamin Pasamanick, Frank R. Scarpitti, Mark Lefton, Simon Dinitz, John J. Wernert, and Harold McPheeters, "Home Versus Hospital Care for Schizophrenics," JAMA, 187 (January 18, 1964), 177-178.

schizophrenic patients in a drug home care group and 23 in a placebo group. Except for the difference in medication—active or inert—all home care patients whether state hospital or ambulatory were seen regularly by public health nurses in their own homes and less frequently by the staff psychiatrist. Their contacts with the psychiatrist as well as with the psychologist and the staff social worker were primarily, but by no means exclusively, for evaluative rather than therapeutic or other purposes. The home visitation of the nurses plus the drug medication given the patients were the principal ingredients in the treatment program. The control patients were cared for in the state hospital and, except for evaluating their functioning, were not subject to any treatment by the project staff.

The state hospital subjects were involved in the home care program for 6 to 30 months. During this lengthy study period, over 77 percent of the drug home care patients as compared to only some 34 percent of the placebo home care cases remained continuously at home. According to our estimates, using the hospital controls as the "natural group," the 57 drug patients were saved over 4800 days of hospitalization and the 41 placebo cases over 1150 inpatient days. Equally important was the finding that even after an average of 83 days of initial hospitalization, the controls failed (required rehospitalization) more often after discharge than did the drug home care cases without any initial inpatient treatment. The results also convincingly showed that home care patients functioned as well or better without hospitalization as did the controls after hospital discharge. The areas of functioning included two types of psychiatric evaluations, a battery of four psychological tests, and the appraisals of "significant others" or responsible relatives.

Despite the tremendous difficulties encountered in its implementation, this carefully designed experimental study confirmed our original hypothesis that home care for schizophrenic patients is *feasible*, that the combination of drug therapy and public health nurses' home visitations is *effective* in preventing hospitalization, and that home care is at least as good a method of treatment as hospitalization by any or all criteria, and probably superior by most.

Even apart from these striking results, which we believe to be both reliable and valid, are the implications which can be drawn from this work. These implications extend beyond the confines of the study itself and its immediate consequences. This study, for example, permits certain interpretations about the nature and management of schizophrenia and other neuropsychiatric and related impairments and their treatment. Just as the treatment model in tuberculosis became the basis for this home care investigation, so the latter has relevance as a model for the problems of aging and of mental retardation, to mention but two, and on a somewhat different level, for chronic alcoholism and other addictions. In theory, the home care model should have utility for various chronic conditions which impair social and psychological functioning to the point that the afflicted become burdensome members to society and require institutionalization. An extension of this home care model to other such chronic conditions now seems warranted, at least at the demonstration program level.

This home care study is also pertinent for the emerging community mental health centers. Not only are continuous, coordinated, and comprehensive services desirable, but also this investigation has indicated the need for a research framework in which each component of these new programs can be tested and evaluated before its inclusion and retention becomes a vested interest. In this respect, this home care study has also raised the issue of the relationship of health to welfare and educational services and how to obtain greater coordination of these in the treatment of community patients.

Perhaps the most significant general implication of this investigation concerns the selection, training, orientation, and education of staff for the future rather than the past programs. Present professional roles are, in view of the direction health care is likely to move, confused and ambiguous. The training of mental health professionals from psychiatrists to psychiatric nurses and social workers, is archaic and maybe even destructive in terms of the goals to be achieved. This study clearly shows what might some day emerge in the way of the recruitment of professional persons not now involved in mental health care, the upgrading of some of the present mental health professionals, the shifting and reorganization of professional roles, and the creation of new settings in which more effective care for more people becomes more of a reality.

Plan of the Book

Chapter 1 concerns the development of the community psychiatry and mental health center movement in the United States. Recent legislation, including the Community Mental Health Act of 1963, and its precursors are described. The second part of this chapter deals with the growth, stagnation and renaissance of the state mental hospital as a treatment rather than as a custodial setting. The various forces leading from the mental hospital back to community treatment including the new role of the federal government, the nature of psychiatric practice and the types of practitioners, the cumulative impact of psychodynamic theories, the growth of the therapeutic community and "open" hospital, and the drug revolution, are discussed in some detail.

Chapter 2 is concerned with some of the antecedent research and demonstration projects which are background for the home care study. This earlier work is divided into three major streams: epidemiological studies centering around unreported and untreated mental illness in the community, posthospital outcome studies, and previous investigations focusing on the prevention of the hospitalization of ambulatory patients.

In Chapter 3, our Louisville home care study design is presented as well as some of the modifications which were required at the outset and which made the achievement of positive results all the more difficult to obtain. These modifications included relocation of the project to another city from the one originally selected, patient selection changes, and alterations in the testing and evaluation procedures.

One of the most fascinating aspects of the study concerned the recruitment, training, duties and responsibilities, and operating procedures and problems confronting the various staff professionals. The role, problems, and trial-and-error solutions eventually arrived at by all members of the team in their respective professional spheres make up the bulk of Chapter 4. Special attention is paid to the public health nurses, whose role in this study program was critical; and to the staff psychiatrist who was confronted by the need to develop a method of mass care for patients in settings far removed from the optimal patient-doctor relationship extolled in most if not all training programs. Descriptions of the work involvement and contributions of the staff psychologist, social worker, and study director are also included in this chapter.

In Chapter 5 the patients are described—demographically, medically, in terms of their previous psychiatric treatment, and in their psychological and social performance. In all, over 20 separate characteristics of the state hospital patients are presented.

The most important section is Chapter 6 in which the results of this home care investigation are detailed. A subsection deals with the differences between the successes and hospitalized patients in both the drug and placebo home care groups.

Chapter 7 is devoted entirely to a description of the ambulatory schizophrenic patients and to the results obtained with these patients. At all points possible, comparisons are made with the state hospital patients in terms of background characteristics and treatment outcome.

Chapter 8 is different from any of the others. To illustrate the method, problems, and outcome, a number of typical cases from the patient registry are presented. As much as possible these cases reflect success and failure, state hospital and ambulatory origin, drug and placebo, male and female, white and nonwhite, and middle and lower socioeconomic status patients. In addition, these cases attempt to include many variations in the types of problems presented. These case presentations serve to make concrete and to personalize the quantitative findings.

The volume ends with Chapter 9 in which the study is briefly recapitulated, the results restated, and the implications, both specific and general, described and discussed.

Acknowledgments

It has now been some five years since the Institute Treatment Center was established in Louisville, Kentucky and charged with carrying out a rather daring experiment in the treatment of the mentally ill. Treating acutely ill schizophrenic patients at home rather than in the mental hospital had never really been tried in the United States. It was such a controversial idea that many knowledgeable members of the mental health community opposed the attempt and one state actually refused to permit the experiment to be done within its state mental health system. But, it was done, and successfully so, because many people had faith in the feasibility of the project and cooperated with it. We want to thank some of them now.

The project was sponsored by the National Institute of Mental Health through a grant (MH 07874) made to the Psychiatric Institute and Hospital, Department of Psychiatry, The Ohio State University. Various members of the staff of the Research Division of the Columbus Psychiatric Institute and Hospital contributed to the overall planning, design, and administration of the study. Of special merit was the work of Dr. Mark Lefton who was primarily responsible for the research instruments. He also worked closely with the Louisville staff during the first two years of the project. Dr. Athan Karras, also of the Research Division, devised the psychological test battery, served as consultant for all matters having to do with the psychological tests, and rendered invaluable assistance in the analysis of these data. Don Smelzer and Paul Bayless were responsible for the computer and data reduction work. They wrote and ran the computer program. Gail Behymer was invaluable in her administrative role in Columbus. Patricia Fulton assumed these duties in the last year of the study and continued the efficient operation of the program. She was also responsible for much of the tabulation and computation work. Julie Smith and Barbara Cole typed the manuscript and its many revisions. Mrs. Smith also contributed significantly in various other phases of the study.

Our gratitude to former Commissioner Harold McPheeters of the Kentucky Department of Mental Health cannot be expressed in words. Had he not offered to allow the study to be done in his state and within his department, it obviously would have not been done at all. His willingness to support innovation and experiment, his active participation in the program, and his thoughtful advice and counsel contributed greatly to the success of the home care study.

Other members of the Louisville professional community were also helpful in getting the project started and seeing that it was accepted as a legitimate treatment agency. In addition to Dr. McPheeters, Dr. Walter Fox, former Superintendent of Central State Hospital, Dr. Spafford Ackerly, Chairman, Department of Psychiatry, University of Louisville, Dr. A. L. Lincoln, former Dean, Kent School of Social Work, University of Louisville, and Dr. Frank Vicroy, Professor of Sociology, University of Louisville permitted their names to be used on project stationery as consultants. It goes without saying that such a distinguished list of "sponsors" helped to legitimize the study in the eyes of the local community. The members of the staff of Central State Hospital especially Drs. Mehmet Arik, George Guanche, and David Stewart, who referred and helped screen patients, the physicians at Louisville General Hospital, private psychiatrists and general practitioners who referred patients, and the many local social workers attached to agencies which helped our patients have all earned our sincere gratitude and respect.

However, the real heroes of this project were the men and women responsible for its day-to-day operation. Operating in new and undefined roles, only grudgingly accepted by their professional peers, and attempting to do a job defined by many as impossible, the project staff rose to the challenge and with missionary zeal and devotion, performed outstandingly. The project succeeded, and the feasibility of home care was tested, because these people gave unselfishly of their talent and energy: Dr. John J. Wernert, psychiatrist, Gene Priddy, psychologist, Ann Davis and Peggy Ann O'Brien, social workers, Elizabeth Baker, Raphaline Kelley, Mary Jane Raverty, Jeanette Sterchi, and Jane Williams, public health nurses, Virginia Immerman, office manager, Mary Lou Miller, Gloria Buchanan, and Dorothy McDermott, office staff, and Dr. Joseph Albini, coordinator of the study during its last year.

No less heroes, though, were the 226 patients and their families who participated in the home care program during its nearly three years of operation. The willingness of the vast majority of them to cooperate with the Institute Treatment Center staff contributed immeasurably to the success of the project. Indeed, there would have been no project had the patients and their families been unwilling to participate in what undoubtedly seemed to them an unorthodox method of treatment. Special appreciation is also due Smith, Kline and French Laboratories and Sandoz, Inc. for furnishing all medications free of charge. These journals permitted us to use passages and exerpts from previously published articles by these authors: *The Journal of the American Medical Association (JAMA)*, Volume 187, January 18, 1964, pp. 177–181; the *Archives of General Psychiatry*, Volume 10, February, 1964, pp. 143–154; the *American Journal of Orthopsychiatry*, Volume XXXV, January, 1965, pp. 1–9; and the *American Journal of Nursing*, Volume 65, June, 1965, pp. 89–95.

Our thanks go to Dr. Daniel Wilner of U.C.L.A., who served as a consultant early in the study. Our due appreciation is also extended to the office of the Vice-President, Research, Ohio State University; and to John F. Cuber and Alfred C. Clarke, colleagues, and with Jack Burton, Editors of the Appleton-Century-Crofts Sociology Series, for their advice and encouragement during the preparation of this manuscript.

B. P.
F. R. S.
S. D.

CONTENTS

1

THE ROAD TO THE COMMUNITY MENTAL HEALTH CENTER

The concept "community psychiatry," and its incorporation into the comprehensive community mental health center for the care and treatment of the mentally ill, are recent and radical innovations in psychiatry. A generation ago, even perhaps a decade ago, community psychiatry and comprehensive health center programs were relatively unknown to all but a few of the avant-garde in the discipline. Although still only vaguely understood by many in terms of goals, content, and approach, community care of the mentally ill has nearly become a cult. Its adherents can hardly restrain their enthusiasm for this "new type of health facility." And, considering the all-inclusive components of the programs subsumed under this approach, it is difficult, indeed, to restrain one's enthusiasm.[1]

The community mental health center movement owes much of its initial impetus to the intervention of the federal government on behalf of improved mental health treatment programs and facilities. Spurred originally by the inability or unwillingness of many states to support and finance mental health programs, and by the grossly inadequate facilities available for treating the large number of military personnel discharged for psychiatric and medical reasons, Congress enacted a series of health and welfare laws including the National Mental Health Act of 1946. Under the provisions of this act, federal grants were made available to the states to aid them in originating and developing mental health pro-

[1] Leopold Bellak (ed.), *Handbook of Community Psychiatry and Community Mental Health*, New York: Grune & Stratton, 1964; H. G. Whittington, "The Third Psychiatric Revolution—Really? A Consideration of Principles and Practices in Community Psychiatry," *Comm. Men. Hlth. J.*, **1** (Spring, 1965), 73–80, and Gerald Caplan, *An Approach to Community Mental Health*, London: Tavistock Publications, 1961.

grams outside of state hospitals. In addition, the National Institute of Mental Health was established by the act as the focal point and coordinating agency for mental health activities. Since then the National Institute of Mental Health has supported both extra- and intramural research and the training of mental health personnel, and has helped the individual states to plan and institute new, expanded, or improved programs and to build new facilities, particularly for mental health research. NIMH support by Congress, a mere pittance at its inception, has increased nearly every year and in 1965 amounted to the handsome but still quite inadequate sum of 223 million dollars of which 35 million dollars were earmarked for the construction of community mental health centers. In 1965 Congress appropriated additional funds to help in the staffing of these centers.

The major ideas and minimal programs inherent in the community mental health center concept had been more or less outlined by the Expert Committee on Mental Health of the World Health Organization. Specifically, this group recommended many of the essentials—outpatient and part-time treatment, for example—now universally included in the definition of a community mental health center program. Beginning in 1954, some states attempted through the passage of community mental health service acts to expand and operate neuropsychiatric services outside the mental hospital system. New York led the way; by 1964, 19 other states had followed suit.

In 1955 Congress reentered the picture. It enacted the Mental Health Study Act under which was created the Joint Commission on Mental Illness and Health. The function of the Joint Commission, consisting of representatives of 36 national and state organizations, was to survey and evaluate the status of mental health programs and resources and to recommend a blueprint for action. Ten reports dealing with the definitions of health and illness, the economics of mental illness, manpower trends, community resources, epidemiological studies, and attitudes and problems, resulted from specialized studies commissioned by and were or will be published under Joint Commission sponsorship. The mental health care blueprint is contained in the final report of the Joint Commission, *Action for Mental Health,* which was submitted to Congress in 1960, five years after the inception of the Commission.[2]

[2] *Action for Mental Health,* (Final Report of the Joint Commission on Mental Illness and Health), New York: Basic Books, 1961.

In addition to specific recommendations regarding manpower, facilities, costs, and research, the tone of the report left little doubt that, rightly or wrongly, the community care adherents had won their point. Although inevitably calling for the improvement of state hospitals and their conversion into combined chronic disease centers, as well as for restricting their size to fewer than 1000 beds, the main thrust of the proposals was on the community care level. The blueprint called for the establishment of one community mental health clinic per 50,000 population. These clinics, to serve all age groups, would theoretically reduce the need of many persons for repeated and prolonged hospitalization. In addition, and to further emphasize the movement away from the state hospital, the report urged the establishment of psychiatric units in those general hospitals having 100 or more beds as a second facility to the community clinic.

> It is the consensus of the Mental Health Study that definitive care for patients with major mental illness should be given if possible, or for as long as possible, in a psychiatric unit of a general hospital and then, on a longer-term basis, in a specialized mental hospital organized as an intensive psychiatric treatment center.[3]

There were, of course, many other recommendations of the same import. The mental hospital, it was assumed, had become archaic and its usefulness was to be limited to chronic cases who had failed to respond to community care. Little wonder, then, that state hospital system people were extremely displeased with the general tenor and specific recommendations in the report. The principle argument of the opponents of the blueprint was that these proposals, if and when implemented, would drain, attract, and lure already scarce funds and personnel into community centers and away from the hospitals which are chronically handicapped in these respects, even without this competition. Further, the treatment in these new settings would merely *delay* rather than *prevent* the need for the hospitalization of many patients.

Whatever the merits of these criticisms of the *Action for Mental Health* proposals, this blueprint was widely acclaimed, and widely endorsed by professional and lay groups. Finally, the late President Kennedy sent a message to Congress in February, 1963, requesting

[3] *Ibid.*, p. xv.

enabling legistlation by Congress to implement the Joint Commission recommendations. Said this historic message, in part:

> Central to a new mental health program is comprehensive community care. Merely pouring Federal funds into a continuation of the outmoded type of institutional care which now prevails would make little difference. We need a new type of health facility, one which would return mental health care to the main stream of American medicine, and at the same time upgrade mental health services. . . .
>
> While the essential concept of the comprehensive community mental health center is new, the separate elements which would be combined in it are presently found in many communities: diagnostic and evaluative services, emergency psychiatric units, outpatient services, inpatient services, day and night care, foster home care, rehabilitation, consultative services to other community agencies, and mental health information and education. . . .
>
> These comprehensive community mental health centers should become operational at the earliest feasible date. I recommend that we make a major demonstration effort in the early years of the program to be expanded to all major communities as the necessary manpower and facilities become available.[4]

Within a year after this eloquent message urging a reorientation in the direction of mental health services, the 88th Congress passed Public Law 88-164 in October, 1963. This act authorized the federal expenditure of 150 million dollars for the 3 fiscal years, 1965–1967, for the construction of community mental health centers in the various states. The federal expenditures of 35 million dollars in 1965, 50 million dollars in 1966, and 65 million dollars in 1967 will constitute from one-third to two-thirds of the total cost of construction. The remainder of the funds, of course, will be supplied on a matching basis by the states or other local agencies. This act, and other congressional authorizations to the states in 1963 and 1964 to aid in the preparation of statewide plans for these centers, represented the first time in our history when all states were constructing new facilities and formulating and implementing mental health programs simultaneously.

In May, 1964, specific regulations concerning the nature of and services to be included in the comprehensive community mental health center were issued. In order to qualify for construction funds a center

[4] John F. Kennedy, "Mental Illness and Mental Retardation," Special Message to the 88th Congress, February 5, 1963.

must provide a minimum of five *essential* services: inpatient services, outpatient services, partial hospitalization (including day care as the minimum), emergency 24-hour services in at least one of the three preceding services, and consultation and education services to community agencies and professional personnel. In addition to these essential activities, an *adequate* center would also include: diagnostic services, rehabilitative activities such as vocational and educational programs, pre- and aftercare services, training, and research and evaluation.[5]

In theory, adequate community treatment programs must meet the criteria of comprehensiveness, coordination, and continuity.[6] By comprehensive is meant that a full range of services is available to all age groups across different diagnostic categories. The second criterion of coordination, while somewhat overlapping with the criterion of comprehensiveness, refers more directly to the need to develop a central agency or clearinghouse facility so that agency participation is better focused. Thus, for example, it is presently possible and quite likely that several agencies serve the same person or family and do so largely independently of one another. Focusing some of these activities through a mental health center is in and of itself a worthy goal. Coordination also refers to the relationship of the mental health center with urban renewal, economic

[5] Community Mental Health Centers Act of 1963, Title II, Public Law 88–164. Regulations, *Federal Register*, May 6, 1964.

[6] These specific criteria of comprehensiveness, coordination, and continuity are defined in section 54.212 of the Regulations as follows:

(c) *Criteria of program.* As used in this section, a program for providing at least the essential elements of comprehensive mental health services must take into consideration the needs of all age groups, assure continuity of care for patients and assure that the relationship between the individual elements of the services meets the following criteria:

(i) That any person eligible for treatment within any one element of service will also be eligible for treatment within any other element of service;

(ii) That any patient within any one element can and will be transferred without delay to any other element (provided that adequate space is available) whenever such a transfer is indicated by the patient's clinical needs;

(iii) The clinical information concerning a patient which was obtained within one element be made available to those responsible for that patient's treatment within any other element;

(iv) That those responsible for a patient's care within one element can, when practicable and when not clinically contraindicated, continue to care for that patient within any of the other elements;

See also, James A. Knight and Winborn E. Davis, *Manual for the Comprehensive Community Mental Health Clinic*, Springfield, Ill.: Charles C Thomas, 1964.

opportunity, delinquency, and other programs. The third objective of continuity of treatment simply means that a person should be able to move easily and freely through the various services such as diagnostic to inpatient or aftercare, or inpatient to home care with sheltered workshop or vocational training or retraining experience. All too often at present persons requiring care are referred from one independent facility to another to the point of getting lost in the byways of agency operation. This referral process, and the inevitable waiting, is not only disenchanting and destructive to patients, but also costly in time and money.

With these guidelines of adequate and essential services, comprehensive, coordinated, and continuous, the Joint Information service of the American Psychiatric Association and the National Association for Mental Health in 1964 surveyed some 234 psychiatric programs and facilities and found that none met all of these standards. In a subsequent report, 11 of the most comprehensive were described in some detail.[7] There is no question but that a great many more centers will in the very near future approximate the model implicit in the act of 1963.

The rapidity of this revolution in the care of the mentally ill, disenchantment with the mental hospital and commitment to the community center as the new hope for the future, is little short of astonishing. In fairness, this movement is a tribute not nearly as much to faith in community programs *per se* as to a revolt against the mental hospital as a treatment center. The mental hospital may perhaps never again have the leading mental health role it once held. To understand the dynamics of this revolution, and of its cult-like aspects, it is necessary to trace the history of the state mental hospital system and the social conditions which gave it life and meaning and, by the same token, the altered social circumstances which have led to its denigration and lesser role in mental health care.

THE MENTAL HOSPITAL

Every society—from the smallest and most cohesive to the largest, most heterogeneous, and sophisticated—is perennially confronted with the problem of managing its deviant, disruptive, and dependent mem-

[7] Raymond Glasscote, David Sanders, H. M. Forstenzer, and A. R. Foley, *The Community Mental Health Center: An Analysis of Existing Models*, American Psychiatric Association, 1964.

bers.[8] And each society has reacted to this problem in its own characteristic "style" and manner, and in conformity with its values, logic, and structure. There are a number of aspects in which the "style" of the reaction may vary: in the definition of what constitutes deviancy and disruption, in the content of behavior deemed aberrant, in the degree of acceptance of such aberrations, in the extent to which a society may be able to institutionalize disruptive behavior, in its sanction system, and on the treatment or care level.

In western history the "style" changed radically in the nineteenth century. At first, and for a very long time thereafter, the acutely or chronically deviant—the mentally ill, psychically handicapped, the mentally retarded, and others—shared a fate much like that of such dependent and noncontributing persons as orphans, illegitimate children, and widows. Prior to the nineteenth century, such dependents and deviants remained mainly the responsibility of the family and the local community.

It is a fact, of course, that the need for custodial institutions for the mentally ill and for other deviants as well existed in some of the larger cities prior to the nineteenth century. Historically, public care for the mentally ill can be traced all the way back to the first known house for lunatics in Byzantium in the fourth century A.D. Thereafter, history records sporadic community attempts at providing care for the insane as, for example, in Cologne where monks began to care for the mentally ill in 560 A.D. A few asylums for the insane are also known to have existed in communities in the Middle East and in England before 700 A.D. By the thirteenth century Spain and Germany also had such institutions. Each succeeding historical period witnessed the building of a few more asylums. By the end of the eighteenth century these early institutions were still relatively rare, and, with few exceptions, were small, prison-like, and foul dungeons. Similar to hospitals for lepers and for persons with contagious diseases the lowest dregs of annoying society were swept into these asylums to die and to be interred quickly. It was surely a dubious choice as to whether it was more desirable to be wan-

[8] There is, of course, an extensive literature on the subject of the mental hospital and its origins and history. For a parallel discussion and elaboration see, Shirley Angrist, "The Mental Hospital: Its History and Destiny," *Perspectives in Psychiatric Care,* December, 1963, pp. 20–26; Albert Deutsch, *The Mentally Ill in America,* New York: Columbia, 1949; and *Action for Mental Health, op. cit.,* Ch. 2.

derers, pariahs, mocked, tortured, burned, or beaten on the outside, or to be more or less certain of a quick death in a community institution or asylum.

These asylums were not for the relatively small number of middle- and upper-class families in the cities. For the most part these families were well able to care for their ill at home where they had adequate space and help. In more severe cases, they could afford private hospital care and a few such private places were established. The peasantry and the villagers who together constituted the bulk of the population were also usually able to maintain their mentally disturbed members at home. Mildly ill or mildly disorganized members could sometimes even contribute to the family economy, if only to a minor degree. In any event, whether productive or not, the mores of family life in the country, villages, and small towns dictated that mildly disturbed family members be kept at home. It was, therefore, primarily the dispossessed and marginal individuals in the growing cities who, if sufficiently ill or aberrant in behavior, would be swept into the bedlams know as asylums. When only mildly ill they were permitted to wander, to beg, or to starve quietly.

Occasional notes of concern for the mentally disturbed were sounded, but the prevailing social structure and economic organization of society and the superstitions and obsessions with devils and sorcery prevented these isolated humane voices from being heard and worse still, from affecting change.

The nineteenth century, a very critical one for the elaboration of the mental hospital, dawned in national and international conflict brought about, in part at least, by the rapid social and economic changes wrought by industrial revolution. Some of the immediate consequences for care of the mentally ill, such as the striking of the chains from the insane at the Salpêtrière and the Bicêtre by Pinel, were symptomatic of the stirrings of concern for the individual, the Enlightenment, which was only then beginning. But unfortunately the mental hospital buildings planned and built under Pinel and his concept of "moral treatment" were isolated events at the time. Despite the reforming zeal of Pinel in France, Tuke in England, and Benjamin Rush in the United States, the few public asylums in this country (14 in all, housing 2500 patients by 1840) continued to operate much as before. Not long thereafter the cumulative effects of industrialization, massive urbanization, the increased complexity of community organization, the weakening of traditional family and local community ties, rural-urban migration, the factory system geared to production, and the many other social changes, led to a construction boom in large, congregate, custodial institutions in France, England, and the United States. The urban industrial community had become so complex that it could no longer feed, clothe, shelter, tolerate, or maintain deviant, disruptive or dependent persons locally or in the family. As a result, the custodial institution—the huge mental hospital and the massive, maximum security prison, now differentiated from the county poorhouse and the workhouse—were created to facilitate the removal from and the care of burdensome and intolerable members from the community on a permanent or long-term basis.

Many of the persons involved in the planning, construction, and staffing of these massive, custodial hospitals were dedicated, enthusiastic, enlightened, and reform-minded physicians. It was their intent that these new institutions or asylums protect the sick from the hostility of society and perhaps even cure them. There is no doubt that to some extent these goals were fulfilled in the beginning. Unfortunately, the social pressures to remove the mentally ill were so great, public apathy so intense, and the institutions so massive, that there began the erosion of earlier dreams for a more enlightened approach to the treatment and care of the mentally ill.

Consequently, it did not take very long for most of the physicians superintending these new asylums to lose their enthusiasm. Indeed, many of the original 13 superintendents, founders of the American Psychiatric Association, left public employment and their superintendencies out of sheer despair and hopelessness. The institutions, more often than not, became political playthings, jobs became sinecures, innovations just about ceased, and custody requirements replaced treatment emphasis. Low budgets and efficient procedures, a minimum of escapees and general tranquility became preeminent measures of successful operation. Competent professional people, however humanitarian, were largely repelled by the isolation of these institutions from the scientific and medical mainstream and, in fact, from the stream of modern life itself. Deliberately located far out in the countryside—presumably to afford the patients an opportunity to help furnish food for the table and to enjoy the benefits of being close to nature—the mental hospital came to be dominated by semi- or even nonprofessional personnel and concerns.

Additionally, the rugged individualism of an entrepreneurial society, the continued popularity of social Darwinism stressing the inherited taint of society's failures, the aging and deterioration of the hospital, the inadequate, untrained, and often callous staffs, and the lack of knowledge concerning the etiology and treatment of mental illness created a climate of intense and unrelieved despair. So much so that as late as the 1920's, psychiatric care in the public mental hospitals seemed no more advanced than it had been 100 years before and in many respects ground had been lost. Mechanical restraints, the dehumanization of patients, desperate overcrowding, epidemics and, above all, hopelessness continued to characterize these unhappy institutions. "Moral treatment" and the concept of cure had all but been lost in the process.

To complete this mosaic, it would be necessary to digress and dwell at some length on the various kinds of patient care initiated in these custodial institutions while they were still viable or in their infrequent periods of change and ferment. Some of these techniques are largely of antiquarian medical interest. Most often they had little lasting effect, and, in general, were similar to efforts in other medical specialties. A few merely reflected the most fashionable ideas of the times.

Thus, at one time or another, homeopathy, venesection, counter irritants, the eradication of focal infections by surgery, hydrotherapy, electrotherapy, and, most recently, lobotomy were acclaimed as important therapeutic breakthroughs and utilized to a greater or lesser extent. Much of the thinking about treatment was cyclical in character. There were periods in which the etiology of the mental disorders was viewed as primarily psychological and other periods when the prevailing view specified organic causation. Similarly, the pendulum swung frequently between the poles of patient activity and inactivity. There was, for example, the total rest program of Weir Mitchell followed by the total push program a few decades later. At present, both are advocated and exemplified in the prolonged sleep work of the Russians and, simultaneously, in their commitment to rehabilitation through work. It is not surprising, then, that hospital administrators and physicians became progressively disillusioned with each of these fads, often to the point of cynicism. A bit of parochial humor frequently encountered was the plea to hospital colleagues to utilize a new "discovery" or participate in a new fad before it was shown to be ineffective.

Still, a few important discoveries did have some appreciable influence on the care and treatment practices in these hospitals. Improved sanitation and related health measures helped prevent epidemics, thereby adding to the overcrowding. Much later the sulfas and the antibiotics did even better in keeping the hospital's daily census figures at a very high level. In between these major landmarks, some specific medical innovations had an impact on patient care and psychiatric progress. The first of these was the treatment of cretinism with thyroid and its prevention by iodides. There was also the treatment of syphilis with arsenicals and the addition of malaria and fever therapy to the arsenicals for neurosyphilis. These latter methods reduced hospital admissions by approximately 10 percent and the resident population, because of the death rate factor, by an estimated 5 percent. Still later, the shock therapies—first insulin, then metrazol, and finally, electroconvulsive—helped dispel some of the futility about neuropsychiatric treatment. Then came the psychoactive drugs.

After more than 100 years of dead-center inertia, this institution can no longer resist change and progress. Despite the continuing lag in mental hospital operation, and the chronic shortages in everything but patients, therapy is beginning to replace mere confinement, as an ideal, if not yet an ultimate reality; the open hospital and the open wards are replacing the closed hospital and the back wards; small, manageable, intensive therapy hospitals are supplanting the massive, deteriorating custodial institutions; and professional people are replacing purely custodial personnel. The entry or reentry of psychiatrists, physicians, psychologists, social workers, and other professionals into the mental hospital setting as replacements for the aides and attendants who, in fact, if not on organizational charts, controlled the destiny of the hospital, portends well for the future. Finally, hospitalization time has been shortened appreciably by home visits, trial visits, family placement, and improved and expanded outpatient care. Thus, although more change has occurred in the mental hospital as a social institution since World War II than in all of its often remote history, the logic of social change is that it tends to supply its own momentum, logic, and necessity. Even before the mental hospital reduces all of its encrusted cultural lag, the revolution in psychiatry has shifted the major emphasis in mental health care out of the institution and back to the community. The forces chiefly responsible for this change have been:

1. federal government involvement in the health and welfare fields
2. the general trend of psychiatric practice in the United States
3. the cumulative impact of psychodynamic theory on public attitudes
4. the development of the "therapeutic" community
5. the drug revolution and the tranquilized hospital.

The Federal Government and Health and Welfare

One of the most significant changes in the entire mental health picture was the intervention of the federal government into the health, welfare, and education fields. Whatever the political attitudes towards this role may be, the origins of and reasons for this intervention are quite clear. Just as the individual states had supplanted the counties in providing services in these areas because most counties could no longer bear the financial burdens involved, so federal action resulted when the states began to fail in these obligations. Given the mass migration—rural to urban, south to north, east to west, the Negro migration to the metropolitan areas of the north, the patterns of segregation necessitating dual facilities and staffs, and the massive and wave-like pattern of immigration up to 1930—many states simply could not provide even minimally adequate services in what is now called the "public sector." Some states and regions were expending a vast percentage of their limited resources and purchasing extremely poor services with no real hope for narrowing the gap between what was needed and what was possible in purely fiscal terms.[9]

In addition, the extent of psychiatric disability and impairment among armed forces personnel during World War II was a sobering experience. Draftees were rejected at a prodigious rate for neuropsychiatric disability. The rate of rejection varied so widely among testing stations that the questions of definition of mental illness and standards of judgment became critical concerns. There was also the problem of how to treat psychiatric casualties in field and base hospitals. The lack of know-how in treating these men, as compared with the readiness and ability

[9] On this matter of expenditures, see, Rashi Fein, *Economics of Mental Health*, (Report to the Joint Commission on Mental Illness and Health), No. 2, New York: Basic Books, 1958.

to deal with men experiencing conventional illnesses and combat injuries, became all too apparent. An occasional and sometimes celebrated case such as an officer slapping or abusing a soldier for "malingering" brought the problem and issues into even closer public focus. Then there was also the far from minor matter of the discharge of over 380,000 men with neuropsychiatric disabilities from military service by the end of the war. The draft and the stresses imposed on men at war made the problem of mental impairment so apparent and critical that it could no longer be dismissed as a low priority matter.[10] By 1946, facilities, staff, and treatment had to be provided for a large cadre of war veterans. The V.A. system was updated and strengthened and veterans' organizations became major and influential protagonists of increased and expanded federal health and psychiatric services.

Congressmen—whether cynical, practical, or deeply persuaded—could hardly resist these legitimate pressures. From the first legislative enactment in 1946, it was clear that Congress meant to do considerably more in the health area, and annual appropriations increases provide reasonable evidence of this. Without federal grants, new construction, especially of community mental health centers, manpower training programs, and research and development projects would very nearly be wiped out in most states. Such optimism as exists that mental illness will some day yield to man's understanding and control rests largely on continued federal support of present and future programs.

Psychiatric Practice and Mental Health Care

Much less significant but still reasonably important in bringing the treatment and care of the mentally ill back into the community has been the formal organization and the economics of medical practice.[11] American medicine has insisted that private medicine is the only legitimate form of practice; group practice, while increasingly familar, is still somewhat tainted. Public medicine, including institutional and salaried practice, has even fewer redeeming aspects to those who publicly represent the medical profession. But mental patients have always been in

[10] See, William C. Menninger, *Psychiatry in a Troubled World*, New York: Macmillan, 1948; also Glasscote *et al.*, *op. cit.*, pp. 3–4.

[11] For a discussion of mental health manpower problems in and out of state mental hospitals, see, George W. Albee, *Mental Health Manpower Trends*, (Report to the Joint Commission on Mental Illness and Health), No. 3, New York: Basic Books, 1959.

hospitals. So added to the generally low rank of psychiatry relative to other medical specialties, the psychiatrist who went into public mental hospital service was confronted with the problem of dealing with psychotic patients of low socioeconomic status in a physically undesirable environment, far removed from the stimulation of the urban area and medical colleagues, and for a traditionally low salary. Why should a physician enter public employment under these circumstances? Few did. For the small number who accepted such positions there were additional disappointments stemming from this atypical practice of state hospital medicine.

When psychiatry finally became a respectable medical specialty under the influence of psychodynamic theories, the Mental Hygiene movement, the decline of the influence of Calvinistic doctrines about human nature, the increase of social stress, and concern about man's identity, psychiatrists turned toward the practice of traditional and therefore private medicine. Such practice presumes a fee-paying client or patient who carefully selects his physician and is treated with dignity and respect in a private office. No third parties, no wards, no stigma. For these and for financial reasons too, most psychiatric residents enter private practice, see mostly middle- and upper middle-class patients who are highly educated and quite respectable. The preferred diagnosis is psychoneurosis, the preferred treatment is psychotherapy, and there is also a preference for not discussing results or outcomes except in institutes and seminars when case failures may be reviewed. The implication, of course, is that such dissection and discussion is educational and necessary for future growth.

As soon, then, as patient care and treatment is returned to the community, it is more likely to become part of the customary practice of medicine. No wonder then that psychiatrists in private practice have spoken up so eloquently, and successfully, for home and community care. Little wonder, too, that psychiatry is, for better or worse, on the way back into the mainstream of American medicine.

Cumulative Impact of Psychodynamic Theories

After years of scientific limbo, medical rejection, and public ridicule, psychodynamic theories finally gained some measure of acceptance by the public in the 1920's, gave way to economic materialism in the 1930's, to war in the 1940's, existentialism in the 1950's, and to civil rights in the 1960's. Although this is hardly descriptive of the whole of American intellectual history in the last 40 years, it nonetheless makes the point that Freudianism and its offshoots began to exert a very powerful influence on the thinking of literati, the playwrights and poets, and the educators and educated long before it affected medical thinking. In stressing nonorganic etiology and the interpersonal aspects of mental disease, psychodynamic theories reduced the distance between illness and health and between normal and pathological. The mentally ill were merely somewhat more impaired than some of the rest of maladjusted humanity. Under these circumstances it was folly, and largely a primitive and punitive societal reaction, to banish the mentally ill into archaic, custodial institutions. With "insight" through psychotherapy, the majority of the psychologically disturbed could be restored to useful, productive, and even creative lives. So great has been the implicit acceptance of this approach that the lay public, and many professionals as well, are currently confused to the point at which they fail to understand that there is, in fact, a significant difference between frustrating problems of living and mental illness.[12] The recommended panacea—psychiatric attention—may be effective in dealing with certain types of disease or disability, but access to such care has come to confer status on its recipients much as a florid ulcer is viewed as a *sine qua non* of entrepreneurial success. The point is that an enormously successful educational campaign has not only altered public attitudes toward mental illness but has, in fact, elevated some of these milder, nonpsychotic disabilities to prestigious disorders. Such has been the amazing legacy of the psychodynamic era.

The Therapeutic Community

Maxwell Jones in England and Solomon, Stanton and Schwartz, Greenblatt, Hunt and others in the United States have pioneered in developing the concept of the therapeutic community which is one of the logical offshoots of analytic psychodynamic theory.[13] Ideologically com-

[12] For an analysis which rejects this concept of difference, see, Thomas S. Szasz, *The Myth of Mental Illness*, New York: Hoeber-Harper, 1961.

[13] See, for example, Maxwell Jones, *The Therapeutic Community*, New York: Basic Books, 1953; Alfred H. Stanton and Morris S. Schwartz, *The Mental Hospital*, New York: Basic Books, 1954; and Milton Greenblatt, Richard H. York, and Esther L. Brown, *From Custodial to Therapeutic Patient Care in Mental Hospitals*, New York: Russell Sage Foundation, 1955.

patible with psychological principles and practices, and especially with Sullivan's conceptions of psychiatry, the therapeutic community exemplifies the revolt against the impersonal, formally structured, and highly rigid mental hospital.

The therapeutic community developed in the early 1940's as a "humane" and "moral" treatment setting. Expanded and elaborated in the 1950's there is little doubt that the therapeutic community movement was a necessary and welcome step in the development of the community mental health center approach.

In theory, milieu therapy or the therapeutic community presupposes that the relationships among patients, between patients and staff, and among staff can be structured to insure the maximum benefit to patients. The goal is to create a conflict-free, warm, encouraging, reassuring environment with a minimum of stress for the patients. In this setting, patients can participate more freely in activities, help and guide each other, gain insight into the nature of their disabilities through meaningful interaction with others and test their behavior against the reality of involvement in group living. The psychological damage incurred in unfortunate interpersonal experiences in the past can be overcome by learning how to establish new and satisfying ones.

Therapeutic communities may feature a number of attributes. They are usually *open* so that patients are free, within limits, to move through the hospital, its grounds and environs. Bars, closed doors, isolation rooms, and other devices which restrain and shame are absent. The sexes are free to interact with one another, as on the outside. Civilian clothes are worn making it difficult to distinguish patients from staff. Again within limits, patients can establish the rules which govern their hospital lives, conduct "gripe" sessions with staff, see visitors freely during the day and evening, and exercise individual initiative.

There can be little quarrel with these methods. In a high stress, mobile, industrial society in which patients and nonpatients alike are confronted with the loss of identity and individuality, providing patients with this "warm-bath" or pressure-free environment comes highly recommended although never empirically tested. On the contrary it may even be that the social interaction demanded is more than many psychotics can tolerate but this claim, too, has not been tested. Tested or not, the open ward, open hospital has been vital in improving community tolerance and acceptance of the mentally ill. The more the mental hospital resembles the general hospital, the less the stigma attached to mental illness.

The Drug Revolution and the Tranquilized Hospital

The drug revolution has probably had a more profound effect on the mental hospital as an institution and as part of a community care program than all the other changes combined. Unlike other discoveries in psychiatry, this one is going to stand the test of time, even though all the early drugs will have long since become oddities. In this respect, the drug revolution is unique.

The advent of the tranquilizers, first used in 1953 and almost universally used with psychotic and other patients since 1955, brought "moral treatment in pill form" into the hospitals. Above all, tranquilizers reduced the hospital ward noise level, all but ended the need for physical and mechanical restraints, and eliminated forever the bedlams.[14]

With tranquilizers, fewer patients need be hospitalized; those hospitalized are easier to work with and to care for; the mental hospital loses its bars and burly attendants and comes to resemble a general hospital; personnel at all levels can be more readily attracted, treatment more easily implemented, and patients more rapidly discharged. On all levels and in nearly all respects, tranquilizers have altered our hospitals and provided the impetus for community care.

Other Variables

Yet with or without the redeeming aspects of the drugs and other changes, the total institution, of which the mental hospital is a classic example, had fallen into nearly total disrepute. For one thing, modern rehabilitation and corrections theory holds that no institution can be therapeutic and custodial simultaneously. The requirements of therapy are totally at variance with the requirements of custody.[15] The latter may be necessary and even desirable, but it cannot be therapeutic.

Implicit also in the present rejection of the total institution, although only rarely mentioned now, was the revulsion with the concentration

[14] *Action for Mental Health, op. cit.*, pp. 39–46.
[15] Erving Goffman, *Asylums*, New York: Anchor Books, 1961.

camp as the symbol of ultimate evil. Any society which had experienced, even vicariously, such an utter collapse of human morality and decency would never again be able to accept the total institution as easily and guiltlessly as before.

On a different level, public mental hospitals and other total institutions have been criticized on several other theoretical grounds. First, it has been suggested that even under the very best of circumstances institutionalization tends to alienate patients from family, friends, and community, making their eventual reintegration into normal activities exceedingly difficult. By removing these interpersonal supports, the patient may lose incentive to recover, and this isolation and enforced estrangement may facilitate further patient withdrawal from reality. Second, the chronic lack of stimulation characteristic of total institutions results in the dulling and decay of intellectual and social functioning—a process called the *social breakdown syndrome* in the American Public Health Association Guide for the Control of Mental Disorder.[16] Third, patient attempts to subvert the hospital structure for their own ends results in the development of an "inmate society" which thwarts the therapeutic goals of the staff and is hardly conducive to patient improvement.[17] Finally, not even patients can fail to be aware of the definition and significance of their institutionalization. The sick role imposed on them by their hospital commitment stigmatizes them long after release.

SUMMARY

In this chapter three major topics were discussed in some detail. First, the origins and development of community psychiatry and of the community mental health center were presented. Second, the community mental health center movement was seen as being a revolt against the traditional public mental hospital. The history of the mental hospital as a total institution, from its inception as a morally superior method of treating the mental ill than other techniques then in vogue, its failure as a treatment center, its sordid history as a dumping ground for the inadequate and sick, and its present signs of rejuvenation, were described in relatively general terms.

[16] *Mental Disorders: A Guide to Control Methods*, American Public Health Association, 1962, Ch. 1.

[17] See, Albert F. Wessen (ed.), *The Psychiatric Hospital as a Social System*, Springfield, Ill.: Charles C Thomas, 1964.

Finally, several major factors were seen as forcing the change from the mental hospital to community care. These include (1) the intervention of the federal government (2) the nature of psychiatric practice; (3) the cumulative impact of psychodynamic theories; (4) the development of the therapeutic community approach; and, (5) the all-important drug revolution.

2

ANTECEDENT RESEARCH

Three separate but related streams of research and demonstration provide the background for our work. These streams—from the broadest and most general to the most specific—are (1) epidemiological studies dealing with disturbed persons who remain unreported and unknown in their communities, (2) studies of outcome of the hospitalization of psychotic patients, and (3) programs and investigations involving the prevention of hospitalization.

EPIDEMIOLOGICAL STUDIES[1]

Although home and community care programs seem visionary in purpose and scope and arouse considerable antipathy and fear in some circles, the fact is and has always been, that many disturbed persons, at any moment in time, remain undetected and untreated and still live *in* their home communities. Whatever the merits, and limitations, of epidemiologic findings, the one result that cannot be argued is that many persons need but do not receive psychiatric treatment. These include mildly ill psychotic individuals whose behavior usually does not lead to hospitalization as well as the entire spectrum of the nonpsychotic. If disturbed and impaired persons can function at some level, albeit minimal, without care, then surely patients should do even better at home with care. Put in these terms, the concept of the community mental health center loses much of its revolutionary impact.

[1] For a review of several of these studies see, Richard J. Plunkett and John E. Gordon, *Epidemiology and Mental Illness,* (Report to the Joint Commission on Mental Illness and Health), No. 6, New York: Basic Books, 1960.

The "Midtown" Study in New York City[2]

There are several epidemiological investigations which can legitimately be cited at this point. Of these, two merit special consideration. The first, the "Midtown" study in Manhattan, was conducted in a densely populated area in Manhattan with a heterogeneous population. Different socioeconomic, ethnic, religious, and occupational groups reside in this area. Community and kinship ties are tenuous. Impersonality, anonymity, and urbanism as a way of life, are characteristic.

From census data, investigators carefully selected a sample of 1660 persons for study. This 1.7 percent sample was representative of "Midtown" on major demographic variables. Interviews were successfully completed with all but 13 percent of the sample group. The interview schedule contained, among other questions, 120 specific items dealing with past or present psychological symptoms of disturbance.

On the basis of self-reported symptoms, the sample was classified into six severity classes: *well* (free of important or major symptoms), *mildly disturbed* (some symptoms but fairly good behavior), *moderately disturbed* (a greater number and qualitatively more important symptoms but everyday functioning still reasonably good), *marked disturbance* (some impairment in performance), *severe disturbance* (performance quite impaired), and *incapacitation.* Persons falling into the first three groups, by virtue of lack of overt disability, were considered to be unimpaired. Persons in the latter three were considered to be impaired. The results indicated that nearly a fourth (23.4 percent) of the sample was or had been impaired. The inevitable conclusion is that one in four people in "Midtown" had experienced psychological difficulties which interfered with functioning.

Caution should be exercised in using this prevalence percentage because, among other compelling reasons, every form and type of mental disorder was included. No distinction was made between the psychoses and other disorders. It is probable therefore that psychotics constituted a small segment of the impaired population. Still, they were at home and not hospitalized, which is the thrust of the argument.

[2] Leo Srole, Thomas S. Langner, Stanley T. Michael, Marvin K. Opler, and Thomas A. C. Rennie, *Mental Health in the Metropolis: The Manhattan Midtown Study*, Vol. 1, New York: McGraw-Hill, 1962.

The Baltimore Study[3]

From 1952 to 1955, the Commission on Chronic Illness, an agency jointly sponsored by the American Hospital Association, the American Medical Association, the American Public Health Association, and the American Public Welfare Association, conducted a study of the prevalence of chronic illness in Baltimore, Maryland. The first phase of this investigation consisted of a survey of 4000 randomly selected households containing a total of 12,000 people. The second and unique phase involved the examination of 809 respondents, half of whom were selected randomly from the larger population sample and the other half consisting of high risks for chronic disorders other than mental illness. In 86 cases (of the 809) a finding of mental disorder was made and substantiated by a psychiatrist who reviewed the clinical data. The chief finding, for our purposes, was that one percent of the Baltimore population was psychotic; *half were institutionalized, the other half were at home or elsewhere in the community.*

OUTCOME RESEARCH

In addition to ferreting out unreported and untreated cases, research studies have also concentrated on determining the success and failure of discharged hospital patients. In these investigations, medical, demographic, functioning, sociocultural and other variables have been related to case outcome. The results have been sufficiently equivocal to frustrate, for the time being at least, the accurate prediction of case outcome. Several of these investigations are presented below:

The London Study[4]

The Carstairs group in London, England, conducted one of the earliest and most provocative of the investigations in case outcome after hospitalization. This work stimulated a renewed interest in tracing the

[3] Benjamin Pasamanick, Dean W. Roberts, Paul W. Lemkau, and Dean B. Kreuger, "A Survey of Mental Disease in an Urban Population: I. Prevalence by Age, Sex and Severity of Impairment," *Amer. J. Publ. Hlth.*, **47** (1957), 923–929.

[4] George W. Brown, G. Morris Carstairs, and Gillian Topping, "Post-Hospital Adjustment of Chronic Mental Patients," *Lancet*, September 27, 1958, pp. 685–689; and George W. Brown, "Experiences of Discharged Chronic Schizophrenic Patients in Various Types of Living Groups," *Milbank Memorial Fund Quarterly*, **37** (1959), 105–131.

posthospital adjustment of discharged mental patients and dispelled some of the gloom about posthospital functioning cast by previous studies both in Europe and the United States.

The study group consisted of male patients, born in England, aged 20 to 65, and discharged to an address in the Greater London Area after minimum hospital stay of 2 years, from seven mental hospitals in or near London between July, 1949, and June, 1956. In all, 240 patients qualified for inclusion in the study; 229 (95 percent) were followed. Of these, over two-thirds were schizophrenics whose average age was 39.4 and more than three-fourths of whom were unmarried at time of admission. Their minimum length of hospital stay prior to discharge was 2 years and the mean 6.5 years. At release 14 percent were rated as recovered, 65 percent as relieved, and 21 percent as not improved.

One year after discharge, 31.6 percent of these long-term former schizophrenic patients had relapsed (failed), 25.8 percent had made a poor adjustment, 17.4 percent a partial adjustment, and 25.2 percent a full adjustment. These outcomes bore little relationship to patients' age, recorded diagnosis, or length of hospitalization. On the other hand, successful outcome was associated with patients' clinical status or severity of impairment at time of hospital discharge, and the settings to which patients went. Discharged patients who accepted residence with siblings or in lodgings did better than those who went to live with parents, wives, or in large hostels. This impact of residence on outcome was significant even after allowing for the fact that sicker patients are sometimes released to parents but rarely ever to lodgings. The obvious implication of these findings is that schizophrenics do better when family pressures are minimal, and quite poorly when subjected to the usual obligations and privileges of family life. Since hospitals are often unwilling or unable to discharge patients except to near and responsible relatives, this very policy may in itself be jeopardizing successful hospital outcome by returning patients to what are often pathogenic family interactional patterns and pressures.

The Massachusetts Studies[5]

The work of the Maudsley Hospital group in England found its almost identical counterpart in the research of Simmons and Freeman

[5] Howard E. Freeman and Ozzie G. Simmons, *The Mental Patient Comes Home*, New York: Wiley, 1963.

in the United States. The latter research is divided into two phases. The earlier pilot studies were organized around the concept of tolerance of deviant behavior as the critical variable in posthospital outcome. Tolerance of deviant behavior was operationally defined as "the continued acceptance of the former patient by his family members, even when he fails to perform in instrumental roles." Thus, structural, interactional, and attitudinal variations in family settings were postulated as affecting the tolerance of deviance level, which in turn was associated with posthospital success or failure.

The initial empirical results seemed to confirm the general thesis. Patients returned to a *parental* situation were hospitalized less frequently but functioned more poorly than patients returned to a *conjugal* setting. In the latter, the patient either performed adequately or his spouse would be more apt to return him to the hospital. Mothers were more tolerant of poor performance than were wives.

The results of a second study of 182 male, white, native-born, discharged hospital patients, aged 20 to 60 tended to expand and confirm the earlier findings. Specifically, Simmons and Freeman found that low level posthospital functioning was associated with (1) the presence of other males in the household who can play the roles and perform the duties of the patients, (2) lower-class status, and (3) low expectations on the part of their families. Conversely, high level performance was related to being the sole role incumbent, middle-class status, and high expectations for functioning. At this point, the tolerance of deviant behavior hypothesis seemed to be a most significant variable in case outcome.

Two later investigations, however, cast serious doubt about the meaning of these relationships. In a much larger study involving 649 of 714 male and female patients released during a 6-month period in 1959 from nine state and three V.A. hospitals in eastern Massachusetts, Simmons and Freeman found that 63.9 percent of the male and 60.2 percent of the female patients succeeded in remaining home for at least 1 year. They also found that symptomatic or bizarre behavior, and florid signs and symptoms rather than inadequate instrumental role performance, was the most probable basis for rehospitalization. Important as are the structural, interpersonal, and cultural variations in family life, these do not in themselves appreciably alter the reaction to bizarre or extreme behavior.

The Columbus (Ohio) Study[6]

In an attempt to determine whether different in-hospital ward therapeutic policies and practices had any discernible lasting consequences on the posthospital functioning of discharged mental patients, a group in Columbus initiated an outcome study comparable in some respects to those described previously. There were, however, some very notable and important differences. The patients studied by the Columbus group were females, acutely rather than chronically ill, who were interviewed in the posthospital setting along with their "significant others" or nearest responsible relatives. Further, two staff psychiatrists, independently of each other and of the interviewer who went into the home, evaluated the mental status of a sample of the patients. Finally, the functioning of each of 100 former patients was compared with that of a nonpsychotic, untreated female neighbor who lived 10 house numbers away. In this way patient-normal comparisons were possible, with race and socioeconomic status controlled.

The Ohio State University Psychiatric Hospital, an intensive therapy, short term, heavily staffed institution discharged 376 female patients in the period December, 1958, through July, 1959. Of these, 287 returned to a residence within the study area, and could be studied intensively. Within 6 months, 14 percent had failed. The results were much as expected. Except for diagnosis, medical and psychiatric variables such as number and length of previous hospitalization were not significantly related to rehospitalization or to the adequacy of posthospital functioning. More important were such variables as class, marital status, type of household (nuclear or parental), and self- and other expectations for performance. Also, the discharged patients as

[6] A series of papers by Shirley Angrist, Mark Lefton, Simon Dinitz, and Benjamin Pasamanick have reported the results of this research. See, for example, "Social and Psychiatric Attributes as Predictors of Case Outcome in Mental Hospitalization," *Soc. Prob.*, **8** (1962), 248–254; "Rehospitalization of Female Mental Patients," *AMA Arch. gen. Psychiat.*, **4** (1961), 363–370; "The Posthospital Psychological Functioning of Former Mental Patients," *Mental Hygiene*, **45** (1961), 579–588; "Instrumental Role Expectations and Posthospital Performance of Female Mental Patients, *Social Forces*, **40** (1962), 248–254; "Social Class, Expectations and Performance of Mental Patients," *Amer. J. Sociol.*, **68** (1962), 79–87; and "Tolerance of Deviant Behavior, Posthospital Performance Levels and Rehospitalization," *Proceedings of the Third World Congress of Psychiatry*, 1962, pp. 237-241.

a group, though drawn from the same socioeconomic level were inferior in their performance and functioning to the normal controls. The greatest difference was in the psychological status of the controls which was clearly superior to that of the former patients.

The conclusions in this study reversed the previous emphasis. It was contended that the social variables—expectations, tolerance of behavior—*reflect* rather than *determine* patient functioning. Significant others relate, test, and revise their perceptions and expectations of patient performance against actual performance; more is expected of an obviously recovered patient than of one who is still clearly ill. Illness cannot be modified by expectations nearly as readily as expectations by illness. As already noted, Simmons and Freeman reversed themselves and concurred in this interpretation after the completion of their last study.

PREVENTION OF HOSPITALIZATION

In both Europe and the United States, the 1950's witnessed not only an interest in posthospital outcome but in the development of new and interesting departures in the provision of psychiatric care apart from, and in order to prevent, institutionalization. This review will be concerned principally with those projects which incorporated research, however inadequate in design or implementation, for evaluation of the new or different services.

The Worthing Experiment (England)[7]

From 1950 to 1955, admissions to mental hospitals in England and Wales increased by nearly 23,000 patients. By 1955 hospitals were overcrowded by nearly 18,000 patients. Without some radical innovations, the situation seemed hopeless. In 1956 Graylingwell Hospital was designated as the institution that would undertake a 2-year pilot experiment providing an outpatient center and domiciliary treatment service. The coastal community of Worthing and its environs with a population of some 160,000 people normally served by this hospital became the focal

[7] Joshua Carse, Nydia E. Panton, and Alexander Watt, "A District Mental Health Service: The Worthing Experiment," *Lancet*, January 4, 1958, pp. 39–42.

point of the project. No patient was admitted to Graylingwell Hospital from the Worthing area without being screened by the new outpatient treatment center in order to insure that hospital beds were reserved for only the most needy.

In the first 10 months of operation in 1957, the new service had seen 1110 new cases and 82 others who had received psychiatric care previously. Over 1000 domiciliary visits were paid to 432 patients by the two full-time and one part-time psychiatrists. Electroconvulsive therapy was used extensively—317 patients each received an average of 4.9 treatments. Modified insulin shock was used primarily in the treatment of tension states with 166 patients receiving such therapy. Individual psychotherapy was the main treatment given to all patients attending the center. A weekly group psychotherapy session was also held.

The results of this experiment were excellent. Admissions to Graylingwell Hospital from the Worthing catchment area fell from 548 in 1956 to 224 in 1957, a net decrease of 59 percent. At the same time admissions from the noncatchment area rose from 603 to 626 or 4 percent in the same period. Based on this experience the Graylingwell Hospital team specify as the minimum criteria for a successful program: (1) good community public relations so that the public ceases to fear mental illness and is willing to seek treatment promptly, (2) cooperation from patients, and (3) relatives who are willing to accept some responsibility for the patient.

The Worthing experiment, even *without the use of psychoactive drugs,* was a most successful pioneering effort. In contrast, a study in California achieved completely opposite results. So negative was the outcome in this investigation that undertaking outpatient care demonstration projects seemed foolhardy.

The California Experience[8]

This project was initiated in 1955 to answer some very important and recurrent questions concerning patient eligibility for inpatient hospital as opposed to outpatient clinic care:

[8] Harold Sampson, David Ross, Bernice Engle, and Florine Linson, *A Study of Suitability for Outpatient Clinic Treatment of State Mental Hospital Admissions,* Research Report No. 1, Department of Mental Hygiene, State of California, 1957.

1. Are there state hospital admissions for whom outpatient clinic treatment is a reasonable alternative?
2. How can clinic eligible patients be readily identified at or shortly after their hospital admission?
3. Will such patients and their families consent to a clinic treatment plan?

Three California state mental hospitals and two state community clinics participated in the study. Every other newly admitted patient in each of the three state hospitals within a 3-month period became a study subject. As a first step in the program, new hospital admissions were classified as unsuitable or potentially suitable clinic cases by the admission ward psychiatrists at two of the hospitals and the examining physician at the third hospital. The intent was to get a liberal judgment of eligibility for outpatient care. Next, suitable patients were seen by a hospital referral team, that is, a psychiatrist and social worker. The function of this team was to screen out those whose families did not wish to cooperate and others who, after more careful and thorough study, seemed unlikely prospects. Finally, a clinic intake team made the final decision as to whether or not to attempt outpatient care in lieu of hospitalization. The research design also required that one half of the acceptable patients be treated and the other half serve as hospital controls.

In all, 504 patients were involved almost evenly divided by sex. Median age was 46.8 years. Two-fifths were diagnosed as psychotic, 64 percent had no previous history of hospitalization, and only 8 percent had any previous outpatient clinic contact.

The results were not only incredible but, in view of later research, most unfortunate. Of these 504 newly admitted patients, 447 or 89 percent were eliminated in the initial screening as unsuitable for outpatient care in lieu of hospitalization. Of the 57 patients reaching the second stage, the hospital referral team, a mere 20 still retained eligibility. Of these 20, only 6 were finally accepted. The cruelest blow of all was that 4 of the 6 should have been screened out of the study because they failed to meet the criteria for inclusion. Of 6 recipients, then, only 2 patients benefited from outpatient treatment.

The MMHC—CES Project[9]

In marked contrast to the startingly negative conclusions of the California research, the Community Extension Service of the Massachusetts Mental Health Center project demonstrated anew the feasibility of outpatient and home care treatment.

The Massachusetts Mental Health Center is a small, intensive therapy, training, and research hospital run under the aegis of both the state system and Harvard Medical School. While it is a relatively simple matter to obtain immediate admission to the local state hospital, the famous and heavily staffed MMHC normally maintains a waiting list of patients. Twenty percent of the patients on the waiting list were not hospitalized, 60 percent eventually entered the MMHC facility and the remainder were admitted to other hospitals. The obvious need to offer professional supervision to waiting list patients brought the Community Extension Service into the picture. CES entered with the conviction that "treatment outside the hospital, when feasible, would nearly always be in the best interests of both patient and the community, and when outpatient and inpatient treatment might both be expected to yield a satisfactory outcome, the former was preferred."

The procedure involved reviewing the additions to the MMHC waiting list each day beginning in October, 1957, and ending in December, 1959. Persons meeting the following criteria became potential subjects: residents of Greater Boston, age 18 or older, and not currently hospitalized anywhere or in the MMHC in the preceding 4 years. The patient's referring physician was then contacted, the program explained to him and his cooperation sought. If he agreed, CES contacted and then interviewed the prospective patient and family at the clinic or in a diagnostic home visit. After securing patient acceptance into the project, treatment then followed. The therapy was broad and inclusive and involved individual psychotherapy, drugs, ECT, casework with patients and relatives, vocational and more general counseling, and day hospital care when required.

[9] Milton Greenblatt, Robert F. Moore, Robert S. Albert, and Maida H. Solomon, *The Prevention of Hospitalization: Treatment Without Admission for Psychiatric Patients*, New York: Grune & Stratton, 1963.

Psychotherapy was the method most frequently used. A staff psychiatrist saw patients as often as three times weekly at the outset and at a reduced frequency later. These sessions continued for an average of 6 months but in some cases lasted up to 2 years. Drugs were used with more than half the patients. Psychiatrists made a considerable number of home visits. Five of them averaged over 110 such visits yearly. Seven others paid an average of 19 home visits. Project social workers and nurses were also extensively involved in the home visiting program.[10]

In order to evaluate the effectiveness of this program, CES conducted a follow-up interview with patients and relatives a year after referral to the MMHC waiting list. In the 27 months of the program, 128 patients were served by CES. Their average age was 35.7 years, 71.9 percent were males, only 39 percent were married, nearly half were Catholic, and nearly two-thirds were at least high school graduates.

Of great importance in assessing the results achieved by CES was the diagnosis and severity of illness of the 128 patients. Psychotics accounted for only 56 percent of the patients; the remainder were diagnosed as psychoneurotic, or personality disturbance, or given some other nonpsychotic classification. Most importantly, only 37 percent were diagnosed as schizophrenic or paranoid reaction.

Again, of the 128 patients, 30.5 percent had been both hospitalized and on outpatient treatment previously; 11.7 percent had been hospitalized only; 25.8 percent had been in outpatient treatment only; the rest, 32.0 percent, had experienced no previous psychiatric contact.

The results were good but not as convincing as they appear to be at first glance. To begin with, *almost half of the patients failed and were hospitalized* (49.4 percent). These exclude the 10.2 percent who were treated by CES in the day care program. Of those who had to be hospitalized, failure occurred within 6 months in all cases. In assessing these findings two considerations should be remembered. First, 20 percent of the patients on the MMHC waiting list were not hospitalized even without intervention. Second, and by far the most critical consideration, was the differential success rate by diagnosis. Of the 24 involutional and manic-depressive patients treated, three-quarters were

[10] The cost of this excellent program was obviously quite large in terms of both funds and staff. In view of the funding available in most communities, the CES program would probably be well beyond their financial means.

hospitalized. Similarly, a majority (59.5 percent) of the schizophrenics failed. The greatest success occurred with nonpsychotic patients, nearly three-quarters of whom remained in the community.

Kings County (Brooklyn) Experimental Clinic[11]

The Engelhardt group attempted in a series of two studies, one within the other, to determine the effectiveness of promazine hydrochloride and chlorpromazine hydrochloride in preventing psychiatric hospitalization. In the first investigation 173 recently discharged patients—18 to 40 years of age, evidencing signs and symptoms of schizophrenia for more than a year prior to clinic admission, willing to take drug medication, and having an English-speaking and cooperative relative—were selected for study. Each patient was randomly assigned to a placebo, (nonactive or inert substance identical in external appearance to the genuine drug), promazine, or chlorpromazine group and the treating psychiatrist did not know which patient received which of the three substances. The findings were very significant. Of the placebo patients, 28.6 percent required hospitalization whereas 18.2 percent of the promazine and a mere 4.8 percent of the chlorpromazine patients were hospitalized. The time period of treatment and of success ranged from 1 to 18 months. However, there was a very serious deficiency in this investigation. The dropout rate was so large that it decreased much of the impact of the study. At the end of 3 months, 35 percent of the study population had dropped out; at 1 year, 65 percent. While this rate was comparable in all three groups, the size of the rate raises a great many doubts about the validity of the results.

In a larger investigation involving 445 patients, including the original 173, Engelhardt *et al* concluded that drug therapy with ambulatory schizophrenics *delayed* rather than *prevented* hospitalization. Comparisons of the results in the earlier and later studies in which minimal participation increased from 1 to 15 months and maximum participation from 18 to 61 months revealed that the drug and placebo

[11] David M. Engelhardt, Norbert Freedman, Burton S. Glick, Leon D. Hankoff, and David Mann, "Prevention of Psychiatric Hospitalization with Use of Psychopharmacological Agents," *JAMA*, **173** (May 14, 1960), 147–149; and David M. Engelhardt *et al.*, "Phenothiazines in Prevention of Psychiatric Hospitalization: II, Duration of Treatment Exposure," *JAMA*, **186** (December 14, 1963), 981–983.

group rates were approaching equality. The overall hospitalization rate increased from 16.7 to 25.4 percent; the placebo rate from 28.6 to 29.6 percent; the promazine rate from 18.2 to 28.0 percent; and the chlorpromazine rate from 4.8 to 19.0 percent. Thus, over time the placebo hospitalization rate exceeded the drug rates by a very modest amount. With additional time even this difference was likely to disappear. (Dropout rates were not reported in this study.)

SUMMARY

These antecedent and parallel studies have been discussed in some detail because of their direct relevance to the home care study to be described in this monograph. The principal areas of significance of these investigations are: (1) the indications that substantial numbers of psychotic and, indeed, schizophrenic persons are able to maintain themselves for greater or lesser periods of time in the community without treatment; (2) that certain sociological factors are critically related to hospital outcome in those cases where patients do receive care and treatment; and (3) that it is possible to prevent or perhaps only delay hospitalization through the establishment of even modest community outpatient programs.

The study with which this monograph is concerned and which is reported in the remaining chapters was considerably more successful in preventing the hospitalization of chronic schizophrenic patients than any of the programs described previously. The extent of its success and the reasons for it should increase optimism for the success of the entire community mental health program.

3

THE LOUISVILLE STUDY: HISTORY AND DESIGN

The Louisville study was designed to determine (1) whether home care for schizophrenic patients was feasible, (2) whether drug therapy was effective in preventing their hospitalization, and (3) whether home care was, in fact, a better or poorer method of treatment than hospitalization. It was our conviction as early as 1957 when the proposal was submitted to the National Institutes of Health for grant support that home care of schizophrenic patients is feasible under the proper public mental health auspices and when used in conjunction with appropriate psychopharmacologic agents.[1]

Three considerations supported this conviction. The first had to do with the general effects of ataractic drug therapy in inducing patient manageability and in providing the setting for the process of recovery. The second involved the feasibility of maintaining protracted medical supervision of long term patients through an outpatient home care facility. The third concerned the possibility that, for a number of patients, recovery, after-progress, and resistance to relapse are facilitated by the patient's continued stay in home and community during efforts at treatment, rather than by removal to an institution.

On the first two points, there already existed by 1957 successful precedent for the proposed treatment method in connection with other diseases. The principal question which remained was whether a psychiatric condition was equally amenable to such procedures. On the third point, there was, of course, the possibility that some family settings

[1] For a review article in this area see, Martin M. Katz and Jonathan O. Cole, "Research on Drugs and Community Care," *AMA Arch. gen. Psychiat.*, 7 (November, 1962), 345–359.

would not be optimal environments for the process of recovery. On the other hand, the primary advantage of recovery in the home is the uninterrupted channel of communication and interstimulation between patient and family and friends and the possibility of maintaining social relationships in work and recreation. In this situation, positive self-appraisal and appraisal by others may be enhanced, thus speeding up the process by which the patient is reincorporated into society as an adequately functioning member.

THE HOME CARE PROJECT: ORIGINAL DESIGN[2]

The basic plan of this home care project involved a study of three groups of patients for a 3-year period. These groups were:

1. *a drug group* kept at home on prescribed dosages of psychopharmacologic agents under psychiatric care and frequent home visits by a public health nurse
2. *a placebo group* treated identically with the drug group, except for the substitution of a placebo for the active drug
3. *a hospital control* group admitted to a psychiatric facility and treated in accordance with "ordinary" hospital procedures.

As originally proposed, all subjects in this program were to be selected from persons at the point of commitment to a psychiatric hospital as first admission cases. The project was to be conducted in Franklin County (Columbus) Ohio. In this community about 450 schizophrenic patients are admitted initially each year to the two hospitals serving the area. About half of these patients are committed through legal procedures; the remainder are voluntary patients.

A study staff consisting of a psychiatrist, psychologist, and social worker plus technical personnel was to make the first contact with potential subjects in a screening clinic set up in conjunction with the admissions procedure. The purpose of this screening clinic was to select eligible subjects for placement in the drug, placebo, and hospital con-

[2] Much of the following material is contained in an earlier article. See Frank Scarpitti, Mark Lefton, Simon Dinitz, and Benjamin Pasamanick, "Problems in a Home Care Study for Schizophrenics," *AMA Arch. gen. Psychiat,* **10** (February, 1964), 143–154.

trol groups. In order to make these assignments, patients at the point of committal or voluntary hospital entry were to be examined and evaluated by the clinic staff. Patients requiring emergency care and those who had previously undergone extensive drug therapy were to be excluded from further study consideration. Preliminary data indicated that of the 450 annual admissions, 210 would be eligible for the study. Of these 210 patients, 90 were to be placed in the drug group and 60 each in the placebo and hospital control groups. These assignments of eligible patients would continue for 2 years and result in a grand total of 420 patients in the drug, placebo, and hospital control groups in the ratio of 4:3:3 respectively.

Hospitalized control patients were to have no routine contact with the study staff. It was hoped that they would follow ordinary hospital procedures, including whatever drug therapy, electric shock treatment, or other therapeutics were prescribed for them. There was, of course, to be contact with the study staff at regular intervals for evaluation purposes.

On the other hand, after initial clinic examination and assignment, follow-up on the home care patients was to begin by the public health nurses functioning as staff members of an outpatient clinic. The plan was to provide home visits by the nurses on a weekly basis for the first 3 months, a bimonthly basis for the next 3 months, and a monthly basis commencing in the seventh month and running through the twenty-fourth month of treatment. Apart from regularly scheduled visits, the home care patients or their relatives were to be able to contact the clinic when the need arose. The entire clinic staff was to be available for outpatient service.

THE MOVE TO LOUISVILLE

Shortly after the National Institute of Mental Health granted funds to the Ohio State University Psychiatric Hospital for the home versus hospital care research, it was learned that, despite previous assurances of cooperation, the study could not be done in Columbus, Ohio, because the local state hospital refused to participate in the program despite an earlier understanding to do so. The Commissioner of Mental Health for the state of Kentucky, learning of this situation, offered the cooperation of his department and proposed the Louisville area as the study site.

Faced with the prospect of abandoning the research, it was decided that the study would be attempted in Kentucky.

Jefferson County, which includes Louisville, is located in the north-central part of Kentucky on the Ohio River. With a population of 610,947 in 1960, it is the largest, most progressive metropolitan area in the state. This seems to be especially true in the area of mental health. The local mental hospital is the only one of the four in the state which is an open-door hospital. Community mental health facilities include several tax-supported outpatient clinics, a half-way house, a chapter of Recovery, and an active citizens' mental health association. For many years several prominent civic and political leaders have been active in developing a better community understanding of mental illness. These factors were considered distinct advantages when the decision was made in early 1961 to accept Louisville as the site of the home care study.

Prior to the move to Kentucky, it was decided that patients would be drawn into the project at the point of admission to the local state hospital, Central State. Since this hospital is located some 20 miles from downtown Louisville, an outpatient clinic easily accessible to home care patients and families had to be established in town. This clinic was, to all intents and purposes, to be part of the Kentucky State Department of Mental Health.

With the exception of the study director, the staff of the clinic was to be composed of local people. A psychologist and five public health nurses were found and employed. A psychiatrist and a social worker, however, were not easy to find. After several weeks of futile searching for a psychiatrist in private practice who would work on a part-time basis, a third-year resident was assigned by the local Resident's Review Board to participate in the research on a part-time arrangement. The quest for a qualified social worker was equally as difficult. The fact that this was to be only a 3-year program did not seem to offer enough incentive to many social workers.

Once recruited, a training program was begun for the staff. The psychiatrist, psychologist, and social worker, who were to be doing work for which they had been trained, needed only to be familiarized with the several instruments and tests which were to be used in the study. The nurses, however, posed a different problem. Although each was an experienced public health nurse, four of the five had never before worked with psychiatric patients. Since their role of liaison between patient and psychiatrist was crucial, they were subjected to a comprehensive and rigorous training program which will be described in Chapter 4.

In the latter part of 1961 the Institute Treatment Center (ITC), a fully complemented clinic, was established in downtown Louisville to begin the home versus hospital care study. The name of the clinic was suggested by a local probate court judge who felt that it should be as innocuous as possible so as to avoid any suspicion or stigma. In order to gain a measure of respectability from the local community and its professionals and to allay suspicion and hostility to the study, the names of five prominent local professionals (three psychiatrists and two social scientists) were listed on the Treatment Center's letterhead as consultants. Letters and study descriptions were sent to all psychiatrists and social agencies in the community, the local medical society, and to all the judges. The program was presented by the Commissioner of Mental Health and study director at local hospital staff meetings and to various professional groups. Because of the experimental nature of the program, knowledge of the study was deliberately restricted to the local medical and social service communities. During the entire course of the study there was never a public announcement of the nature of the Center's program.

Since the private psychiatrists appeared especially resistant, many of them were seen individually and their objections heard and answered. Despite our efforts, the local psychiatrists seemed unconvinced that the research was worthwhile. Most of them voiced two main objections to the study: the use of placebo medication for some home care patients and the use of public health nurses as the liaison between patient and clinic staff. The private psychiatrists, however, were not the only ones to voice these objections. The medical staff at the State Hospital also opposed the use of placebo medication for some patients and seriously questioned the ability of public health nurses to function in their assigned role.

From the beginning of the program, the relationship between the Treatment Center and the State Hospital was somewhat difficult. Physical distance accounted for some of this. The fact that the clinic was 20 miles from the state hospital meant that it had to operate as an independent agency. Although the clinic was supposed to be a functional part of the state mental health system, no one really believed this. It appeared to the study staff that the hospital staff sometimes viewed the Treatment Center as a competitor with whom they had to cooperate grudgingly. The tremendous turnover of hospital staff (below the administrative level) also resulted in poor communications and a lack of understanding as to the nature of the home care program.

MODIFICATIONS OF RESEARCH DESIGN

A careful analysis of the admission statistics for the local state hospital revealed that certain modifications of the research design had to be made before the study began. Although the original design specified the use of first-admission schizophrenics only, the admission statistics clearly showed that there were so few of these that this limitation was not practical (*e.g.*, there were only 48 first-admission schizophrenics admitted to the state hospital in 1962, the first full calendar year of the program). The decision to include all patients admitted to the hospital who were diagnosed as schizophrenic and who met the other criteria of selection was one of necessity and not of choice. This modification meant that more difficulties in treatment and more home care failures could be anticipated. After all, multi-hospitalized patients were likely to be sicker than those never before hospitalized.

A corollary problem arose in that very few patients admitted to the state hospital had not had some prior drug therapy. An overwhelming number of admissions had had some contact with general practitioners, private psychiatrists, and psychiatrists at outpatient clinics, who had prescribed tranquilizing drugs. Although the original study design called for the rejection of patients who had undergone extensive drug therapy, the practical problem of finding enough patients who met the unalterable criteria of the program caused us to remove this stipulation. This modification, like the previously mentioned change, was expected to lead to an increased hospitalization rate since patients were now included who had already failed on drugs. Far from compromising the design, therefore, these modifications made it more difficult to obtain significant differences between home care and hospital control patients.

After consulting local mental health officials, the staff psychiatrist, and staff public health nurses, two other modifications in the original design were made before the home care program got under way. First, it was felt that the use of only one drug did not give the prescribing physician enough of a choice for effective treatment. Therefore, the number of available drugs was increased to three: chlorpromazine, trifluoperazine, and thioridazine. An antidepressant, tranylcypromine, was also made available as was trihexyphenidyl. Second, drawing a blood sample to test for toxicity on a weekly basis seemed to the staff physician and nurses to be excessive and unnecessary. This had been deemed desirable during the early days of drug treatment in 1956 when the original design was drawn up but largely unnecessary by 1961. It was decided therefore that blood samples would not be taken on a regular basis but whenever the medical staff deemed it advisable. As it happened, there were only two such occasions during the entire study.

Once these modifications were made, it was possible to compose a list of criteria for selection of patients to be treated on the home care program. The following were the minimum qualifications or characteristics needed to determine a patient's eligibility for treatment:

1. All patients must be schizophrenic. The psychosis must be severe enough to warrant hospitalization.
2. Patients must not be homicidal or suicidal.
3. Patients must be adults between the ages of 18 and 60.
4. Patients must have families or family surrogates willing to accept and supervise them in the home and to report on their progress throughout the course of the study.
5. Patients must reside in Jefferson County or one of nine surrounding counties within a radius of approximately 60 miles from Louisville.

The setting up of a semi-independent clinic several miles from the hospital meant that certain mechanical procedures had to be worked out for the screening and selection of patients. Arrangements were made to employ a psychiatrist at Central State Hospital (CSH), working on a part-time basis, to screen all newly admitted patients to determine eligibility for study inclusion. This screening occurred immediately after the patient was admitted to the hospital, in many cases the very same day. When a patient met these screening criteria, the information was phoned to the Treatment Center where the social worker immediatly began making arrangements to interview the family.

Every effort was made to get the family in for an interview as quickly as possible. The patient was brought into the clinic and evaluated at the same time as the family was scheduled for an interview. Since this usually varied from 1 to 4 days after the patient's admission to the hospital, the patient was held on the hospital admission ward without treatment in the interim.

At the time of the family interview, the social worker confronted the family with the possibility that the patient might be sent home to be treated by the Institute Treatment Center on an oupatient basis. The family was told that the decision for home treatment or continued hospitalization was to be made by the staff psychiatrist. The responsible family member was asked, "If the psychiatrist recommends home treatment, is the family willing to accept the patient back into the home and to work with the staff in the treatment program?" Refusal on the part of the family to take the patient back, after a due amount of persuasion by the social worker, terminated consideration of the patient. Most of the families were willing to abide by the decision of the psychiatrist. In these cases, the social worker took an extensive social history.

While this was going on, the patient was transported from the hospital to the downtown clinic by two clinic aides. The clinic staff psychiatrist examined the patient in order to confirm the diagnosis and to satisfy himself that the patient was not dangerous to himself or others. He also conducted a mental status examination and prescribed medication. After the psychiatric interview, the patient was seen by the psychologist who administered a battery of psychological tests.

Once the psychiatrist was satisfied that the patient was acceptable for the program, he relayed this information to the project director who had already been informed by the social worker of the family's decision. If the family was willing to accept the patient, the project director then drew the next *randomized* card from his file which determined this particular patient's group assignment: home on drugs, home on placebo, or hospital control. The appropriate staff members were then informed whether the patient was to go home or was to return to the hospital as a member of the control group. *No one but the project director, however, ever knew whether the home care patient was on drug or placebo medication.*

Before sending a patient home from the clinic, the chief public health nurse once again explained the program to the patient and his family. She also explained the visiting schedule of the nurses and gave the patient his medication. The hospital was notified of our decision to send the patient home and he was placed on convalescent leave for a 1-year period.

Patients designated as hospital controls were returned to the hospital. Their families were told that the psychiatrist felt that continued hospitalization was best for the patient at the present time. Needless to say, patients found unacceptable for the program were also returned to the hospital immediately.

The public health nurse made her first visit to the home care patient the day after he was sent home. Thereafter, the same nurse visited the patient and family weekly for the first 3 months, each time taking a week's supply of the patient's medication. The nurse's visiting schedule conformed to that of the original study design. After each home visit the nurse submitted a written report to the psychiatrist who reviewed the patient's progress. Every other week the nurse recorded the responses of the patient's significant other (husband, wife, parent) to standardized questions pertaining to the patient's behavior and completed an evaluation of the patient's behavior (modified Lorr scale). These, too, were reviewed by the psychiatrist. Data pertaining to the patient's and the relative's conception of his progress were collected every third month by the nurse.

Although the patient could see the psychiatrist whenever he wished or whenever the nurse felt it necessary, each patient was seen at least every 3 months. After 6 months and again after 18 and 24 months at home the patient was given a repeat battery of psychological tests. As with the psychiatrist, the patient and family could see the social worker whenever they desired to do so or whenever it seemed necessary to the nurse or psychiatrist. However, contrary to the original design, the social worker had no routine contact with the patients, and the nurses collected all data of a social nature once the initial social history had been taken.

Patients who did not "succeed" on home treatment were admitted to the hospital. Of necessity, home care success was a subjective evaluation often influenced by the amount of family pressure or agitation. Although the Treatment Center had a 24-hour answering service in the first year of operation, families would occasionally return a patient to the hospital without consulting the treatment staff. Most, however, were admitted to the hospital only after numerous medication changes failed to allay a worsening of the patient's condition. Whenever circumstances allowed, the decision to hospitalize was made by the staff psychiatrist. Once hospitalized, treatment was left to the discretion of the hospital and the patient was dropped from active participation in the program after release. This did not preclude our following them for study. Hospitalized patients were seen by the psychiatrist and psychologist at periodic intervals in order to assess any change in status.

Patients returned to the hospital as members of the control group were also followed. One month after release from the hospital, a public health nurse visited them and systematically questioned them about their present condition and posthospital functioning using the same instruments as for the other two groups. Similar questions were asked of the released patient's family. In addition, these patients were also reevaluated by the psychiatrist and psychologist at periodic intervals.

Within a few months after the home care program began in Louisville, it became evident that even with the modified criteria of selection the state hospital could not supply enough acceptable patients to meet the needs of the research. Louisville General Hospital was consequently asked to refer schizophrenic patients to the Treatment Center and consented to do so. However, since the General Hospital sent those patients who did not respond to a short period of intensive treatment on to the state hospital from which they could be referred anyway, this new source did not account for a very large number of new patients.

To further supplement the supply of patients, all outpatient clinics, social agencies, and physicians in the area were asked to refer schizophrenics or suspected schizophrenics to the Treatment Center. This appeal produced many people who were not schizophrenic and to some degree forced the study clinic to become a screening agency for individuals with a variety of emotional problems. Nevertheless, some ambulatory schizophrenics were uncovered, and if their illness was assessed to be severe enough to warrant hospitalization, they were accepted into the program.

These ambulatory schizophrenics who had been receiving treatment on an outpatient basis from clinics or family physicians could not be handled in the same way as the hospital referrals. When the randomized card for study group selection indicated hospital control, these patients refused to hospitalize themselves and the families concurred. Rather than lose the patient altogether, a separate deck of random cards was made specifying only two groups: home on drugs or home on placebo.

PERSISTENT PROBLEMS

The high percentage but relatively small number of patients referred and found acceptable for the program posed several problems in two areas of operation. Of greatest concern was the fact that the sample did not grow as rapidly as was expected. Whereas it was originally hoped that the number of patients in the study would total approximately 400 after 2 years, it soon became clear that that figure would have to be modified considerably.

In addition to purely research problems, the lack of patients created staff problems during the first 8 months of the program. The morale of the staff, especially the public health nurses, deteriorated during this time because of insufficient work. After several months of training and indoctrination, this period of inactivity resulted in a let-down which was only aggravated by the generally negative attitudes of the local professional community and the fear that the program might be abolished. Later, however, with the increase in the number of patients to the point of total utilization of nursing time, staff morale improved. In fact, it might be said that the uniqueness and importance of the home treatment program created a missionary spirit for many staff members which might not be totally realistic.

Families of patients were usually reluctant to take the patient home, even with home treatment. This was especially true when the family was approached 1 or 2 days after the patient's admission to the hospital. They could not imagine the patient's being "well" enough to go home so soon after hospitalization. The social worker's explanation of the program as a substitute for hospitalization was usually not sufficient to counter the preconceived notion that a hospital would not release a sick patient. Hence, the response of the family seemed to fall into one of three categories: adamant refusal to take the patient home, ambivalence coupled with a willingness to do whatever the psychiatrist felt was best, or willingness to take the patient home because of a feeling that the patient must be better and ready for release. Unfortunately, those relatives who fell into the latter category were often disappointed when they saw and heard the patient.

One criterion of selection for patients eligible for home care was having a family to which they could return and which would cooperate in the supervision of the patient and in reporting the requisite functioning data. Although this prerequisite seemed rather simple, it was the source of some problems. Mention has already been made of the difficulties in getting families to agree to the program. In addition, staff members sometimes felt that the pathogenic family situation may have been a major contributor to the patient's illness. Because of a lack of alternatives, it was necessary for the patient to return to the same situation with the hope that the social worker and public health nurse would be able to relieve some of the family pressures.

Patients living alone prior to hospitalization were accepted if they consented to live with their families during the course of the program. Perhaps the lure of hospital release fostered this agreement on the patient's part, but it was usually forgotten a few weeks after the patient returned home. These arrangements were seldom successful and the patient was likely to strike out on his own again. If the relative was able to maintain frequent and intimate contact with the patient, he was kept on the home care program. Otherwise, the patient was returned to the hospital.

A similar problem of supervision arose when acutely ill patients were sent home and had to remain alone or with small children for a great part of the day. This usually occurred because the patient's significant other (SO) was employed and had to be away from the home. Not to accept these patients would have been to penalize the individuals who returned to fairly normal family situations. However, whenever possible the family was urged to provide some adult supervision for the patient.

Despite the condition of the patient when he was sent home, both the patient and his family tended to lose interest in the program once they believed he was "cured" or even improved. There was a general unwillingness to accept the fact that most patients needed continuing care to prevent repeated episodes. When the patient began to function "normally," the home visits and medication regimen were seen as nuisances. At that point, the patient and family frequently became less cooperative and more difficult to maintain on the program.

At the beginning of the program it was decided that all medications would look exactly alike. Instead of the customary tablets, the drugs were placed by the pharmaceutical companies in #2 pink capsules. Unfortunately, this caused many difficulties. Many patients taking both a tranquilizer and an antidepressant became confused since both medications looked alike. On occasion, a patient or a family, thinking that two different medications were the same, would mix them together. To help avoid this confusion, different medications were placed in different colored slide boxes when they were given to the patient. Another problem arose when the psychiatrist changed a patient from one medication to another. Since all looked alike, the patient was usually dubious about whether his medication was really changed. All that could be done for this patient was to reassure him that a change had been made and that no one was trying to trick him.

When the Institute Treatment Center sent a patient home, it became the agency responsible for the patient's care. This responsibility extended beyond mere treatment for psychiatric illness. The bulk of the home care patients were members of disorganized or dependent families which needed and expected numerous services. The Treatment Center was the agency to which the patient and family turned for counseling, welfare assistance, legal help, and many other types of aid. Although the Institute Treatment Center attempted only to refer the individual or family to the proper community agency, this task grew tremendously with the rising patient load and the increasing demands for information placed on the staff by other agencies. Nevertheless, these needs of the patients were not frivolous and could not be ignored if one wished to maintain the patient in the community.

This was particularly true of the patient's physical ailments. A hospitalized mental patient who was physically ill would ordinarily be treated for these ills while hospitalized. When the patient was sent home within a day or two of his admission, these physical ills went unattended unless some arrangements could be made in the community. This compounded the difficulty for the treatment staff which had to treat the patient's psychiatric illness and also see to it that his physical illness was treated through whatever community facilities were available. In other words, home treatment in lieu of hospitalization placed on the home care clinic responsibilities which would ordinarily have been shared by several agencies.

For the first year of the program, patients and families were told that they could call a 24-hour answering service at any time if unusual problems arose. The answering service would then call one of the five nurses who would return the call to the patient or family. If the problem was serious enough, the nurse would phone the psychiatrist for his opinion before she would advise the family or patient. In a very short time, the number of these calls grew to the point where it was unfair to ask the nurses to assume this responsibility at all hours of the night. In addition, very few of the calls turned out to be real emergencies or crises. It was estimated that at least 95 percent of the calls could have waited until the next day when someone was in the office. Therefore, after a year's experience, the answering service was instructed to inform all callers to call back after 8:30 AM the next day or, if the caller insisted that an emergency existed, to advise him to call the police department for aid.

Of course, the potential danger and the risk involved in having acutely psychotic patients in the community, many on placebo, was a continual source of concern for the study director and the clinic staff. Although the risk was probably little greater for this population than for a nonpsychotic population, there is little doubt that any major act of violence on the part of one of the study patients could have ended the home care program. As it turned out, during the 3-year course of the study there were no such incidents, although two patients did make unsuccessful attempts at suicide.

The persistent problems which have already been enumerated were generally problems pertaining to program design and patient maintenance. In addition, another source of concern was the basic orientation of the staff and their adjustment to new roles. Although these problems will be examined at length in the next chapter, a word is in order at this point. The professional study staff consisted of a project director who had no direct contact with patients in a treatment role, a psychiatrist, psychologist, social worker, and five public health nurses. With the exception of the project director, the others were service-oriented people with little or no research background. In general, this meant only a superficial understanding of many of the demands and requirements placed on the staff by the research objectives. The use of a placebo, sending an acutely ill patient home, returning a patient to an unfavorable environment, and the inability to solve many of the patients' social problems were but a few of the things which the staff found hard to accept. This basic treatment and service orientation to the ill was, on the other hand, an attitude which probably accounted for much of the success of the home care patients.

INSTRUMENTS

Five types of measures and instruments were used in an attempt to evaluate the effectiveness of the home care program. In retrospect, perhaps too frequent ratings of patient functioning were secured. Certainly, one of the major problems in the study involved the collection of these evaluations at the regularly scheduled time. The test battery included periodic assessments of all aspects of patient functioning which could be reasonably obtained.

Psychiatric Evaluation

Two separate instruments were used to assess the mental status of each patient. The staff psychiatrist was wholly and solely responsible for obtaining these ratings. The first instrument, administered at admission and at 6 and 18 months as well as at discharge was the *Inpatient Multidimensional Psychiatric Scale* (IMPS) of Lorr and associates.[3] This scale had been standardized with functional psychotics who can be interviewed. It consists of brief, unlabelled rating scales and dichotomous items which combine into 10 syndromes. These syndromes, in turn, combine into three morbidity scores which are excitement-retardation, perceptual and thinking distortion, and schizophrenic disorganization. The IMPS had been selected because of previous favorable experience with it and also because it yields a schizophrenic disorganization morbidity score.

The second mental status measure used was the Psychiatric Inventory. This instrument was a modification of the Adult Outpatient Initial Psychiatric Interview developed at the Lafayette Clinic in Detroit. In principle, this checklist inventory was designed to obtain quantitative and qualitative assessments of the same material which normally goes into the write-up of a case history. The Psychiatric Inventory contains the following sections: history of present illness, prominent features of

[3] Maurice Lorr, C. James Klett, Douglas M. McNair, and Julian Lasky, *Inpatient Multidimensional Psychiatric Scale (IMPS) Manual*, Veterans Administration, 1962.

present illness, past history, mental status examination results (motor, facial, speech), emotional reactions, disturbances in thinking, and diagnosis and prognosis.

Psychological Tests

Four psychological tests were administered by the staff psychologist on the same schedule as the psychiatric evaluations: the Wechsler Adult Intelligence Scale (WAIS), a reaction time test series, the Bender Gestalt, and the Porteus Mazes tests. The WAIS is a standard intelligence test which has been widely used with mental patients. The reason for selecting this or any other test of intelligence was that it provided a baseline on the intellectual impairment of the patients, and of improvement or change with time.

A complex reaction time test was used previously with chronic schizophrenic patients by the psychological consultant, Dr. Athan Karras, and was included as one of the four psychological measures because of the highly satisfactory results which had been obtained. The test involves the presentation of a series of five lights which the subject turns off as each appears. The lights are presented in five blocks with twenty trials per block. The initial presentation is sequential from left to right and later presentations are also sequential but in a more complex pattern. Response speed is electrically timed. The median block scores are summed and the means derived. Functional impairment is theoretically directly related to the mean reaction time.

The Bender Gestalt is another standard psychological test in which the patient is presented with a series of cards containing geometric patterns which he must reproduce with each card in front of him. The Pascal and Suttell scoring system yields a perceptual-motor disorganization score. The lower the score, the less the pathology.

The Porteus Mazes was the fourth psychological test used in this study. The test consists of a series of mazes of increasing difficulty which the subject traces from a peripheral starting point to an inside end point. Two scores are derived. The first, IQ, is considered to be a measure of the ability to plan action; the second, the QE, is an error score and is considered to be a measure of pathology.

A fifth psychological test, the Minnesota Multiphasic (MMPI) was used in the pilot study and was discarded because there was insufficient variation in response profiles among the subjects to warrant inclusion in the test battery.

Social History

A complete social history was taken by the social worker. Demographic variables and family history composed Part I of this schedule. Part II dealt mostly with the psychiatric treatment history. Part III included sections on the patient's behavior and problems, social participation and activities. Part IV applied to male patients only and attempted to elicit information regarding prehospital employment and general functioning as well as expectations for role performance. Part V, restricted to females, substituted performance of household duties for employment performance and expectations. Part VI applied only when the patient had a child 16 years of age or younger. It sought to get at parent-child relationships and such things as parental attachment and aspirations for the child. The respondent was *not* the patient but rather the significant other of the patient, usually husband, wife, father, or mother.

Nurses' Reports

Most of the large number of research instruments which had to be completed were the responsibility of the nurses. Specifically, there was the Multidimensional Scale for Rating Psychiatric Patients (MSPP), a behavior chart checklist, a physical and general status rating sheet, a nursing report, and a significant other report.

The MSPP instrument is identical to the Lorr IMPS. The nurse completed this form, which deals with psychological symptoms and signs, on each visit to the home. In this way a weekly, bi-weekly, and later a monthly record of the patient's mental status was available. The second instrument, the behavior chart checklist, originated with the staff psychiatrist and was also completed on each home visit. It was simply a listing of 37 adjectives mostly associated with poor mental health. The nurse merely checked those adjectives which appeared descriptive of patient behavior at the time. The chart was submitted to the psychiatrist after each visit. The third form completed at each home visit was a physical and general status form. On it were recorded the patient's temperature, pulse, and blood pressure as well as comments on general physical condition and appetite. Most importantly, it contained an open ended section in which the nurse summarized her impressions of changes in patient functioning and problems gleaned from the home visit. These comments became the basis for the continuing narrative about selected patients to be found in Chapter 8.

Two measures were obtained on a monthly basis. The first of these was called the SO (significant other) Rating Report. This rating form is a parallel version of the IMPS ratings of the psychiatrist and the MSPP ratings of the nurses. The significant other was asked to indicate the presence or absence (yes or no) of psychological symptoms in the patient since the last visit.

The final parallel instruments were completed every 3 months. Both the patient and relative were asked about the patient's performance and expectation for performance. The instrument was the same as Parts IV or V of the social history depending on whether the patient was male or female. On the same visit a Public Health Nursing (PHN) Report was also collected. This form required judgments from the nurse about the nature and suitability of the household in which the patient resided both from the point of view of adequacy of supervision of the patient and of the effect on the family of having a patient at home.

These instruments, except the standardized psychological tests and the reaction time program, are included in Appendix A.

SUMMARY STATEMENT OF PROCEDURES

Because of possible confusion in following all of the various stages in the design of this study from intake to discharge, a 21-step summary of the procedure concludes this chapter.

1. Patient arrived at Central State Hospital and was placed on the admission ward with no immediate treatment.
2. If the initial diagnosis, usually made within a day, was schizophrenia, the patient became eligible for study consideration and the hospital psychiatrist checked further to determine if the other criteria were met: not dangerous, proper age, residence in Louisville area, and some family.
3. When a patient qualified, the ITC was phoned and arrangements were made to have him brought to the Center as quickly as possible.

4. The patient's family was called by the ITC social worker who arranged for them to be at the Center when the patient was examined.
5. At the proper time the patient was transferred from the hospital to the center where he was examined by the staff psychiatrist who determined psychiatric eligibility.
6. While this was being done, the social worker was explaining the program to the family and determining their willingness to take the patient home. She also completed an extensive social history at this time.
7. Once the family expressed willingness, the social worker relayed this information to the study director.
8. When the psychiatrist completed his interview with the patient, he informed the study director of the patient's eligibility.
9. If the psychiatrist found the patient acceptable and if the family was willing to take the patient home, the study director pulled the next randomly assigned card to determine the patient's study group: home on drugs, home on placebo, or hospital control.
10. This determination having been made, the study director informed via the telephone both the psychiatrist and the social worker.
11. The social worker relayed this information to the family, saying that the psychiatrist had decided that the patient could best be treated at home or in the hospital.
12. Once the patient was definitely accepted as part of the study, he was tested by the ITC staff psychologist.
13. Patients returning to the hospital were taken back immediately. Those going home were placed on convalescent leave as soon as the hospital was informed of the ITC's decision.
14. Before a home care patient and his family left the Treatment Center, the study director prepared the proper medication as per the psychiatrist's prescription and the study assignment.
15. The chief public health nurse again explained the program to the patient and his family and instructed them as to when the medication must be taken.
16. The patient's regular nurse made her first home visit the next day and once each week after that for the first 3 months.
17. At the end of 3 months, the patient returned to the Center for an examination by the psychiatrist. Such reexaminations by the psychiatrist occurred every 3 months thereafter.
18. Between the fourth, fifth, and sixth months of home care, the nurse visited the patient every other week. After the sixth month, the visits were restricted to once a month.

19. The staff psychiatrist completed a formal psychiatric inventory for every study patient after 6, 18, and 24 months on the program.
20. After 6, 18, and 24 months on the program, all patients, home care and hospital controls, were given the entire battery of psychological tests.
21. Patients still at home after at least 24 months of home care were discharged from the program.

4

PERSONNEL PROBLEMS AND POLICIES

It is well known that acute shortages exist in all categories of professional health personnel, but it is not as well known that it is unlikely that there will be any change or radical improvement in the near future. Thus, if community mental health centers are not to become still another competitor for already scarce personnel, these centers will have to recruit competent staff members from the nonmental health professions and related disciplines. General practitioners, public health and practical nurses, guidance counselors, and others without extensive previous experience in treating the mentally ill will have to play a major role in these projected programs.

Not only will it be necessary to recruit personnel from the nonmental health disciplines, but it will also be necessary for certain professions to function in new and as yet largely uncharted roles. It is quite probable that in these new treatment settings the traditional roles of service-oriented professionals will have to be modified to include new functions. By the same token, old and established functions may well become obsolete and impractical. Until such time as a new balance can be struck, it will be necessary to experiment with new roles as well as redefine the old.

In this home care study, the role expectations of several traditional professions were modified to meet both treatment and research needs. The psychiatrist, public health nurse, psychiatric social worker, and psychologist each performed valuable and necessary functions, but not necessarily the same functions that they would have performed in another type of psychiatric care setting. This chapter discusses the role of each of these treatment oriented professionals in an experimental, home care project.

ROLE OF THE STUDY DIRECTOR

Before discussing the roles of each of the other staff participants in the Louisville ITC study, the critical role of the study director deserves mention. The study director and coauthor of this monograph was an advanced graduate student in the Department of Sociology at the Ohio State University in 1961 when he agreed to undertake direction of and assume responsibility for this home care study. His initial and continuing responsibilities were primarily administrative. They included such varied activities as negotiating a lease for the clinic building, purchasing the office furniture, hiring all of the personnel, arranging for the training of the nurses, supervising the daily activities of the staff, scheduling vacations, signing vouchers, and ordering and dispensing drugs. These and other duties were necessary merely to keep the Center running smoothly.

The study director was also responsible for maintaining complete and continuous liaison with Central State Hospital, the general hospital, and other treatment centers, and for maintaining good relations with the Department of Mental Health and the various professional groups in the community. Some of these public, professional, and community relations responsibilities were shared with the staff psychiatrist and the other members of the ITC staff. The Commissioner of Mental Health also helped a great deal in these areas. Nevertheless, fence-mending and community relations problems occupied a considerable proportion of the director's time.

In the area of research, the study director was responsible for training the personnel in the use of the instruments, emphasizing and explaining again and again the need for the seemingly endless data collection, making sure the data were gathered as scheduled, and setting up the random card files for patient assignment as well as for dispensing the medication —drug or placebo.

In the third year of the study, the original director was replaced by a new director, also a recent graduate of the doctoral program in Sociology at Ohio State University. In addition to maintaining the staff, patients, and the research program the new director later was responsible for curtailing patient intake, getting patients either discharged from the

ITC program or transferred to other outpatient facilities in the area, and for eventually closing the Center itself.

ROLE OF THE PSYCHIATRIST

Two part-time psychiatrists were members of the home care study staff. One, on the Central State Hospital medical staff, screened all new patients admitted to the hospital. Any patient whose illness was diagnosed as schizophrenia and who appeared to meet the other criteria of patient selection was referred by him to the Institute Treatment Center. This was meant to be a rough screening, or the first gate, since final determination of patient acceptability would come later. Therefore, the hospital psychiatrist was primarily interested in the patient's diagnosis and in seeing to it that potential ITC patients were held on the admission ward without treatment until transferred to the Center.

The final decision as to a patient's psychiatric acceptability for the program rested with the part-time staff psychiatrist responsible for patient treatment. He had to answer three important questions: (1) Is the patient's illness schizophrenia? (2) If so, is it severe enough to warrant immediate hospitalization? (3) Is the patient potentially suicidal or homicidal? To answer these questions and to determine the patient's mental status, he examined every person considered for the home care study. In the beginning of the study, the initial examination at the Institute Treatment Center included a physical checkup as well as a psychiatric evaluation. Later, when the patient load and referrals increased, the physical examination was modified to include only a check of the patient's temperature, blood pressure, and weight. If the patient was diagnostically and otherwise acceptable for study inclusion and was assigned to the home care group, the psychiatrist prescribed medication.

Immediately after the initial interview with the patient, the psychiatrist completed the Psychiatric Inventory and the Lorr IMPS. These measures of the patient's current mental status went into the psychiatrist's file for future reference along with his notes on the case and any medical records requested from other hospitals, clinics, or physicians. For a short period of time, the psychiatrist dictated a medical report on every patient accepted for the study. This too was later abandoned when the case load increased.

Patients accepted as part of the study were then seen by the psychiatrist at regular intervals. Home care patients were seen every 3 months for reevaluation, although the mental status inventories were completed only at 6-month intervals. Hospital control patients were evaluated again after 6 and 18 months whether or not they still were hospitalized.

Experience indicated that the 3-months reevaluation schedule was not a realistic goal in every case. It was necessary for the psychiatrist to see many patients much more often than that. When the nurse was wary of a patient's behavior or when she thought his vital signs were irregular she asked that the patient be seen. Families, and patients themselves, often demanded that the psychiatrist see the patient more often than every 3 months. Whenever possible, therefore, the psychiatrist saw every patient as often as he could.

Aside from the initial diagnosis and prescription of medication, the psychiatrist's contact with the patients was quite limited and he depended wholly upon the public health nurse to keep him informed. Each week he read the nurses' reports on their patients and, in effect, decided whether or not to continue the current treatment unchanged. This often demanded that the psychiatrist consult with the nurse and question her further about the patient's condition. Therefore, a significant portion of his mornings at the Center were devoted to such patient maintenance activities. Another significant portion of his time was devoted to what might be called "nurse maintenance" activity. The nurses needed and demanded a great deal of support from the psychiatrist. Often unsure of what they should do and say in particular situations, they frequently came to the psychiatrist for advice and information. Although he seldom gave them explicit instructions, he did listen to them and help them work through their own difficulties. He performed the same role in staff meetings when the nurses aired their frustrations and fears about particular patients.

From the beginning of the study the staff psychiatrist was able to devote only 2 days each week to the program. First as a third-year resident, and later as he fulfilled an employment obligation to the State Department of Mental Health, he was forced to handle his duties as the Treatment Center's psychiatrist on only a part-time basis. This, of course, created many problems, especially for the nurses who often felt that their questions about a patient's behavior or condition could not wait until the psychiatrist was again at the Center. In cases of emergency the psychiatrist was always accessible by telephone, but to have a long talk with five nurses over the telephone three mornings a week was impossible.

Out of a feeling of unfilled need, the nurses began turning to the psychiatric social worker for advice and counsel.

The limited time of the psychiatrist also meant that discussions with family members who desired to see him had to be limited. It was quite rare for him to consent to see a family member who had questions about the patient's illness. He felt that the nurse and the social worker should handle this and free his time for patient supervision. Unfortunately, many families, especially those of the ambulatory patients who were accustomed to speaking with private physicians whenever they desired, were not satisfied with talking to a nurse or social worker. This created problems for the staff and especially for the nurse who was very dependent upon the rapport she had to establish and maintain with the patient's family.

Like the other service-oriented professionals associated with this study, the staff psychiatrist also had initial qualms about the use of placebo medications. However, unlike some of the other members of the treatment team, he quickly overcame his misgivings about this phase of the study design and proceeded as though all patients were on drugs. As any psychiatrist in a similar outpatient clinic, he had to rely mainly upon the psychoactive drugs to keep the patient in the community. The lack of precedent for treating this type of patient at home dictated a certain amount of experimentation in prescribing medications. In the early stages (first 6 months) of the program dosages were quite conventional and in line with amounts prescribed for outpatients. Later, however, as the patients' tolerances proved to be greater than expected, the use of drugs became bolder and patient success increased. Other factors, of course, might also have been significant for this improvement.

The problem of drug defectors is one that is common to outpatient clinics and had to be faced by the psychiatrist on this program. Many patients simply refused to take medication, or at least the prescribed dosage. To help detect these patients, the psychiatrist asked that some method be established to help determine whether or not the drugs were being taken. As a consequence, all drugs used in the home care program contained 0.5 mg. of riboflavin. This acted as a tracer which could be detected in a urine specimen placed under an ultraviolet lamp. The identification of drug defectors was important since those patients taking placebo may have shown a similar lack of drug effectiveness. When the defectors—drug and placebo—were discovered, they were urged to take their medication as prescribed or face the possibility of being returned to the hospital. However, the use of riboflavin as a tracer did not prove to be the answer since it was soon discovered that taking only one capsule per day had the same effect on the color of the urine as taking any other number of capsules. After about 18 months of using riboflavin as a tracer it was abandoned and, as a last resort, the psychiatrist simply had to urge the nurse to threaten the patient with hospitalization if he continued to refuse to take his medication as prescribed.

Threatening hospitalization in these cases was quite out of character for the psychiatrist. In practically every other instance, he was much more willing than other members of the treatment team to keep a patient at home even under the most difficult of circumstances. Often, in the face of demands by the family that the patient be hospitalized and ambivalence on the part of the nurse about the efficacy of continued home care, the psychiatrist refused to order hospitalization until a medication change had time to become effective or he had an opportunity to see the patient personally. It was obvious that his expectations for patient functioning were not as great as those of the families or the nurses and he was, therefore, more tolerant of what to others seems like intolerable behavior. Of course, when necessary, he did make the decision to hospitalize patients when, but not usually before, all else seemed to have failed.

In a home care program such as this, ultimate responsibility for the patients is vested in the psychiatrist. In this role he must decide if a patient is dangerous, prescribe medication, supervise the nurse's program of care, and make the decision if and when to hospitalize the patient. He is responsible for sicker patients, and for more patients than is a private psychiatrist or one in an outpatient clinic. He must defend and explain the program to family physicians who may be recommending that the patient return to the hospital. Unfortunately, these perplexing problems are inherent in any program of this type and defy simple guide lines and do's and dont's.

ROLE OF THE PUBLIC HEALTH NURSE[1]

This study as noted before was patterned on the home care for tuberculosis patients model because it was felt that schizophrenia as a chronic disease had many similarities, both medical and social, to tuber-

[1] In this connection, see, Ida Gelber, *Released Mental Patients on Tranquiliz-*

culosis and might therefore be treated in a comparable manner. This treatment model and other reasons, too, prompted the selection of public health rather than psychiatric nurses as the principal participants in this program. First, the public health nurse, by virtue of her training and experience and traditional service activities as friend, counselor, advisor, general supporter, observer, and informant on patient and family life, is uniquely equipped to function in a home care mental health program. Second, the public health nurse normally commands well-earned respect and support and is a welcome figure to most families and in most communities. Third, despite a shortage, public health nurses numbering 30,000 nationally, are more readily available than are psychiatric nurses. Fourth, since this project was to represent a considerable departure from previous practices, it was felt that the public health nurse would be more amenable to the innovations involved in this program as well as to its specific research aspects.

Because an intimate knowledge of the community was necessary, 5 local, experienced public health nurses were recruited from a pool of 35 applicants. Once recruited, a training program was initiated for them. Because the nurses would have to serve as a liaison between the patient and the clinic, and collect an enormous amount of material on each visit, they were subjected to a rigorous training program which provided them with the knowledge and techniques they would need. This training program was administered by the staff of Central State Hospital and entailed a 2-week orientation program designed to familiarize the nurse with such areas as social service work, psychiatric nursing, general concepts employed in psychiatry, and specific treatment procedures. Employing lectures, films, discussions, and demonstrations, members of the hospital staff presented various aspects of working with the mentally ill. After this 2-week program of formal training, the nurses remained at the hospital for another 4 weeks. During this time, they circulated on the wards, observing and talking with patients, members of patients' families who visited, and with staff. They also practiced using the patient rating forms which they would later employ with their home care patients.

Toward the end of this 6-week training period, the Institute Treat-

---

ing Drugs and the Public Health Nurse, New York: New York University Press, 1959; and Frank Scarpitti, Joseph Albini, Elizabeth Baker, Simon Dinitz, and Benjamin Pasamanick, "Public Health Nurses in a Community Care Program for the Mentally Ill," *Amer. J. Nurs.,* **65** (June, 1965), 89–95.

ment Center psychiatrist visited the hospital frequently and interviewed patients in the presence of the nurses. During these interviews, each nurse would rate the mental status of the patient, using a standardized rating scale. After the interview, the nurses discussed their ratings with the psychiatrist and exchanged opinions as to why they had rated the patient as they did. The nurses also took turns interviewing patients while being observed by the psychiatrist, thus enabling him to evaluate their techniques and offer suggestions for improvement. Following this training period within the hospital, the nurses spent several weeks interviewing recently discharged mental patients and their significant others in the home. This provided them not only with the opportunity to experiment with the instruments and schedules but to talk with recently discharged mental patients and their families in the home setting. It was only after this extensive training period which included considerable patient contact, that the study director and psychiatrist felt that the nurses were ready to begin the home care program.

THE RESEARCH ROLE OF THE NURSE

Once the study got under way, the nurse's role was divided into two aspects, research and treatment. The nurse began her series of visits to the home care patient the day after he was accepted into the program. At each visit she recorded the patient's temperature, pulse, respiration, blood pressure, and weight, and obtained information regarding sleep pattern and appetite. She also wrote any comments about the patient which she thought were pertinent. These data were submitted to the staff psychiatrist after every home visit along with the patient's behavior chart—a check list of characteristics pertaining to general behavioral status. As already noted, the psychiatrist relied greatly upon this information for his continuing assessment of the patient's condition.

During every home visit the nurse was required to rate each patient on the Multidimensional Scale for Rating Psychiatric Patients (MSPP). The staff psychiatrist also rated the patients using the same instrument. The results indicated that the nurses' ratings tended to show a lesser degree of patient impairment, and the two sets of ratings—psychiatrist and nurses—at patient intake showed a correlation of +.53.

In addition to the nurse's evaluation of the patient, the significant other was also asked a series of questions about the patient's behavior.

This SO Rating Scale consisted of 128 questions which were very similar to the items in the MSPP and were answered either yes or no. These questions were asked of the patient's relative on a monthly basis.

Every 3 months, the nurse submitted a lengthy progress report for each patient. This report consisted of a structured instrument indicating the patient's current status, the significant other's perceptions of the patient's functioning and behavior, the family's attitudes toward home care, and the patient's own feelings about his condition and ability to function in the home and community environment. The nurse was also given an opportunity at this time to give her subjective impressions of the patient's progress, his family and their ability to look after him, and any "movement" or changes she felt were occurring in either the patient or family.

Unfortunately, some patients were not successful on home treatment and had to be readmitted to the hospital. When such "failures" occurred, the nurse immediately visited the family and completed the SO Rating Scale and a progress report. In addition, the nurse wrote a report on each "failure" which was a synopsis of the case and the reasons for and precipitants of the patient's inability to remain at home.

The staff nurses also had research contact with the group of hospital control patients. One month after a member of this group was released from the hospital, a nurse would visit him in his home and explain that the State Hospital was interested in finding out how he was getting along. During this visit, she would talk with the patient and his significant other and complete the following schedules: MSPP, SO Rating Scale, and progress report. Other than this, the nurse had no contact with the hospital control patient.

THE TREATMENT ROLE OF THE NURSE

The nurse's research role was meant to complement her treatment role although there were times when she found the two quite incompatible. As a researcher she was expected to gather and record data in an unbiased and objective fashion. At the same time, however, she could not lose sight of her primary goal of home care for the mentally ill patient.

The assignment of a nurse to a patient was based upon the nurse's case load and to a lesser extent on the patient's geographic residence.

Once assigned, however, the same nurse visited the patient throughout his stay in the study. This was done because it was believed that the effectiveness of the nurse would depend upon the degree of rapport she established with patient and family. This rapport, it was felt, would be enhanced by having the same nurse visit the home repeatedly and acquiring an intimate knowledge of the patient and his environment.

The official treatment duties of the nurse seemed quite simple. On each home visit she would bring the patient enough free medication to last until her next visit. She would then check the patient's vital signs, after which she would advise and counsel the patient and his family in the traditional public health fashion. This essential function, in terms of keeping the patient out of the hospital, turned out to be more difficult and complex than in the usual visiting nurse case. A large number of patients came from multiproblem families and needed assistance in many areas. They turned to the nurse for help regarding physical illness, economic problems, and family problems, as well as for assistance in understanding and combating mental illness.

The patient-nurse relationship was sometimes the only stable relationship many patients had ever experienced. More than anything else, the nurse, who was not trained to provide therapy, apparently played a very therapeutic role simply by showing interest in the patient and permitting him to talk about his problems. At no time did the nurse attempt traditional psychotherapy, but merely offered commonsense advice and reassurance to the patient. The patients generally seemed satisfied by this supportive therapy.

The patient, however, was not the only one who needed and looked forward to the nurse's support. In most cases, other members of the patient's family needed the continual reassurance of the nurse and came to depend upon her as much as did the patient. The families of the patients sought the nurse's guidance regarding the management of the patient's difficult behavior, how they should relate to the patient, what they should tell neighbors about the patient, and a host of other problems.

Needless to say, the nurse was not always equipped to handle the more difficult problems presented in the home situation. Whenever necessary, the nurse would recommend that the patient or family visit the staff psychiatrist and or social worker for help she did not feel competent to render. It was not unusual for her to call into the clinic from the patient's home and make an appointment for him to see one of the other treatment staff members.

At least twice a week the nurses discussed with the clinic psychiatrist any persistent problems they were having with a patient or family. During these sessions, he was often able to interpret or clarify many of the patient's actions and indicate the best way to handle difficult situations. To a greater extent, however, this was done by the psychiatric social worker with whom the nurses had almost daily contact.

PROBLEMS ENCOUNTERED BY THE NURSES

Since this project is to some degree a likely prototype of programs to be instituted under the aegis of the comprehensive community mental health centers, some of the problems encountered by the public health nurses, and their reactions to them, deserve consideration. These problems will be discussed under two headings—research and general problems.

The Use of Placebos

The most persistent research problem confronted by the nurses was their certain knowledge that many home care patients were receiving placebo medication. Although the need for this procedure had been painstakingly explained to them at the beginning of the study and discussed with them on innumerable other occasions and was clearly understood by all, it still violated their conceptions of the nursing role and remained a difficult problem throughout. Wrote one of the nurses when queried about this problem of the use of placebos: "No good nurse approves. Enough said." Said another:

> This was a very 'bitter pill' for the nurses to take even after talking with Dr. ________. We were very worried that there might be violence on the part of a patient taking placebos and that he would harm himself or others. I feel, however, that we adjusted to the fact that it was part of the program and a very necessary part. However, because of the use of placebos, I think we were probably more apt to bring all the little problems to the attention

of the psychiatrist to help take the share of blame from our shoulders if there were any disasters.

A third nurse summed up her reactions as follows:

> Never having worked on a research project before, it was hard for me to accustom and reconcile myself to the placebo and I never did fully. I felt frustrated and rather belligerent when I felt a patient might be on placebos who might have a good chance of functioning well if he were on drugs.

Collection of Research Data

A close second as a major and continuing problem to the nurses was the never-ending collection of research data. As previously indicated these included patient progress reports, patient functioning schedules, significant other reports of patient functioning, a general report form, and one designed to obtain information requested by the psychiatrist. This questioning tended to irritate the significant others and sometimes the patients as well. One nurse described this problem as follows:

> The significant others frequently became resentful and sarcastic. They avoided these interviews when they could. The patients would say 'not that again' but didn't show their resentment as openly as the significant others.

Patients who Failed

In the beginning, the nurses were inexperienced and probably fearful. This appeared to be reflected in the relatively high drug home care failure rate in the first 6 months which occurred despite the fact that the nurses had more time available for each patient than at any subsequent time. In the second 6 months, with greater experience and less fear and with the added incentive of keeping patients at home lest the study be discontinued, the drug failure rate dropped. Thereafter, this lowered rate was more or less maintained. The placebo patients, however, failed at more like the same rate throughout the study. It may very well be that in the drug patients the combined effect of drugs and more experienced nursing care served to lower the failure rate after the initial 6-month period. However, the numbers involved in each 6-month period were too small to say this with any degree of certainty.

A corollary problem concerned the necessity of preventing study "dropouts." Many of the dropouts, of whom there were only 11 among the state hospital patients in the 30 months of the program, left the state or area and consequently presented few problems. The remainder were either noncooperative, or, more commonly, sought and received private care. In any case, gathering data on the mental status of these patients for research purposes was a difficult and, not infrequently, unrewarding burden.

In addition to these specific difficulties occasioned by the nature of the research itself, certain more general problems are likely to be present in any community program.

Acceptance of the Nurses

By and large, the public health nurse was very well accepted in the home. The patients and families were usually grateful for her attention and the free service that they were receiving. It must be pointed out that the vast majority of the study patients were of lower-class status and they were acquainted with the public health nurse tradition. She was a familiar sight in their neighborhoods and her visiting the home was not seen as conferring social stigma. This was not the case, however, with the few middle-class patients treated on the project. They were much less accepting of a uniformed public health nurse visiting the home and were often worried about what the neighbors would think if they saw her. Three of the nurses were asked to remove their hats before visiting, by at least one each of their middle-class families, so that they would be less conspicuous. One nurse reported that one of the families wanted to pay for her services and the medication she left. Still another nurse reported that her middle-class patients wanted to be discharged from the project as soon as there was some improvement in mental status.

Along with this minor amount of resistance and embarrassment on the part of the middle-class patients, the nurses also had some trouble with patients who worked. Not only did the nurse not wish to stigmatize the patient but there was also the problem of leaving his medication for him while he was on the job, and also of interrupting his lunch hour in the process.

It is a tribute to the five staff nurses that there was so little resistance by patients and families and it confirmed the original belief that the public health nurse is well suited to supervise and manage schizophrenic patients at home.

Supportive Therapy and Length of Visits

In contrast to the generally well defined role of the public health nurse in dealing with physical illness and communicable diseases, her role within the new area of community mental health presented some definite differences in the functions she was expected to perform. Experience confirmed that the care of the psychiatric patient in the home differs significantly from other types of public health care. Whereas the average nonspecialized public health nurse may be expected to make about eight home visits per day, the nurses participating in this project were able to visit only four patients per day. Although these visits were lengthened by the data collection duties, and the large amount of travel time in covering the Louisville metropolitan area, the major reason can be traced to the patient's need to talk with the nurse. Consultation with the psychiatrist and social worker also consumed a good deal of time.

The insecurities and lack of understanding surrounding mental illness and its manifestation placed both the patient and the significant other in a somewhat precarious position. Unlike physical illness where some explanation of the cause and effect conditions of the illness can be offered with some degree of intelligibility to the patient and family, an attempt at explanation in mental illness is not so easily accomplished. The nurses simply answered some of the questions raised by patients and families as best they could and with a considerable lack of confidence in their explanations. Some very typical and unanswerable questions were: What are the chances ______ will be cured? How soon will this happen? Will he be able to work again? How long will he have to take medicine? Will he relapse? Why did they send him home so soon from the hospital?

Although she could not always allay the anxieties of both patients and families, the nurse did offer at least one form of aid—the consolation of listening to their problems. While this did not necessarily solve any of the particular problems at hand, the nurses felt that in listening, they established stronger rapport with the patient and family. This high degree of rapport also served to improve the cooperation of patient and family in keeping appointments for the psychological testing evaluation. Because of the essential nature of the nurse's home visit to the program, it was impossible for the nurse to limit her visit to any specified length of time. As a result, the nurses serving in this program, unlike those dealing with other aspects of public health nursing, found their daily number of possible home visits greatly limited.

The Use and Misuse of Medication

Central to this minimal home care program was the use of tranquilizing drugs and antidepressants. Not only did the nurse not know which of her patients were being given placebos, but she also did not always know whether her patients were actually taking the prescribed medication. In a few instances, over- rather than undermedication posed a threat to the patient's welfare. In a few others, excessive drinking complicated the difficulties.

Generally speaking, most patients cooperated in taking the prescribed medication. Those who did not specified all sorts of reasons for failing to do so. These reasons given the nurses by drug defectors, included such things as, "forgot about taking pills," "didn't need medication," "drugs didn't help," and also that improvement was so great that drug use was discontinued. In such cases, the nurses cajoled recalcitrant patients, urged the significant others to exercise additional supervision in this area, and sometimes even felt compelled to threaten hospitalization for the defector. This threat, for a period of time at least, was sufficient to improve cooperation in taking medication. In the few cases where even this threat did not appear to be effective, an appointment was scheduled for the patient with the staff psychiatrist who tried to prevail upon him to resume taking medication as prescribed.

Psychotic Episodes

Although periodic episodes are quite common with chronic schizophrenics, and the nurses had been so advised time and again, these episodes continued to create problems both for the family and the nurse. Families usually reacted in patterned ways. Some insisted on immediate rehospitalization, others on changes in medication, some wanted an immediate appointment with the staff psychiatrist, and most expressed a feeling of utter helplessness and futility. Some unhappy significant others blamed themselves, and lamented their fate, and in a very few cases expressed the feeling that the patient was simply being "mean." In response to these episodes, nurses would try to schedule an immediate appointment for the patient with the psychiatrist, or request a change in medication, or both. Nurses would also schedule extra visits to the home. Above all, they would expend enormous efforts in reassuring the family and in counseling significant others. All of this was quite a strain on the nurses. As one of them wrote:

> I often felt depressed and very inadequate. As in all fields of nursing I would ask myself what I did wrong or what else could I have done to help. My emotions about episodes or failures varied greatly at the end of the program compared to the beginning. I had only been told that episodes were not unusual—that there would be ups and downs. At the end of the program I had experienced this many times. I felt protective toward the patient and was annoyed by home conditions that I felt were the direct cause of the episode and toward the family that seemed not to care enough, try enough, or who seemed sick themselves and also at society for allowing many of these conditions to exist. Sometimes my emotions about a patient's episode were partially controlled by the variable of how I felt myself that particular day.

Relations with Other Team Members

The nurse, of course, carried the largest share of the program and the most immediate responsibility for the patients and families involved. Nevertheless others—the psychiatrist, social worker and psychologist—were equally members of the team and the nurse remained as dependent upon them as they upon her in the conduct of this study. Generally, the nurses looked to the staff psychiatrist for advice on how to manage the patients and for understanding the nature of their patients' problems. There were two problems—both accentuated by the use of placebo medication and the fact that patients were often returned home while still acutely sick—which appeared time and again to the mutual discomfiture of the nurses and psychiatrist. One involved the desire of the nurses for direct orders as to how to proceed and what to do in dealing with their patients. The other concerned the desire of the nurses, often under extreme pressure from the families, to hospitalize an acutely sick patient sooner than the psychiatrist deemed advisable. These problems between psychiatrist and nurses as perceived by the nurses, were described as follows:

This was my first contact with a psychiatrist and at first I expected him to act as any other physician with whom I had worked before, expecting direct orders as to what to do and say and exactly how to handle the patients. To my amazement and confusion, I would tell him that a certain patient, on my visit, would rant and rave quoting the Bible one minute and calling me names the next and finally throwing a glass of water in my face and he would listen but not comment, or ask, "was she taking her medicine," and I would leave the office feeling I was no better off than before I went in. I would feel I talked too much and then before I would come out I would answer all my own questions.

Having such close contact as we had in our small group, we probably talked to the psychiatrist more than the ordinary nurse talks to a doctor and I feel that maybe a lot of the things I took to him were trivial and now feel possibly this was his way of making me do my own thinking and therefore recognize symptoms, etc.

I believe the main value in telling the psychiatrist all these things was a sense of relief in the fact I had told him, so if anything happened, it was his responsibility to make the decisions and to know what was going on.

The staff psychologist had less involvement with the nurses than did the psychiatrist or social worker. Still, the nurses relied upon him for various kinds of information and advice. Said one nurse, typifying the general assessment of the other nurses as well:

It was helpful to know the results of the psychologicals and to discuss with him areas that he felt the patient could be helped with. It was often gratifying to learn that you shared the same opinion regarding the patient's condition as the psychologist even though you arrived at this conclusion by different routes—the nurse by visiting and the psychologist by testing.

Of all the team members, the nurses came to rely most heavily on the social worker. The latter not only performed her traditional role in the clinic setting but also came to serve as a type of traffic director for problems. The nurses tended to consult with the social worker about problem patients or families. If the social worker could not resolve them, they were then taken to the staff psychiatrist. Said one of the nurses expressing the consensus:

> The social worker is a key person and the nurse must rely on her to make contacts with other community agencies, to assist the patient and his family obtain additional medical care, financial assistance, vocational rehabilitation, child care services, etc. The nurse does not have the time or know-how to make these contacts herself.

The social worker kept the nurse informed as to the methods employed by the agency to assist the patient and family and the progress that was being made in that direction. She also frequently interpreted the patient's behavior pattern to the nurse and reassured her about questions of relationship and evaluation of the patient. In addition, the social worker acted as a liaison person between the psychiatrist and nurses.

Another aspect of the relationship between nurse and psychiatric social worker was indicated by a nurse as follows:

> I felt restricted at times with the significant others due to my close relationship to the patients and felt that the social worker could best help the significant others with their problems.

ROLE OF THE SOCIAL WORKER[2]

During the course of this project the social worker, like each of the other professionals, performed some duties which had been clearly defined at the outset of the program, and others which developed as the study continued. At the beginning of the study, the social worker was seen as being responsible for providing three services. First, upon referral of a patient to the Center, the social worker had to arrange an interview between the patient and the psychiatrist and, far more importantly, to interview the family member or others willing to provide supervision. Second, it was necessary to take a detailed social history based upon information obtained during the interview with the family

[2] Joseph Albini, Ann E. Davis, Frank Scarpitti, Simon Dinitz, and Benjamin Pasamanick, "The Social Worker in an Experimental Home Care Study of Schizophrenics," unpublished paper.

or other interested person. Third, and of an entirely different order, to act as consultant to the public health nurses regarding problems relating to the patients' welfare. Later in the program these functions were extended to include direct consultation with patient and family and, where and when necessary, the accompanying process of referral to community agencies.

Although all the functions performed by the social worker throughout this project were important, probably the most vital involved an activity which falls outside the traditional role of social work; mainly, obtaining the sample for the study.

Patient Recruitment: Explanation and Orientation

Most of the patients in this study were obtained from Central State Hospital. Since Central State Hospital could not provide a sufficient number of patients to fulfill the requirements of the original research design, other sources of referrals had to be utilized. These principally included Louisville General Hospital, private general physicians and psychiatrists, and various social agencies. Irrespective of the source, once the referral was made, the social worker discussed with the family or other interested person why the patient had been referred to the clinic. Also, at this time a brief description of the home care program was given in order to determine whether or not the family or others were interested, willing, and capable of providing adequate supervision for the patient and of cooperating in the data gathering.

Few families refused to cooperate at the time of the initial request. The most difficult problem was simply one of reaching them. Some did not have telephones; hence, they had to be sought by letter. In some cases, both telephone calls and letters were necessary before any contact was finally made. In any event, if the significant other expressed interest in the patient and the program, an appointment was made for both the patient and the SO (significant other) to appear at the Center.

The interview during which the social worker discussed the possibility of home care with the family was normally filled with concern on the part of the family or those others assuming responsibility for the patient. When confronted with the possibility of taking the patient home, the significant other was often apprehensive about the feasibility of such a plan. These patients, it must be remembered, were quite ill.

Hospitalization had, in most cases, been necessitated initially by the family's inability to tolerate the patient's behavior. Then, within one or at most a few days of hospitalization, the family was told that the patient could go home again. It was difficult for the family to accept what they thought was the doctor's opinion that the patient was "well enough" to return home. Throughout the interview, the social worker made no attempt to discuss the condition of the patient's health but merely kept repeating that it was the psychiatrist's opinion that the patient could be treated effectively at home. Generally the context of this affirmation was expressed to the following effect:

> There are many patients whose illness is of such a nature that home care is out of the question. On the other hand, thanks to the new drugs, there are many patients who can benefit from treatment at home. Dr. _______, our psychiatrist, feels that _______ is the type of patient who can be treated at home. I don't think that Dr. _______ would recommend this type of treatment unless he was sure that _______ could benefit from it.

Very few families offered outright resistance to the psychiatrist's final decision. It appears that the authority of the doctor's statement that the patient could be treated at home was sufficient to convince most families to attempt the plan. It was obvious to the social worker that many of the families believed that the psychiatrist's decision was incorrect; however, they refrained from open disagreement. When the family agreed with the plan, the social worker, as she had done throughout the interview, again assured the family that they would have the continued support and help of the clinic staff, particularly the public health nurse who would be visiting the home at periodic intervals. Those few families who adamantly refused the home care program generally involved cases where the family stated that the patient was beyond their ability to control or exhibited intolerable and grossly bizarre antisocial behavior. There was no independent corroboration of these reasons since patients were not examined when families absolutely refused to cooperate.

It goes without saying that the entire intake process generated a great deal of anxiety and difficulties for all concerned. This can best be illustrated by the following case:

> Mrs. _______ was referred to the clinic from Central State Hospital. Upon referral the clinic social worker was given the name of the patient's

husband whom she phoned. After explaining the program to him he readily agreed to cooperate and an appointment was made for him to appear at the clinic. The hospital was notified of the appointment time so that arrangements could be made to have the patient at the clinic at the same time. Shortly afterwards, the clinic social worker received a call from the social worker at Central State Hospital informing her that the patient had become quite upset upon learning that plans were being made for her to return home to live with her husband. During this conversation the clinic social worker was also informed that the patient had not been living with her husband prior to admission but was being cared for by the patient's sisters and mother. It was pointed out that the patient's sisters and mother expressed negative attitudes toward the husband and indicated the belief that the husband was largely responsible for the patient's becoming ill.

After getting this new information, the clinic social worker decided to proceed with the appointment as planned and thus be afforded the opportunity to evaluate the husband, the home environment, and the patient's real feelings about going home.

The interview with the husband indicated to the social worker that he was a responsible person willing and capable of supervising the patient. The patient, in turn, told the clinic psychiatrist that she had no objections to going home to live with her husband. When asked about his in-laws' negative attitudes toward him, the husband verbalized negative feelings against them and stated that the in-laws were basically causing his marital difficulties.

After reviewing the facts, the social worker and psychiatrist decided that the patient should return home with her husband. Later, during the same day, the patient's sisters each in turn called the clinic expressing strong disapproval of the plan. When they were assured that the clinic would not alter its plan, one of the sisters called to demand an interview with the psychiatrist. She maintained that the patient had called and told her that she was afraid her husband would injure her physically. As the conversation continued, the sister became very upset and again demanded an appointment with the psychiatrist. An appointment was made for the following day. The interview with this sister revealed she and several of the other sisters had psychiatric problems of their own and believed, as well as reinforced, the patient's paranoid delusions concerning the husband. The sisters were again assured that the patient would not be harmed and that the Center, through visits by the nurse, would keep close surveillance on the patient's condition. Despite these assurances the sisters insisted that the patient be removed from the husband's home and threatened to sue the psychiatrist if he did not. At this point, for the welfare of the patient, it became necessary for the psychiatrist to establish firm rules regulating the relationship between the patient and her family. These rules stipulated that the patient not be permitted to visit, be visited, call, or receive calls from her family. All information and contact between patient and family had to be arranged through the clinic. Within a relatively short period of time the patient responded to medication at which point she herself was in a condition to assure the family that she was doing well and that she definitely desired to remain with her husband.

This case illustrates some of the problems faced by the social worker during the intake process. In performing this intake function the social worker was required to adopt an approach which has not traditionally been part of her role—*providing for the patient's return home at a time when he is still seriously ill.* It is true that the accepted role of the social worker in the past has incorporated the task of preparing the family and patient for the patient's return home. Such planning, however, usually begins at a time when the patient is felt to be sufficiently improved to warrant hospital discharge or after a reasonably lengthy period of hospitalization. In the ITC project the opposite was the case. The social worker was required to work with patients who had been committed or otherwise admitted to the state hospital for only a very short period of time before coming to the Center. Little wonder that families and significant others often found it very difficult to accept such a plan, making it necessary for the social worker to orient them to the goal of a community mental health program. As part of this orientation the worker had to "educate" them in terms of the types of problems they would be likely to encounter as well as give them some knowledge of how to cope with them. She explained, for example, that the patient would probably continue to manifest behavior similar to that displayed prior to hospitalization, but that, with drug therapy and with time, the patient should improve. More importantly, the worker instructed the family member to try to accept the patient's less extreme behavior. Family members were told, above all, not to argue, contradict, or threaten the patient in any way. Instead, they were urged to create a setting of assurance, support, and stability.

Despite the fact that the families were assured that the visiting public health nurse would help them, it must have been very difficult for these people, who knew very little about mental illness and much less about techniques of handling the mentally ill, to be willing to cooperate in such a venture. Thus, when community mental health centers finally emerge, it is safe to assume that this function of "educating" families will become a vital and integral part of the social worker's role.

Obtaining a Social History

Along with the tasks of education and orientation, a second major function of the social worker's role was to obtain an extensive social history. This history consisted of a 52-page schedule of questions regarding the patient and the significant other. Included were questions eliciting information about the patient and family's educational background, religious preference, employment history, source and amount of income, recreational activities, patient's previous hospitalizations, number and length of duration of the patient's previous marriages, and information concerning the patient's children. Also, the inventory incorporated scaled questions concerning the significant other's attitudes toward the patient as well as toward mental illness in general. The format of this inventory was structured in such a manner as to make the answers easily amenable to coding for later analysis. Factual questions were often interspersed with emotionally loaded queries, and the social worker was frequently confronted with the problem of "preparing" the respondent for "anxiety-producing" questions. This the worker accomplished, to a large extent, by prefacing these types of questions with a reassuring phrase, such as "I know this will probably be a very difficult question to answer . . ." or "I realize that this next question is very personal, but could you tell me . . ."

In most instances the completion of the social history was an arduous task, generally requiring at least 2 hours to accomplish. Often the significant other interrupted the worker with questions revealing areas of personal anxiety as, for example, in one case where a father from a middle-class background became very concerned about what the neighbors would think if they saw a public health nurse making regular visits to his house. Another, a wife, was concerned about the family's financial condition during the interim of her husband's recovery. In such cases during the interview the worker was forced to stop and discuss these and similar issues before resuming the completion of the history.

Consultation with Nurses

A third important aspect of the social worker's duties in this project involved her consultation with the public health nurses. Again, necessity obliged the social worker to take on a function not usually associated with her normal duties. Although psychiatric social workers have sometimes served as advisors to others, the responsibility of systematically acting as consultant to other professional groups is rather new. In this project, since only one of the five nurses had previous psychiatric nursing experience, the nurses needed as much support and guidance in working with their patients as they could get. The responsibility of keeping seriously ill patients in the home setting, who otherwise would certainly have been hospitalized, resulted in serious emotional strain for the nurses. Their major fears centered about whether or not they had said or done the "right thing" in regard to a problem which had been presented by a patient or family. In this respect the social worker had to introduce the nurses to some basic casework techniques in dealing with the patient and family. Also, the nurses needed someone who could take direct action in the event that a patient or family presented a problem necessitating immediate referral to a social agency.

Since the staff psychiatrist was available to the nurses only 2 days a week, the social worker became the principal consultant. Because the roles were not clearly defined, the establishment of the initial consultant relationship between the worker and nurse was difficult. As the program continued, however, the relationship became more structured and the limits of both roles within this relationship became much more definite. The invaluable service provided by the social worker in her consultant's role is best reflected by the nurses' comments at the end of the program:

> I feel that the social worker was a necessity and great asset to the nurses in this type of program.

> I feel the social worker was very useful and cooperative in referrals, helping patients obtain jobs, and talking with the nurses.

> She frequently interpreted the patient's behavior pattern to the nurse and reassured the nurse in questions of relationship to and evaluation of the patient.

One nurse very concisely reflected the attitudes of the others when she stated:

> The social worker made me feel that I was helping the patient to the very best of my ability and as a result of this I feel I was able to establish good rapport with the patient and family.

Social Services

Another important function performed by the social worker, and one that is well within the traditional role, was that of offering direct social services. As the project continued, the need for direct social services to home care patients increased. Although the program was oriented toward research, the patients viewed the Center, like most other clinics, as a treatment agency. It was not unusual for patients or family members to come to the Center unannounced, seeking advice regarding marital problems, financial assistance, child rearing problems, and many other difficulties. Since, because of her many other duties, the social worker had little time to devote to this function, most of the patients received help only in the form of short term services and referrals. In a few special cases long term consultation, particularly in the area of marriage counseling, was attempted. This was eventually discontinued because of the time limitations on the social worker. Short term services generally consisted of referrals to other community agencies in order to help the client meet medical, financial, recreational, employment, housing, and other needs. A variety of agencies were utilized, including a half-way house for the mentally ill, various assistance programs, the juvenile court, children's protective services, the state vocational rehabilitation service, general hospital medical services, and the marriage counseling services of the family and children's agency. Unfortunately, these agencies were unable, because of staff shortages and other limitations, to render much service to ITC patients. In seeking these direct services, one of the most difficult tasks was that of helping a family through a period of crisis while they were simultaneously caring for an acutely ill patient. In these situations, the staff was confronted with the possible disorganization of the entire family unit. During such emergencies requiring immediate attention, the social worker, both in her role as consultant to the nurses and as a source of contact with social agencies, provided an extremely valuable service to the nurse, the patient, and the family.

Follow-Up Scheduling Function

As the study progressed, another task of a routine nature and not within the usual domain of psychiatric social work was performed by the social worker. This involved scheduling appointments at the Center for follow-up interviews and psychological testing. Since this task often required skillful persuasion which necessitated an understanding of the patient's background and problems, the social worker seemed to be the most logical choice. Later, it became necessary for the psychiatrist and psychologist to test and evaluate a few of the less cooperative patients at home. The social worker tried to prepare the patient and family for such visits. All too often the function of scheduling and rescheduling patients became a tiresome and disheartening task. The social worker was constantly beset by the problems of patients cancelling appointments at the last minute, not appearing for their appointments, and changing addresses without notifying the Center. Many of the patients had no telephones thereby making it necessary to schedule appointments by mail. At the beginning of the project, return postcards were used, but later a form letter was sent. A particular problem with the use of both the postcard and the letter was the frequent lack of reply from patient or family, affirming their receipt of such. When this occurred, the worker could not determine whether the patients had deliberately failed to keep their appointments or, because of change of address, had not received the letter. Eventually the social worker found it necessary to send registered letters, a procedure which proved to be quite effective in obtaining replies.

Collecting School Data

Near the end of the program and for only a short period of time, the social worker was assigned the added task of collecting the school records of the children of the patients. Permission slips were obtained from the parents of these children, and the school officials consented to make the records available. Obtaining these school records necessitated going to each school, instructing the school officials as to the information desired, and then duplicating the material on a photocopy machine. Later, this function was shared by one of the public health nurses.

Final Referrals

As the study approached termination, the social worker became involved with transferring out those home care patients who were still on the program. This called for conferences with the psychiatrist and nurse during which the patient's progress, present needs, and possible sources for referral were discussed. At this time the psychiatrist and social worker were informed by the study director as to whether the patient had been receiving drugs or placebos, so that this information could be transmitted to the referral agency. In the transferring-out process, the nurses sought the support and advice of the social worker as they faced the ordeal of severing relationships with their patients. Despite their attempts to avoid emotional involvement, the nurses were quite unhappy when the patient was to be discharged or transferred. Here again, the social worker's supportive help proved invaluable.

ROLE OF THE PSYCHOLOGIST

The psychologist's role in this home care project was primarily one of testing. Once a patient was accepted as either a home care patient or a hospital control, he was given a battery of psychological tests by the psychologist. These tests, described elsewhere, included the Wechsler Adult Intelligence Scale, a reaction time test series, the Bender Gestalt test, and the Porteus Maze test. After the initial test on the day the patient was accepted into the study, the same tests were repeated for each patient after 6, 18 months, and again after 24 months. Once the patient had completed each battery of tests, the psychologist scored them and wrote a brief summary of the results.

In addition to this function, the staff psychologist also served as advisor and counselor to the nurses. He was able to explain to them the extent of a patient's pathology and what type of behavior they might expect him to exhibit. Although he played no direct treatment role with the patients, which in future programs would certainly be one of his chief responsibilities, he was a valuable resource person for those staff members who were involved in direct contact with the patients.

SUMMARY

In this chapter the roles of the study director, psychiatrist, public health nurse, psychiatric social worker, and psychologist were discussed. These roles were concerned with treatment of the mentally ill outside of the hospital, and, as such, they may well serve as prototypes of professional roles in future community mental health programs. Admittedly, some duties and responsibilities of the professional staff were unique because they reflected both the research and treatment demands of the program. But, even without research, it is obvious that neither the psychiatrist nor the social worker will be able to function in precisely the same manner in the new settings as they have in the hospital or even posthospital outpatient clinics. For the public health nurse, a whole new area of service has developed in the form of community mental health. Her special talents make her exceptionally qualified to assume a major role in this type of psychiatric care.

5

THE PATIENTS

In the course of 25 months of patient intake, the Institute Treatment Center accepted a total of 163 cases for the study from the Central State Hospital. All of these patients met the following criteria: a diagnosis of schizophrenia at the time of admission to Central State Hospital which was corroborated by the ITC psychiatrist after independent examination, between 18 and 60 years of age, residence in Greater Louisville, and having a family willing and able to provide supervision at home.[1] Using the random sampling procedures discussed previously, the 163 patients were assigned either to the drug home care group, to the placebo home care group, or to the hospital control or natural group. For the purposes of this analysis, 11 of these patients—7 drug and 4 placebo—have been omitted from consideration. These 11 cases were study dropouts who left the project to seek private care (3), or because the patient or family refused to cooperate (5), or because the patient left the community (3). Analysis indicated that the dropouts were similar to the patients who remained in the program in all major respects.

STUDY POPULATION CHARACTERISTICS: DEMOGRAPHIC

The remaining 152 patients in the three study groups—home on drugs (57), home on placebo (41), and hospital controls (54)—were similar to each other in almost all the important demographic characteristics except that the controls were significantly lower in education and

[1] These 163 cases represented approximately 30 percent of the patients admitted to Central State Hospital and eventually classified as schizophrenic; and over 87 percent of the patients passing the initial hospital screening (age, diagnosis, residence, family) and referred to ITC.

higher in residential mobility. A detailed description of these background characteristics follows.

Age, Sex, and Race

The average age of all 152 ITC patients was 36.6 years at time of admission to the project. The age range was 18 to 56 years. Drug home care patients averaged 35.9 years at admission, placebo home care patients 36.2 years, and hospital control patients had a mean age of 37.6 years. In contrast, all schizophrenic patients admitted to Central State Hospital averaged 41 years of age, and first admissions with schizophrenic reactions in 271 public mental hospitals in the United States, 34.5 years.[2]

The ITC patient population drawn from the State Hospital was heavily weighted with females. Slightly over two-thirds of the 152 patients were females (see Table 5-1). However, this ratio was not too different from the sex distribution of diagnosed schizophrenics admitted to the Central State Hospital, which was approximately 60:40, female to male. The small sex difference between the ITC and the Central State Hospital patients is probably attributable to the increased willingness of families and psychiatrists to risk the inclusion of a female patient over that of a male. In public mental hospitals generally, the ratio of schizophrenic males to females is approximately 47:53 among newer, previously hospitalized admissions.[3]

The study population was composed of 102 white and 50 Negro patients or a 67 to 33 percentage split. White ITC patients constituted 68.4 percent of the drug, 68.3 percent of the placebo, and 64.8 percent of the hospital control cases. There was a larger percentage of white schizophrenic patients in Central State Hospital (78.4 percent) than in the study population probably because of our insistence on returning the patient to a supervised family setting. In general, Negro families even though frequently disorganized, are probably more likely to accept patients for home care since it has been repeatedly demonstrated that

[2] *Patients in Mental Institutions, 1962, Part II: State and County Mental Hospitals*, Public Health Service, National Institutes of Health, U.S. Department of Health, Education, and Welfare.

[3] *Ibid.*, Tables 3 and 6.

the lower the social class position, the greater the tolerance for deviant behavior[4] (see Table 5-1).

Socioeconomic Status

Education. School grade level completed was the prime demographic characteristic which significantly differentiated the home care patient from the hospital controls. Of the 148 patients on whom educational data was available, 1 in 7 (14.2 percent) had completed the sixth grade or less, and over 7 in 10 (71.7 percent) had not finished high school. The comparable percentages for the drug patients were 12.5 and 62.5; for the placebo patients, 10.0 and 65.0; and for the hospital controls, 19.2 and 86.5 percent (see Table 5-1). The control patients were thus considerably overrepresented among the poorly educated cases. This lower educational attainment of the controls is apparently a fortuitous occurrence. Despite random assignment, when a sizeable number of characteristics of a sample are examined one by one, a few may be expected to be significantly different by chance alone.

Occupation. It is more difficult to describe the exact occupational status of the patients than their educational level. It is clear, however, that almost all of the male patients, and the husbands of female patients as well, were either blue-collar workers or unskilled laborers. Excluding housewives, 93 patients had actual occupations. Of these, 3 were at the lesser professional or lower administrative level, 17 involved clerical or sales work, only 5 were skilled, 30 were at the semi-skilled or machine operative level, and 38 were unskilled. The same pattern prevailed also for the husbands of the married female patients. A large proportion were in the lower blue-collar range. There were no significant differences among the three groups on the dimension of occupation, but the controls as might be anticipated from their lower level of education occupied a greater number of the lowest status jobs.

The Hollingshead Index of Social Position.[5] As a more stable, and

[4] Howard E. Freeman and Ozzie G. Simmons, "Social Class and Posthospital Performance Levels," *Amer. sociol. Rev.*, **24** (June, 1959), 345–351. On the other hand, for a modified version of this thesis see, Mark Lefton, Shirley Angrist, Simon Dinitz, and Benjamin Pasamanick, "Social Class, Expectations, and Performance of Mental Patients," *Amer. J. Sociol.*, **LXVIII** (July, 1962), 79–87.

[5] August B. Hollingshead, "Two Factor Index of Social Position," 1957, (Mimeographed). See also, August B. Hollingshead and Frederick C. Redlich, *Social Class and Mental Illness*, New York: Wiley, 1958.

possibly sharper measure of socioeconomic status, the Hollingshead Index of Social Position consisting of the weighted factors of education and occupation was used. Patients were scored on their own occupations or, when necessary, in terms of the occupations of their husbands or fathers. On this Index, the highest possible status commands a score of 11; the lowest, a score of 77. Only 1 patient had the highest status; 15 were at the very bottom of the scale. The patient cohort is probably reasonably representative of the low socioeconomic status of hospital admissions for schizophrenia in Kentucky and in public mental hospitals in the United States. The mean socioeconomic score for the total group was 62.2. Placebo patients were of somewhat higher status at 58.8, drug patients were intermediate at 60.5 and the hospital controls lowest at 64.9 (see Table 5-1). These intergroup differences in mean scores were not statistically significant.

Income and Class Identification. Although these income figures apply to the period of patient intake (November 1961 to December 1963), it is clear that the low socioeconomic status of the patients was matched by the small annual income of their households. The median income of patient households in all three study categories was in the $3500–$4000 range. At the time, 8 of the households were receiving welfare aid, and 15 others needed and received outside help other than home relief. On the other extreme, half a dozen households were near, at, or over the $9,500 annual income mark.

Purely as an interesting sidelight and to round out the socioeconomic description of the cohort, of the respondents willing to indicate their class identifictaion, most gave in answer the working class, a small number the middle, and only a very few the upper class. When asked about people who reside in their area, an even greater number indicated that working-class families typified their neighborhood.

Residence

Residence History. All of the patients and almost all of their fathers and mothers were native born; an overwhelming majority of the patients and of their parents were born in Kentucky. The social histories indicate that the birthplace of nearly one-half the patients was in a rural area or small town. A slightly higher but not significantly greater proportion of the control patients were of rural or small town origin.

Prior to hospitalization, however, only 10 patients lived on farms, 5 lived in a semirural area, and 8 resided in a small town. The remainder were from urban Louisville. The control group had the largest number and percentage of the nonurban patients. This difference in residence is possibly related to the lower educational and occupational attainments of the controls.

Residential Mobility. The patients probably typify both a schizophrenic population and an urban lower-class group in terms of their residential mobility pattern. While over one-fourth of the patients maintained the same residence address in the 5 years preceding hospital admission, nearly 13 percent averaged one or more residence changes a year. The least mobile were the drug cases; the placebos were intermediate; the hospital controls, the most mobile. Translated into percentage figures, 35.1 percent of the drug, 29.3 percent of the placebo, and only 19.2 percent of the controls remained at the same address throughout the 5-year period (see Table 5-1).

Another way of gauging the residential mobility of the patient cohort is to examine the length of time they lived at their present address. When this is done, it appears that over one-third of the patients have resided at their last address for less than 1 year. This was also the case with one-fourth of the drug, and about 4 in 10 of the placebo and control patients. On the other side of the ledger, 18.3 percent of all patients, and 21.4 percent of the drug, 25.6 percent of the placebo, and but 9.5 percent of the control cases lived at their current address for a decade or more.

Family Setting

The principal demographic variables, of interest in this study because of the home care supervision requirement, centered around the nature of the family situation to which the patient was returned. Each of the more important of these family variables will be discussed.

Marital Status. At the time of admission to Central State Hospital and to the ITC project, half of the patients were married, 22.4 percent were single and never previously wed, and 26.9 percent were widowed, separated, or divorced with the latter two categories accounting for the bulk of these cases. There were only minor variations in the marital status of the patients across the three study categories (see Table 5-1).

Of the married patients, the largest number by far had married but once, a few twice, and an insignificant number had any more than two previous marriages. One hospital control, however, had been in and out of at least eight previous marriages. On another level most of the last previous marriages of the patients at time of acceptance into the project had been legalized by the law or clergy or both, but at least four were either common-law relationships or casual alliances.

In contrast and rather surprisingly the last or most recent marriages of the patients in all three study groups seemed to have endured longer than might have been anticipated in view of the illness of the patients. Including marriages later dissolved by divorce, separation, desertion or widowhood, 8.5 percent of the marriages were in their first year or had lasted less than 1 year. At the other end of the continuum, over 54 percent had lasted over 10 years, and 17.9 percent had remained intact for 20 or more years.

Marital Adjustment. Based on responses of significant others, the marital adjustment of the patients was reasonably good. For example, all but a very few of the spouses indicated that neither they nor the patients wanted to end the marriage. Just 7 patients and 9 spouses had serious reservations about continuing the marital relationship as opposed to 48 patients and 53 spouses who were content with their marriages. Similarly, a minimum of hostility on the part of the patients towards the spouse was reported by the significant other. Finally, again based on the interview responses of the spouses, the sexual relationships were reported to be good with only a few indicating otherwise. These data, whatever their intrinsic validity, do tend to confirm subjectively the objective and hard fact that these significant others were willing and able to take responsibility for the patient in the home. It would certainly be erroneous to assume that the spouses of schizophrenic patients as a whole are equally as adjusted in their marriages as were the significant others in this study. However, since only 5 percent of the families interviewed by the ITC staff refused to accept patients for home care, this degree of marital adjustment is better than anticipated for a patient population.

Children. The ITC patients, both married and single, were for the most part still well within childbearing age. More than three-fourths were under 45 years of age. Hence, the number of children born to these cases is by no means the final total. One of the patients, for example, had three pregnancies while in the ITC program. As of the time of admission to the program, however, the 118 married or previously married patients were parents to an average of 2.76 children. The drug and placebo patients average about 3 children each; the controls 2.29 children. This nonsignificant difference was mainly attributable to the greater proportion of childless control patients. A fourth of the controls, nearly 1 in 7 of the drug, and but 1 in 10 of the placebo patients, were childless.

Table 5-1. Selected Characteristics of ITC State Hospital Patients by Study Group*

	Drug (*N*=57)	*Placebo* (*N*=41)	*Control* (*N*=54)	*Total* (*N*=152)
Average age	35.9	36.2	37.6	36.6
Percent female	64.9	68.3	70.4	67.8
Percent white	68.4	68.3	64.8	67.1
Percent grade school diploma or less	12.5	10.0	19.2	14.2
Percent high school graduates	37.5	35.0	13.5	28.4
Hollingshead Index of Social Position (mean score)	60.5	58.8	64.9	62.2
Percent residing at same address for last 5 years	35.1	29.3	19.2	28.0
Percent married	54.4	43.9	51.9	50.7
Percent never married	24.6	26.8	16.7	22.4
Mean number of children born to married patients	3.1	3.0	2.3	2.8

*Appendix Tables I-X contain specific distributions of these and other characteristics.

PSYCHIATRIC TREATMENT HISTORY

Previous Hospitalization and Outpatient Care

At the time of admission to the study, patients in the drug group had averaged 1.9 previous mental hospital admissions, placebo patients 2.0 such admissions, and controls 2.3 previous admissions. These differences were not statistically significant. The average of all patients was 2.08 previous hospitalizations.

Put a little differently, nearly one in five drug patients had never before been hospitalized, more than half had been institutionalized once or twice, and one-fifth more had been hospitalized on three or more separate occasions. In the placebo group, almost one-fourth of the patients were first admissions, 37 percent had been institutionalized once or twice, and 39 percent three or more times. Of the hospital controls, 15 percent had never before been hospitalized, 47 percent had been hospitalized once or twice, and 38 percent at least three times before. Regardless of study placement, 19.2 percent of all the patients were first hospital admissions, 47.0 percent had been hospitalized once or twice before, and 33.8 percent had been previously hospitalized from three to nine or more times. These indications of serious illness were confirmed by the findings on patient symptoms and level of functioning at admission to the study.

Translating hospital admissions into cumulative inpatient time, about 8 percent of all patients had spent less than 1 week in any mental hospital, 42.3 percent less than 1 month, nearly 60 percent less than 3 months, and some 82 percent less than 1 year. Only 18.1 percent had spent over a year in mental hospitals, and, of these, better than half had been institutionalized for 4 or more years. The controls recorded more inpatient time since, as already noted, they had the greater number of previous hospital admissions.

Apart from hospitalization, many of the patients had previously received outpatient psychiatric treatment. Of the 57 drug cases, 44 percent had been under outpatient care. Sixteen of the 41 placebo patients, 39 percent, and one-third of the 54 control cases had also received such attention. Overall, 39 percent of the patients had been in outpatient treatment. For most of the patients this care had been for a reasonably short period or periods of time. The total time in outpatient treatment only rarely exceeded 1 year in duration.

When inpatient and outpatient experiences are combined, it is obvious that a very considerable number of our 152 patients had received some type of psychiatric care previously. These were chronic patients both in terms of their diagnosis as well as their previous illness histories. Of the total group, only 14.5 percent had experienced neither previous in- nor outpatient care, while 34.2 percent had received both types of service. The remainder had been hospitalized or, in only a few instances, had been in outpatient care alone. There were only minor variations among the three categories of subjects—drug, placebo, and hospital control—with regard to the type of psychiatric service received previously. These data which further attest to the composition of the sample population as one with considerable psychiatric involvement prior to admission to this study, are presented in Table 5-2.

Without belaboring the issue, the ITC emphasis on drug therapy was by no means a new form of treatment for the majority of the patients. Of the 123 previously hospitalized patients, 81 had been on drug medication while institutionalized. Sixty patients, mostly the same ones, had been on a drug regimen as outpatients. Additionally, 56 patients had received from 1 to more than 60 electroshock treatments in prior hospitalizations and 7 had been given ECT as outpatients. Psychotherapy had been rather sparingly provided the ITC patients as either in- or outpatients—a situation not very atypical with lower- or even lower middle-class patients as Hollingshead and Redlich and others have shown. Only 19 of the 122 previously hospitalized patients had had any psychotherapy, and 28 had received psychotherapy as outpatients. Group psychotherapy had been extended to only 3 of the ITC patients in previous hospitalizations and to only 11 as outpatients.

Present Illness

The nature of the illness which led to Central State Hospital admission and to the ITC project was classified as either acute, intermediate, or insidious. Acute patients were those whose symptoms came to the fore within 2 months prior to admission, intermediate patients had exhibited these symptoms for a somewhat longer period (2 to 6 months), and insidious cases were those whose illness extended back longer than 6 months. In these terms, the onset of illness for about 40 percent of the patients was acute, for 22.5 percent intermediate, and for the remainder, 37.8 percent, insidious. There were no significant differences among the drug, placebo, and control patients in this respect.

It is also interesting to note the person or agency recommending hospitalization. Of the 152 patients, 11.8 percent admitted themselves to Central State Hospital, 45.4 percent were urged to seek care by family members, 27.6 percent were referred by physicians or were medically certified, and 15.1 percent were sent or committed by the police, court, or by a social or legal agency. Although there were some variations

Table 5-2. Total Psychiatric Case Histories of Drug, Placebo, and Hospital Control Patients

	Drug		*Placebo*		*Hospital Control*		*Total*	
	N	%	*N*	%	*N*	%	*N*	%
No hospital or outpatient care	6	10.5	9	22.0	7	13.0	22	14.5
Both hospital and outpatient care	20	35.1	15	36.6	17	31.5	52	34.2
Hospital only	26	45.6	16	39.0	29	53.7	71	46.7
Outpatient only	5	8.8	1	2.4	1	1.9	7	4.6
	57		41		54		152	

See also Tables XI and XIII in Appendix B.

among the three groups in this respect, these differences were not statistically significant.

FUNCTIONING:

Mental Status: Psychiatric Evaluations

All patients were evaluated by the staff psychiatrist using the revised Inpatient Multidimensional Psychiatric Scale (Lorr IMPS) at intake to the ITC project. As already noted elsewhere, this scale contains 10 factor syndromes which cumulatively provide an overall weighted score. In different combinations these factor syndromes form the three morbidity scores, *i.e.* excitement versus retardation, perceptual and thinking distortion, and most importantly, schizophrenic disorganization. At admission to the ITC project there could be little doubt that the 152 patients, as a group, were severely impaired. These baseline data indicate that the drug, placebo, and hospital control patients had mean total weighted syndrome scores of 85.5, 94.6, and 100.4 respectively (see Table 5-3). The difference between the drug and control patients was statistically significant indicating greater initial impairment on the part of the hospital controls.

On the excitement-retardation morbidity scale, however, the controls showed the least extreme scores. The mean score differences on this measure among the three study categories were not statistically significant. In the perceptual and thinking distortion area, the placebo group was lowest but not significantly more so than either of the other study groups.

Finally, the mean schizophrenic disorganization score was 39.6 for the drug home care patients, 48.6 for the placebo patients, and 43.5 for the hospital controls. These mean scores were not significantly different from each other and all were higher than the one- and two-rater mean scores obtained by Lorr for his norm sample of hospitalized patients. Thus, the 152 ITC patients did not constitute the better risks or the less impaired in this respect. Table 5-3 contains these mean scores.

The nurses also evaluated each of the drug and placebo home care patients on the first home visit using the IMPS. Since each nurse saw only her own patients, it was impossible to obtain any measure of interrater reliability. Nevertheless, two points need to be made regarding the nurses' ratings. First, on every morbidity scale, the nurses rated the drug and placebo patients as significantly less impaired than the psychiatrist had rated them. Second, the nurses saw greater pathology in the placebo than in the drug cases on two of the three morbidity scales. The amount of pathology on the schizophrenic disorganization measure was significantly greater in the placebo group. Thus, the direction of the nurses' ratings paralleled that of the psychiatrist but at a lesser impairment level. These initial nurses' ratings are also presented in Table 5-3.

The Lorr IMPS, it will be recalled, was altered so as to make it better suited for use with the significant others of the patients. Named the SO rating scale, this instrument contained 121 items or statements of psychological symptoms paralleling those in the IMPS. Significant others were asked to indicate the presence or absence of each of these symptoms in the patients. Comparable weighting and morbidity scores were used in the psychiatrist's and nurses' ratings as described above.

At the time of admission of the cases to the ITC program, significant others viewed the drug patients as less impaired than the placebo or hospital controls. The differences in means, however, were not quite great enough to rule out chance variations (see Table 5-3).

In summary, the drug patients were seen by all the raters—psychiatrist, nurse, and significant other—as somewhat less impaired than the placebo and control group patients. While the direction was consistent, the actual mean differences failed to reach statistical significance in all but one instance.

Mental Status: Psychological Test Scores

The psychological battery administered to the subjects at admission to the ITC project and at subsequent intervals thereafter consisted of a sequential reaction time test, the Wechsler Adult Intelligence Scale (WAIS), the Bender Gestalt, and the Porteus Mazes. In the initial administration the drug, placebo, and hospital control patients did not systematically or consistently differ from each other on most of these measures although the hospital controls did not score quite as well as the home care groups (see Table 5-4).

In looking at the total of the medians of 20 blocks of 5 trials each, the three groups did not differ significantly from each other in reaction

Table 5-3. Psychiatrist's, Nurses', and Significant Other Initial Evaluations of Drug, Placebo, and Hospital Control Patients

	Drug		*Placebo*		*Hospital Control*	
	Mean	σ	*Mean*	σ	*Mean*	σ
Psychiatrist's Evaluations						
Total weighted score	85.5	31.6	94.6	47.0	100.4	43.7
Excitement vs. retardation	−7.7	21.4	−11.9	32.0	−2.3	30.9
Perceptual and thinking distortion	16.1	20.6	16.7	25.8	20.8	25.1
Schizophrenic disorganization	39.6	20.3	48.6	28.6	43.5	21.2
Nurses' Evaluations						
Total weighted score	47.5	32.4	61.0	46.7		
Excitement-retardation	+5.3	21.6	+2.5	31.9		
Perceptual and thinking distortion	6.2	12.2	8.4	16.1		
Schizophrenic disorganization	16.5	15.4	25.8	20.5		
Significant Other Evaluations						
Total weighted score	28.0	27.5	38.5	32.7	38.1	27.6
Excitement-retardation	+1.2	3.4	+1.8	4.6	+2.2	4.1
Perceptual and thinking distortion	12.1	16.1	19.5	20.8	18.6	19.3
Schizophrenic disorganization	7.8	6.3	10.3	8.4	9.8	5.8

Table 5-4. Psychological Test Scores of Drug, Placebo, and Hospital Control Patients

	Drug		*Placebo*		*Hospital Control*	
	Mean	*σ*	*Mean*	*σ*	*Mean*	*σ*
(Log) Reaction time*	3.2860	166.7	3.2965	176.8	3.2748	131.5
WAIS	81.2	16.4	80.1	19.1	72.6	17.2
Bender Gestalt**	107.5	24.9	99.9	26.3	97.0	34.8
Porteus Mazes						
QE+	61.0	16.3	58.4	12.8	55.7	15.2
IQ	80.7	32.5	80.8	32.0	68.0	28.9

*Composite of 20 blocks, 5 trials per block.
**Reciprocal of Z.
+Square root transformation of QE.
Source: Dinitz, Scarpitti, Albini, Lefton and Pasamanick, "An Experimental Study in Prevention of Hospitalization of Schizophrenics: Thirty Months Experience," *Amer. J. Orthopsychiat.*, 35 (January, 1965), 6.

time. The hospital controls were the speediest in their 100 trials and the placebo patients were the slowest. On this test, then, the hospital controls evidenced the lesser deterioration and impairment.

On the two IQ measures the WAIS and one derived from the Porteus Mazes—the controls were significantly lower than the other two groups. On the WAIS the IQ mean scores of patients in the drug, placebo, and hospital control groups were 81.2, 80.1, and 72.6 respectively.[6] Mean scores for the same groups on the Porteus Mazes IQ were 80.7, 80.8, and 68.0. Thus, there was considerable impairment in intellectual functioning in cases in all three study categories. In addition to the affect of the illness on the IQ scores, the generally low mean quotients were probably also a function of the low socioeconomic and poor educational backgrounds of the patients.

On the two measures of pathology—the Bender Gestalt and the QE (error quotient) mean on the Porteus Mazes—there was an interesting reversal in direction. On the Bender Gestalt, with use of reciprocals of Z scores derived by Pascal and Suttell, the controls showed somewhat, but

[6] The WAIS scores were prorated from six subtests. See, Athan Karras, "Predicting Full Scale WAIS IQ's from WAIS Subtests for a Psychiatric Population," *J. clin. Psychol.*, **19** (1963), 100.

not significantly, more pathology than the home care patients.[7] But on the Porteus Mazes, the controls showed less pathology than the home care subjects. These inconsistent and statistically nonsignificant results indicate that, as on the other scales and instruments, no study group was overloaded with the sicker patients or the poorer risks although the controls generally did more poorly than the two home care groups.

Patients as Problems

Since one inflexible criterion of admission to the study was the ability and willingness of a significant other to supervise the patient in the home, it seemed important to determine just how much of a burden the patient had been immediately prior to hospitalization. A problems or burden subschedule was included in the intake history and was also a major part of the Progress Report. This problems subsection consisted of 22 items dealing with various aspects of patient behavior that presented difficulties in the household or community. The higher the score, the greater the burden imposed on the family by the patient.

At admission to the ITC study program, the mean problems score was lowest for the controls (32.1) and highest for the drug patients (33.2). These mean score differences were slight and not statistically significant. The major burdens presented by the patients in all three study categories to the significant others included being noisy or wandering about during the night, odd speech and idea patterns, and general worry and concern about the behavior of the patients. Patients did not seem to induce much fear or confer shame on the part of family members (see Appendix B, Table XIII).

Domestic Performance (Females)

It is, of course, one thing to be considered a problematic member of a household and quite another to be unable to perform the necessary activities consistent with one's role and status. Instrumental role performance in the case of the female inevitably involves domesticity; in the male, remunerative employment.

[7] G. Pascal and B. J. Suttell, *The Bender Gestalt Test: Quantification and Validation for Adults*, New York: Grune & Stratton, 1951.

As a consequence of a previous study in which an attempt was made to relate case outcome to performance, an eight item domestic functioning subscale was included in the intake and the Progress Report schedules. These items previously were shown to perform as a scale. This domestic performance subscale attempted to elicit information about the ability of the patient to handle customary household duties such as cleaning, shopping, meal preparation, and budgeting.

At admission, the mean domestic functioning score of the 37 female drug patients was 13.8. The 28 female placebo patients had a somewhat higher mean score of 15.9; the 38 female controls were intermediate at 14.0. The higher mean score (better functioning) of the placebo patients was not significantly higher than that of the drug patients or of the controls; nor was there any significant variation by individual domestic activity. Between 40 and 60 percent of the female patients were wholly or partly unable to perform each of the specific activities normally associated with the female role prior to admission to the project (see Appendix B, Table XIV).

Employment (Males)

Considerable data were obtained on the work histories of the male patients in the study program. Immediately prior to their hospitalization at Central State Hospital and subsequent admission to the ITC project, 14 of 20 male drug patients, only 2 of 13 male placebo cases, and 6 of the 16 male hospital controls were gainfully employed. Despite the small numbers involved, the drug patients were significantly different from the placebo cases in this respect. Of the unemployed patients, all but 4 in the drug, 3 in the placebo, and 1 of the control group had been employed previously. Much of the unemployment occurred in the 3 months preceding the most recent onset of illness. On the other extreme, a considerable number had held the same job for reasonably long periods of time. Thus, nearly half of all the males had had just one job in the preceding 5-year period. A fourth of the patients had held the same job for 5 or more years. The jobs held by the patients generally involved full-time work. As best we could ascertain, the employed patients, prior to hospitalization, had excellent absenteeism records and experienced few difficulties on the job prior to or between the onset of episodes of illness. According to the significant others, the patients had experienced far greater work difficulties immediately prior to hospitalization than in the periods of absence of florid symptoms which, of course, merely confirms the expected.

Social Participation

In general, the information gathered from the significant others at time of admission of the patients to the project indicated that while certainly not joiners of or members in a host of organizations or participants in many activities, the patients did engage in leisure pursuits to some extent. Fifteen items dealing with the social participation of patients were included in the schedule. The activities tapped by these items ranged from movie-going on the one hand, to the entertainment of relatives and friends on the other. Passive and solitary activities such as watching TV or listening to the radio seemed to predominate over the active ones such as attending meetings or extending oneself in visiting or entertaining others. There were no major or significant variations among the three categories of patients in this respect. In terms of the number and type of activities in which the patients participated, it did appear though, that the hospital controls were somewhat less involved than the home care patients. There was little, if any, discernible difference between the drug and placebo groups (see Appendix B, Table XV).

SUMMARY

Since at least 23 separate characteristics—demographic, medical, and functioning—were used to contrast the 57 drug, 41 placebo, and 54 control patinets, a short summary of these comparisons seems warranted in concluding this chapter.

The 152 ITC patients were relatively young (36.6 years mean age), predominantly white (67.1 percent), females (67.8 percent). They were lower socioeconomic status persons as measured by education, occupation, family income, and self-identification. Nearly 72 percent had not finished high school. They, or their husbands or fathers, were primarily semi- and unskilled workers, and with very few exceptions the family income was not very high. On the Hollingshead two-factor index their socioeconomic status was quite low. The residential mobility of the patients was moderately high and reasonably typical of lower-class persons and families in urban areas. About half of the patients in all three study categories were married, the marriages had been quite durable, and, for the most part, the spouses indicated a high degree of marital adjustment.

On the medical-psychiatric side of the ledger, the 152 patients had experienced an average of over two previous mental hospitalizations. About 40 percent also had been in outpatient treatment previously. Only 22 of the 152 cases had previously received neither in- nor outpatient care. Most of the treatment had consisted of drug or shock therapy rather than psychotherapy. In view of the low socioeconomic status of the patients, this was hardly unanticipated. As for the illness which eventually led to admission into the ITC program, most of the patients began to experience symptoms within 6 months of hospitalization; for a considerable percentage, the onset was still more acute. Overwhelmingly, hospitalization was a consequence of family insistence and pressure and less frequently of medical advice.

On the functioning level, the 152 patients were indisputably quite ill. On the schizophrenic disorganization morbidity score of the IMPS, the patients scored as high or higher than the norm hospital population used by Lorr in standardizing the instrument. The weighted scores and the other morbidity scores also indicated pathology. Similarly, serious pathology was indicated on the psychological examinations including the sequential reaction time tests, the WAIS, the Bender Gestalt, and the Porteus Mazes.

With regard to social functioning, the patients proved burdensome to their relatives in many respects, and particularly in those involving ideational problems and odd speech patterns. They did not, however, create much fear in the relatives or confer much shame on the family according to the significant others. Similarly, about half of the female patients were unable to function effectively in one or more aspects of their roles as homemakers. For the males, the work histories were correspondingly inadequate. Finally, neither the male nor female patients were much involved in social or leisure activities. Most of such involvement as did occur was of a passive and solitary nature.

Generally, although there were few significant variations among the three groups of patients and many reversals across characteristics, the drug home care patients seemed to be the least impaired while the placebo home care patients were frequently intermediate and the controls were often the poorest.

6

FINDINGS

Despite the inherent risks and the difficulties encountered in the execution of this experimental home care study, the unequivocal findings and their enormous potential for more effective and practical care of the mentally ill require a categorical verdict of dramatic success for the enterprise.

The Louisville study was designed to determine (1) whether home care for schizophrenic patients was feasible, (2) whether drug therapy was effective in preventing their hospitalization, and (3) whether home care was in fact a better method of treatment than hospitalization. The answers to these questions are all in the affirmative. The results constitute hard evidence for the feasibility of home care and the effectiveness of drug therapy as part of a home care program. The findings also indicate that if home care is not a superior method of treatment than hospitalization, it is at least every bit as good for successful treatment of the types of schizophrenic patients described in the preceding section.

The purpose of this chapter is to examine in detail the kinds of data which support the above assertions, the precise degree to which each is true, and, in short, the "stuff" of the experiment.

THE PREVENTION OF HOSPITALIZATION

During the course of the study, 44 of the 57 drug home care patients (77.2 percent) remained continuously at home. These successful patients spent an average of 532 consecutive days at home. The least number of days continuously in the community was 203 and the greatest was 827 days. In contrast, significantly fewer of the placebo home care cases—14 of 41, or 34.1 percent—remained continuously at home during the same time period. These 14 successful placebo patients also averaged

532 consecutive days at home and the range was 203 to 877 days. Naturally, all 54 control patients experienced hospitalization. This initial institutionalization averaged about 83 days. Conversely, only 24 percent of the drug, but 66 percent of the placebo and all of the controls were hospitalized during the study. Figure 6-1 presents this striking contrast.

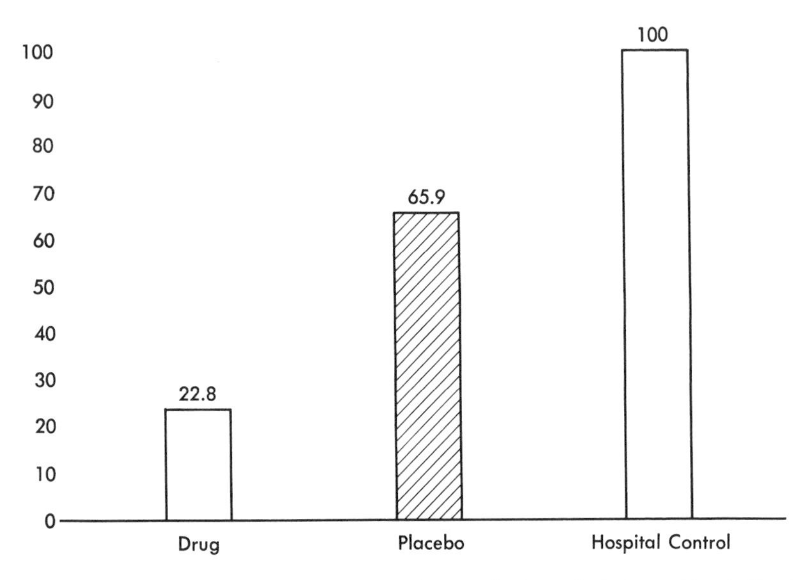

Figure 6–1. Percentage of Drug, Placebo, and Control Patients Hospitalized During Study

This success in keeping drug patients from being institutionalized is also reflected in the percentage of time spent at home and in mental hospitals by the drug, placebo, and control patients. During the course of the project the 57 drug patients spent 28,601 days out of a total of 31,710 days at home. The 41 placebo patients spent 18,327 days of a total of 22,895 days at home. The hospital controls were home for 23,136 of 30,834 days in the program. Translated into percentage figures, the drug patients were home 90.2 percent of the time, the placebo cases 80.0 percent, and the control 75.0 of the total time on the project. These results are presented in Table 6-1 and in graphic form in Figure 6-2.

Table 6-1. Number of Days Spent at Home by Drug, Placebo, and Hospital Control Patients

	Drug	*Placebo*	*Hospital Control*
Days home	28,601	18,327	23,136
Days in hospital	3,109	4,568	7,698
	31,710	22,895	30,834

Using the experience of the hospital controls as the baseline, it is estimated that the placebo patients were saved 1156 days of hospitalization and the drug patients 4818 days during these 30 months.[1] Most of these savings, of course, were a function of the prevention of initial hospitalization. Thus, of the total of 7698 days spent by the controls

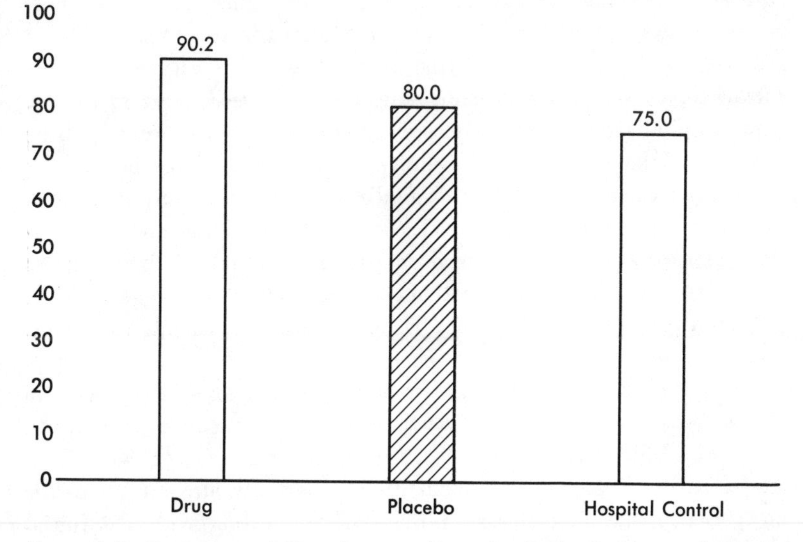

Figure 6–2. Percentage of Time Spent at Home by Drug, Placebo, and Hospital Control Patients

[1] At the annual average United States rate of $5.81 per day in 1962, the dollar savings for the placebo patients were about $6700 and for the drug patients about $28,000. However, adequate home care, and no doubt other community mental health programs are by no means less expensive than hospitalization, except as measured by effectiveness.

in the mental hospital, 4504 days or 58.5 percent were a function of the initial hospitalization.

Since over three-quarters of the drug patients were not hospitalized at all, the savings, from an administrative point of view, are even greater than these 4504 patient bed-days. Institutional personnel, always in scarce supply, could devote proportionately more of their time and energies in treating fewer and sicker patients more intensively. Ultimately, this is one of the principal gains of community psychiatric programs.

SUCCESS AND LENGTH OF TIME ON PROJECT

Considerable controversy has occurred over the use of the phrase "prevention of hospitalization." It has been argued that home care merely delays, rather than prevents, institutionalization. Specifically it has been said that the proportion of successes falls off very sharply with time, so that if a sufficiently long period is used, most of the patient hospitalization ostensibly prevented has in effect merely been deferred.[2] Whatever the face validity of this contention, the data in this study clearly suggest that hospitalization has been truly *prevented*. The attrition in the number of successes with time was not nearly as great as expected. Further, the drug patients maintained their relative advantage over the placebo patients through all of the time periods, thus indicating that the treatment, however limited and modest in scope, was effective.

For the drug patients, the percentage of successes declined from 78.2 percent for those patients on the project for 9 months or more to 60.0 percent for patients under ITC treatment for 2 years or more. Even this relatively small amount of attrition is partially attributable to the inexperience and fearfulness of the staff in dealing with the initial group of patients and to other variables such as the fact that a few of our successful patients left the project or the community before the end of the study, thereby decreasing the number of successes.

Still, *to keep three out of five patients who had actually been sent to a mental hospital out of the hospital for at least 2 years constitutes*

[2] David M. Engelhardt, Bernard Rosen, Norbert Freedman, David Mann, and Reuben Margolis, "Phenothiazines in Prevention of Psychiatric Hospitalization: Duration of Treatment Exposure," *JAMA*, **186** (December 14, 1963), 981–983.

not only a major achievement in itself but clearly implies effective prevention in a difficult treatment field. The percentage of successes in the placebo cohort fell from 31.6 to 22.2 in the same time periods. These data are displayed in Figure 6-3.

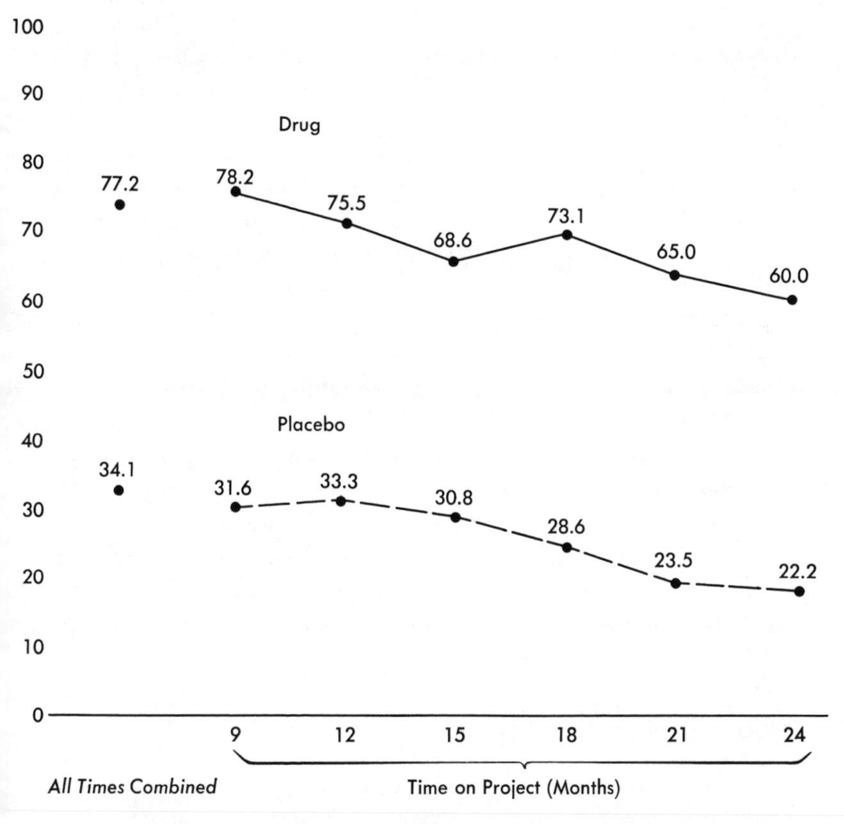

Figure 6–3. Percentage of Home Care Success and Length of Time on Project

SUCCESS AND TIME PERIOD IN THE PROJECT

One of the interesting aspects of the findings, though admittedly somewhat peripheral to the major issues, concerned the role of the staff in conserving successful patients. Remarkable also is their clear improvement after the initial shakedown of the study. At the outset, the nurses were inexperienced and frankly fearful of the dangers and risks in keeping schizophrenics at home. Four of the nurses, except for their intensive training on the project, had never cared for mentally ill persons before. Other staff people, including the ITC psychiatrist, were also unlikely to take undue chances in keeping the patients at home. Underlying this fear and cautiousness was the fact that some of the patients were receiving placebo medication, and the staff members did not know which of their patients were in the drug and which were in the placebo cohorts.

All of this was consequently and inevitably reflected in the disproportionately high drug home care failure rate in the first 6 months of the study. Despite having more time available for each patient than at any subsequent period in the project, the drug success rate for patients treated in the first 6 months of the study was only 67 percent. The success rate in each of the respective 6-month periods thereafter was 100, 82, and 90 percent. The first 6 months of treatment of the placebo patients were also the least successful. The initial rate of success was an unimpressive 43 percent. The peak of success occurred in the fourth 6-month period, and the rate at that point was 78 percent (see Appendix B, Table XVI).

In examining and analyzing these results it seems plausible to contend that for the drug patients the combined effect of the drugs plus more experienced nursing care served to improve the success rate after the initial 6-month period. The numbers involved however, do not permit much certainty about this conclusion.

DRUG AND PLACEBO FAILURES

Previous studies of posthospital outcome have convincingly demonstrated that most failures occur within 6 months of hospital discharge. The reasons for this are well known and might be summarized by saying that the initial adjustment period places the patient under the greatest stress. Roles have to be altered and responsibilities undertaken and fulfilled. Although crises may and do occur thereafter, if the patient can make a reasonably good initial adjustment, the odds on his continued success increase. What applies to the posthospital situation when the patient's symptoms and problems may have been modified appreciably in his hospitalization, applies with even greater force when acutely ill patients are returned home prior to treatment and within a very short time of their commitment to the hospital.

The results, as expected, show that the patients requiring hospitalization (the study failures) failed early. This was especially characteristic of the placebo patients for whom even the support, advice, and services of the public health nurse on her home visits soon proved to be insufficient to prevent hospitalization. In concrete terms, of the 13 drug home care failures, 5 were hospitalized within a month, 8 within 3 months, and all but 1 within a year. Of the 27 placebo failures almost one-quarter within a fortnight, two-fifths within 3 months, three-fourths within 6 months, and all but 2 within a year.

Thus, to maximize successful implementation of the findings of this study the greatest effort must be expended in the initial stages of home care. Although the nurses visited each patient and family on a weekly basis for the first 3 months of home care and were accessible on a 24-hour telephone basis (during the first year of the study), increased visitations and attention at the point of return to the community would appear to be warranted.

The same pattern was also seen in the cases where hospital controls were discharged and later had to be readmitted. Rehospitalization occurred for 25 of the 54 control patients. Hospital readmittance took place within a fortnight in 36 percent of the cases, in 64 percent within 6 months, and in 88 percent within a year.

PRECIPITANTS OF FAILURE

Despite the reluctance of the staff to hospitalize patients unless it was readily apparent that institutionalization was required, 13 drug and 27 home care patients could not succeed in the program. The reasons for failure were varied but very often the onset of acute symptoms prompted either the family, the patient, or ITC to commit the patients to the hospital. The project staff and the families were each responsible for about 45 percent of the commitments. The remainder involved voluntary commitments on the part of the patients or hospitalization on the recommendation of a family physician.

Without detailing all the cases, a few of the precipitants, leading to hospitalization, usually of the "last straw" type, as stated in the failure reports of the nurses are presented below:

"Patient destructive, mischievious. Family refused to have her in the home any longer."

"Family frightened of patient's potentially violent behavior."

"Patient refused to take medication or see nurse."

"Patient extremely agitated. Husband took her to the family physician who urged immediate hospitalization."

"Patient stopped taking medication. Thought ITC was trying to kill her and that medicine was poison."

"Patient insisted on going to the hospital to receive shock treatment."

"Patient violent and abusive."

"Patient completely uncontrollable. Incontinent."

"Significant other moved. Left patient alone. No supervision available."[3]

As far as could be determined, the precipitating factors prompting the hospitalization of drug and placebo failures were quite similar. Bizarre, aggressive, destructive, or other such behaviors did not appear to be any more common among the placebo failures than the drug failures. On the contrary, the reverse may well have been the case.

THE HOSPITAL EXPERIENCE OF HOME CARE FAILURES

Whatever the basis for failure on home care, the drug failure cases on the average spent considerably more time in the hospital subsequently than did the placebo failures. The 13 drug home care failures experienced 30 separate admissions which amounted to 3109 inpatient days or an average 239 days. The 27 placebo home care failures were institutionalized 45 times and accumulated an average of 169 hospital days. It is well to recall that once hospitalized, the failure patients were treated in accordance with customary procedures. Study failure patients received no further care from the ITC staff after hospital release.

This very important finding concerning the much lengthier hospitalizations of the drug failure patients leads to the conclusion that they were so ill that neither the shifts in medication prescribed by the psychiatrist nor the ordinarily adequate dosage of medication could maintain them at home. The placebo failures included not only such

[3] See, Kathleen Smith, Muriel W. Pumphrey and Julian C. Hall, "The 'Last Straw': The Decisive Incident Resulting in the Request for Hospitalization in 100 Schizophrenic Patients," *Amer. J. Psychiat.*, **120** (September, 1963), 228–233.

comparably sick patients but others who probably could have succeeded in the community on drugs. These latter, less seriously ill patients, tended to reduce the average length of hospitalization of the placebo failure cases.

This finding highlights the contention of the proponents of community mental health care that the function of the mental hospital should be to treat only those patients for whom community care, even when continuous and intensive, fails, and greater supervision is required. From this perspective the hospital should be the end of the funnel. When this finally transpires, the hospital will revert to its initially conceived function as a humane treatment institution serving a limited clientele. On the other hand, the opponents of community care claim that the hopelessness inherent in large custodial institutions at present would be multiplied in future institutions which, under community mental health and home care programs, would receive only the very sickest patients with the poorest prognoses. This latter argument is largely refuted by the data in the section which follows.

The hospitalization data on the failure patients are displayed in Table 6-2.

Table 6-2. Number and Mean Length of Hospitalization of Home Care Failure Patients

	Drug			*Placebo*		
Hospitalizations	*N*	*Days Hospitalized*	*Mean*	*N*	*Days Hospitalized*	*Mean*
First	13	2233	171.8	27	3597	133.2
Second	8	419	52.4	9	672	74.7
Third	5	384	76.8	4	244	61.0
Fourth or more	4	73	18.3*	5	55*	11.0

*Hospitalization still incomplete at conclusion of experimental investigation.

HOSPITALIZATION HISTORIES OF THE CONTROLS

The outcome for the home care patients must, to have meaning, be seen against those of the hospitalized controls. This is the baseline for measurement. It will be recalled that all of the controls were permitted to undergo routine hospital treatment *without ITC intervention.*

The 54 control patients spent an average of 83 days in initial hospitalization with a range of 2 to 595 consecutive inpatient days. Every control patient had been returned home and none was left lingering on a back ward which in itself speaks well of the state hospital and of changed practices regarding discharge. After return home and a stay ranging from 6 to 788 days, 25 of the controls failed and required rehospitalization. This rehospitalization averaged over 102 days and accounted for fully one-third of all hospital inpatient time accumulated by the controls. Seven patients were hospitalized a second time, four a third time, and two patients a fourth time. These latter hospitalizations amounted to 8.2 percent of all inpatient time. Table 6-3 contains these results.

Even after hospitalization and presumable remission of symptoms, the controls continued to exhibit greater failure rates when returned home than did the drug patients. This indicates the significant effect of continuous home care intervention of even the modest nature described, in contrast to the usual state hospital aftercare clinics.

Table 6-3. Hospital Experience of Controls

	N	*Days Hospitalized*	*Mean*
Initial hospitalization	54	4504	83.4
First rehospitalization	25	2564	102.6
Second rehospitalization	7	339	48.4
Third rehospitalization	4	121	30.3
Fourth rehospitalization	2	170*	85.0

*Hospitalization still incomplete at conclusion of experimental investigation.

DEMOGRAPHIC AND MEDICAL CHARACTERISTICS AND SUCCESS AND FAILURE

Age, Sex, and Race

For the most part home care success or failure was not significantly related to the demographic and other background variables which were examined. The principal reason for this lack of association was the small number of drug home care failures and placebo home care successes. A second explanation is to be found in the large number of more immediate variables which determined the outcome, including of course the extent and severity of psychological symptoms.

Briefly, then, at the point of study intake drug successes were somewhat older than drug failures, while the reverse applied for the placebo group. Drug successes were an average 35.8 years of age and drug failures 31.7 years. Placebo successes and failures were 35.2 and 37.2 years of age respectively. Not only did the direction reverse, but the age differences were not statistically significant.

It was thought that proportionately more females would succeed in both home care groups since the fear and anxiety of female patients is presumably less than that of male patients. This is the same principle which possibly favored the induction of somewhat more females than males into the study in the first place. While the hypothesis did not find statistical verification as such, the direction of difference in the drug group, at least, was as predicted. Of the 20 male drug patients, 65 percent succeeded in contrast to the nearly 80 percent success ratio for females. On the other hand, only about a third each of the male and female placebo patients succeeded.

Nor were the findings significant with regard to race. Of the 30 white drug cases, about 80 percent succeeded as did 72 percent of the Negro drug patients. As for the placebo patients, race was an equally unimportant variable in the case outcome. This finding negates one of our subsidiary hypotheses about the differential willingness of white and Negro families to tolerate deviant persons and behavior.

Education

There appeared to be some support for the hypothesis that home care success is more frequent among the better educated and occupationally higher status persons. This is direct confirmation of the findings in an outcome study of consecutive female discharges. In that investigation, which was discussed in Chapter 2, posthospital performance was positively related to education and occupation.[4] Posthospital failure cases and poorly functioning successful patients were dispro-

[4] Simon Dinitz, Mark Lefton, Shirley Angrist, and Benjamin Pasamanick, "Psychiatric and Social Attributes as Predictors of Case Outcome in Mental Hospitalization," *Soc. Prob.*, **8** (Spring, 1961), 322–328.

portionately drawn from the poorly educated. Findings in the present study indicate that 56 percent of the drug successes as against 85 percent of the drug failures had less than a high school education. In the placebo group, 57 percent of the successes and 70 percent of the failures had not completed high school. These results are subject to a number of interpretations. One of the most intriguing, however, is that failure patients were sicker to begin with and that their illnesses were of long duration possibly dating back to childhood. This in turn curtailed their education. Albee, for instance, has found that adult schizophrenics as children had lower IQs and poorer school performance than their siblings. This would indicate that they were functioning poorly long before they presented symptoms of schizophrenia.[5] More definitive support for this hypothesis would require longitudinal analysis with a very large cohort of subjects.

Marital Status and Parental and Conjugal Households

There is a considerable body of research data both here and abroad which indicates that patients who are married do better in the posthospital setting than do single persons. Additionally, patients who return home to a conjugal family fail more often but generally function better than patients released to a parental setting. All of these findings are part of the tolerance of deviance proposition which was discussed in the literature review section (pages 24 to 26).

The outcome data in this study, neither statistically nor in the direction of the difference of results, tend to substantiate these hypotheses. There was absolutely no difference in percentage of successes and failures in terms of the marital status of the patients in either the drug or placebo cohorts. Specifically, of the 28 drug patients who were returned to a spouse, over 78 percent succeeded; but so did 73.3 percent who were returned to a parent and over 78 percent who went to a sibling or other relative. The comparable percentages in the placebo cohort were 37.5, 40.0, and 26.7. Whatever the importance of the type of household in determining success or failure, its role was wholly subsidiary to the fact of drug or placebo treatment. These results are so noteworthy that they deserve specific mention. Of the patients returned

[5] Ellen A. Lane and George W. Albee, "Childhood Intellectual Differences between Schizophrenic Adults and their Siblings," *J. Orthopsychiat.*, **35** (July, 1965), 747–753.

to a spouse, 78.6 percent who were on drug medication remained at home in contrast to the 37.5 percent on placebo medication, and nearly three-fourths of the drug patients who went back to a parental household were able to remain home as opposed to only two-fifths of the placebo patients.

Previous Hospitalizations and Success and Failure

The data on previous hospitalizations and success and failure in the program testify to the correctness of the original study design which assumed a patient population never previously hospitalized. Had such been possible, the drug success rate might have been somewhat higher than the 77 percent rate obtained, although the placebo rate would likely have remained at about the same level. Based on numbers that are too small to permit any but the most qualified conclusions, it was found that 10 out of 11 first admission drug home care patients succeeded as did only 3 out of 10 first admission placebo patients. By way of contrast nearly 73 percent of multiple previous admission drug cases and 55 percent of such placebo patients succeeded. Thus, previous hospitalizations tended to be associated with greater failure in the drug cohort but not for the placebo patients.

Previous outpatient psychiatric care, on the other hand, seemed to have little or no bearing for successful outcome in the ITC program. Nor did, as far as the subjective answers are concerned, the status of the illness—acute, intermediate, or insidious—appear to have any significant relationship to outcome in either cohort. This latter finding is especially interesting since it is the prevailing impression that patients with insidious or gradual onsets (*process schizophrenics*) have by far the poorest prognoses.

FUNCTIONING VARIABLES AND OUTCOME

Mental Status

Psychiatrist's Evaluations. Three major findings were obtained from the ratings of the staff psychiatrist who evaluated the drug, placebo, and hospital control patients on the Lorr IMPS at intake and after 6, 18, and 24 months on the project. First, the mental status of patients, regardless of study group, was much improved with time. Second, reduction of symptoms and signs was equally great in the drug, placebo, and hospital control groups. Third, the greatest gain was achieved in the intake versus the 6 months' ratings with little additional improvement thereafter.

In terms of total weighted scores, the mean scores of the 55 drug patients fell from 85.4 to 32.0 from the intake to the 6 months' assessment and thereafter, for the 24 remaining drug patients, to 27.0 at 18 months, and 21.6 at the end of 24 months. The 39 placebo patients scored 95.8 at intake and 44.6 at 6 months. The 42 controls had a mean score of 103.9 at admission and 51.6 at 6 months. Analysis of variance indicated that all three groups had improved significantly and that there had been no greater improvement in any one than in the other groups. Table 6-4 shows these results.

With regard to the perceptual and thinking distortion morbidity

Table 6-4. IMPS Total Weighted Mean Scores of the Same Drug, Placebo, and Hospital Control Patients at Various Points in Time

	Drug		*Placebo*		*Hospital Control*	
*Time**	*N*	*M*	*N*	*M*	*N*	*M*
Admission	57	85.5	41	94.6	54	100.4
Admission	55	85.4	39	95.8	42	103.9
6 months	55	32.0	39	44.6	42	51.6
Admission	36	82.4	13	91.2		
6 months	36	30.0	13	28.5		
18 months	36	26.0	13	34.1		
Admission	24	79.5	8	112.4		
6 months	24	29.7	8	33.4		
18 months	24	27.0	8	38.8		
24 months	24	21.6	8	37.5		
First evaluation	56	85.2	41	94.6	48	101.0
Last evaluation**	56	26.1	41	39.0	48	40.3

*At admission to the ITC program there were 57 drug and 41 placebo patients. At 6 months there were two sets of data on 55 drug and 39 placebo patients. At the 18 months' testing, three sets of scores were available for 36 drug and 13 placebo patients and at 24 months, there were four scores for each of 24 drug and 8 placebo patients.

**The last evaluation is exactly that. It may have occurred at 6, 18, or 24 months.

scale results the drug patients who had some distortion at intake showed practically none at 6 months or in later testing periods. The placebo cases also improved substantially as did the controls. The analysis of variance results indicated a significant reduction in perceptual and thinking distortions of patients in all groups with approximately the same degree of improvement in all.

Table 6-5. IMPS Perceptual and Thinking Distortion Mean Scores of Drug, Placebo, and Hospital Control Patients at Various Points in Time

	Drug		Placebo		Hospital Control	
Time	*N*	*Mean*	*N*	*Mean*	*N*	*Mean*
Admission	57	16.1	41	16.7	54	20.8
Admission	55	16.3	39	16.9	42	21.5
6 months	55	1.3	39	4.4	42	6.2
Admission	36	15.9	13	12.5		
6 months	36	0.5	13	3.9		
18 months	36	0.8	13	5.8		
Admission	24	17.5	8	13.3		
6 months	24	0.7	8	5.0		
18 months	24	1.2	8	6.4		
24 months	24	0.3	8	11.3		
First evaluation	56	16.2	41	16.7	48	20.5
Last evaluation	56	1.5	41	4.8	48	1.2

Finally, the findings on the important schizophrenic disorganization scale showed the identical pattern. Drug and placebo and hospital control patients improved markedly in the 6-months as compared with the initial evaluation of the psychiatrist. Improvement on later assessments for the drug and placebo patients was only minimal. Analysis of variance showed the improvement within subjects over time to be statistically significant and that there was no significant differential improvement in any one category of patients.

Nurses Evaluations of Mental Status. Nurses' ratings of their patients differed from the assessments of the psychiatrist in several ways.

Table 6-6. IMPS Schizophrenic Disorganization Mean Scores of Drug, Placebo, and Hospital Control Patients at Various Points in Time

	Drug		*Placebo*		*Hospital Control*	
Time	*N*	*Mean*	*N*	*Mean*	*N*	*Mean*
Admission	57	38.9	41	49.0	54	43.5
Admission	55	38.6	39	49.8	42	42.9
6 months	55	17.9	39	24.4	42	24.7
Admission	36	37.0	13	49.0		
6 months	36	16.8	13	12.3		
18 months	36	14.1	13	11.5		
Admission	24	30.5	8	62.8		
6 months	24	14.9	8	14.5		
18 months	24	12.8	8	13.3		
24 months	24	12.7	8	15.8		
First evaluation	56	38.4	41	49.0	48	42.5
Last evaluation	56	15.9	41	22.6	48	23.6

First, the nurses rated only the drug and placebo patients since the hospital controls were inaccessible to them. Second, because of the home care failures who were hospitalized, there was greater attrition of numbers and consequently somewhat less stability in ratings after the 18-month testing period. Third, a comparison of the evaluations of the psychiatrist and the nurses on the same instruments showed that the physician scored the patients as having considerably more pathology. The mean scores were about one and one-half to two times greater than the respective mean scores of the nurses (see Table 6-7). This phenomenon in which the psychiatrist systematically finds greater pathology than do the nurses or other raters, including relatives, has been found before. A number of explanations have been suggested the most plausible of which is that by training and experience, the psychiatrist is likely to go deeper thereby finding greater pathology. Also psychiatrists tend to interpret the same signs and symptoms from an illness context rather than a social and interactional context and consequently attach greater significance to various behavioral manifestations.

Despite these differences, the general direction of the results was similar to that of the psychiatrist's results. First, patients improved in their mean scores from the initial to the 6 months' ratings. Second, there was little or no gain after the 6 months' assessment, and on one morbidity score, perceptual and thinking distortion, the placebo patient even lost a little ground from the first to the last testing.

Analysis of variance tests indicated that the nurses found significant improvement in both the drug and placebo patients over time with no greater improvement for either population on the total weighted mean score. No difference in either group before and after or between was found on the distortion scale. A gain with time was found on the schizophrenic disorganization scale, but this improvement was as great for the placebo as for the drug patients.

Significant Other Ratings. The ratings of the relatives of the patients on the modified Lorr IMPS scale are in accord in all important

Table 6-7. Mean Morbidity Scores Based on Nurses' Ratings of Drug and Placebo Patients

	Drug				*Placebo*			
Time	*N*	*Mean**	*Mean***	*Mean****	*N*	*Mean**	*Mean***	*Mean****
Admission	55	47.5	6.2	16.5	41	61.0	8.4	25.8
Admission	51	46.6	6.5	15.3	28	55.4	6.9	25.9
6 months	51	28.7	2.1	11.2	28	45.3	4.9	20.0
Admission	46	47.1	6.6	15.6	15	49.5	5.5	20.7
6 months	46	24.8	1.1	10.4	15	39.3	3.8	13.3
18 months	46	28.6	1.2	13.0	15	38.7	2.8	10.1
Admission	28	43.5	5.6	14.9	9	57.8	8.2	26.2
6 months	28	25.4	1.4	9.5	9	38.9	3.8	12.8
18 months	28	31.0	1.3	12.4	9	41.0	0.9	12.8
24 months	28	25.5	2.8	11.5	9	50.2	15.2	13.2
First evaluation	51	46.6	6.5	15.3	28	55.5	6.9	25.9
Last evaluation	51	30.3	3.2	14.1	28	47.8	9.2	18.1

*Total weighted
**Perceptual and thinking distortion
***Schizophrenic disorganization

respects with those of the psychiatrist and the nurses. Although the small number of cases remaining due to the hospitalization of 27 placebo patients presented a major problem in the analysis, it is still quite clear that there was a decided improvement in the mental status of the patients in the first 6 months, whereas there was no gain and an occasional loss thereafter in the few patients tested. The relative improvement was no greater in the drug group than in the placebo category on all three scores.

Table 6-8. Mean Morbidity Scores Based on Ratings of the Significant Others of Drug and Placebo Patients

	Drug				Placebo			
Time	*N*	*Mean**	*Mean***	*Mean****	*N*	*Mean**	*Mean***	*Mean****
Admission	55	28.0	12.1	7.8	41	38.5	19.5	10.3
Admission	49	27.2	11.6	7.7	31	38.1	19.3	9.9
6 months	49	7.7	1.2	3.3	31	19.2	7.5	7.2
Admission	44	28.0	12.4	7.9	18	32.9	15.0	8.1
6 months	44	5.7	1.0	2.4	18	12.1	5.1	3.4
18 months	44	7.4	2.3	2.8	18	11.3	3.7	4.4
Admission	25	32.8	15.4	7.8	9	42.2	20.7	8.4
6 months	25	5.0	0.7	2.0	9	8.6	2.2	2.8
18 months	25	5.0	1.0	1.8	9	8.6	1.3	3.2
24 months	25	5.3	0.7	1.9	9	15.1	5.9	4.8
First evaluation	49	27.2	11.6	7.7	31	38.1	19.3	9.9
Last evaluation	49	10.2	2.8	4.0	31	20.6	7.9	8.1

*Total weighted score
**Perceptual and thinking distortion
***Schizophrenic disorganization

These very consistent results regarding the mental status of the patients at various points in the study are significant in at least two respects that require mention. First, these subjective evaluations confirmed the hard facts presented earlier. These were very sick patients at the time of intake and they exhibited some very florid symptoms. In the first 6 months some of the symptoms disappeared and the severity of some of the grosser ones lessened. Once the acute stage was over

Table 6-9. Initial Psychiatric Ratings and Success and Failure in Home Care

	Psychiatrist's Ratings			*Nurses' Ratings*			*Significant Others' Ratings*		
Drug	*Mean**	*Mean***	*Mean****	*Mean**	*Mean***	*Mean****	*Mean**	*Mean***	*Mean****
Success	86.2	17.6	38.4	48.1	6.3	14.6	27.5	12.4	7.5
Failure	83.2	10.9	43.8	44.8	5.5	23.5	30.1	10.9	9.0
Placebo									
Success	83.4	8.0	49.3	47.0	5.3	19.1	29.7	14.1	6.8
Failure	100.4	21.1	48.3	68.2	10.0	26.8	43.1	22.3	12.1

*Total weighted score
**Perceptual and thinking distortion
***Schizophrenic disorganization

there was little further improvement possible in many of the cases as their chronic problems tended to persist. Second, and of a wholly different order, it is at least interesting that so much consensus occurred in the three sets of ratings of the psychiatrist, nurse, and relative. Perhaps more attention should be paid as a general rule in evaluating patient status to the assessments of the relatives who after all know the patients best. In this investigation the significant others provided reasonably accurate judgments of patient functioning as determined by the relation of these evaluations to those of the nurses and the psychiatrist.

Initial Psychiatric Evaluations and Success. One admittedly tangential issue is of sufficient import to warrant some consideration before closure on the psychiatric ratings. This issue concerns the prediction potential of these evaluations. Using the initial Lorr IMPS assessments by the staff psychiatrist and the nurses, and the evaluations of the significant others on the modified IMPS rating scale, there was a pronounced trend for the future placebo successful patients to have been rated as less impaired than the future failures. Unfortunately, the small numbers of cases of failure and the large intragroup variance prevented these differences from being conclusive (see Table 6-9).

Psychological Test Results

The four psychological tests administered to the patients at intake, at 6 months, at 18 months, and at 2 years included a reaction time test, the WAIS, the Bender Gestalt, and the Porteus Mazes. The findings obtained with these instruments wholly corroborate the results with the psychiatric measures of mental status.

The validity of some of these psychological measures is attested to by their ability to predict success or failure or at least to distinguish future failures from the successes and by their correlation with all the other functioning instruments. This will be discussed later. Briefly, all three groups of patients showed improvement in the first 6 months or between the initial and 6-month testing periods. The gains thereafter were minimal.

Reaction time. The reaction time test, described previously, indicated that drug, placebo, and hospital control patients exhibited an increased speed of reaction from the initial testing period to the 6-month period but not very much between the 6- and 18-month periods. Using the log transformation mean scores, these results are presented in Table 6-10. An analysis of variance test showed significant improvement in the reaction time of subjects in all three study categories but no greater gain in any one of the groups. This is taken to mean, since the reaction time test was one of the more objective measures of pathology, that the patients functioned much better as the severity of their symptoms decreased or became less florid. Hospitalization was equally as effective as home care in this respect.

Table 6-10. Reaction Time Scores of Drug, Placebo, and Hospital Control Patients at Various Points in Time

	Drug		Placebo		Hospital Control	
	N	*Reaction Time**	*N*	*Reaction Time**	*N*	*Reaction Time**
Admission	56	3.2860	39	3.2965	51	3.2747
Admission	54	3.2880	36	3.3058	41	3.2666
6 months	54	3.1666	36	3.2473	41	3.2406
Admission	31	3.2756	23	3.2982	25	3.2569
6 months	31	3.2226	23	3.2485	25	3.2222
18 months	31	3.2218	23	3.2176	25	3.2167
First test	54	3.2880	38	3.3012	42	3.2649
Last test	54	3.1661	38	3.2252	42	3.2379

*Scores are log transformations.

WAIS Scores. There were three major results obtained with the WAIS. First, while the drug and placebo patients had about the same relatively low IQ mean scores at the onset, the controls' scores were lower and significantly so. Second, all three groups increased their mean IQ scores significantly between the initial and final tests. The drug cases went from 81.2 to 83.5, the placebo cases from 77.8 to 83.6 and the hospital controls from 69.7 to 76.8. Third, the controls while still with poorer scores were no longer significantly lower at the last testing than the other two groups of patients.

Table 6-11. WAIS Scores of Drug, Placebo, and Hospital Controls at Various Points in Time

	Drug		*Placebo*		*Hospital Control*	
	N	*IQ*	*N*	*IQ*	*N*	*IQ*
Admission	57	81.2	40	78.1	54	71.3
Admission	57	81.2	38	77.7	46	69.7
6 months	57	84.2	38	82.1	46	75.5
Admission	34	81.1	24	82.0	29	69.1
6 months	34	82.8	24	85.3	29	75.4
18 months	34	81.5	24	87.5	29	77.5
First test	57	81.2	39	77.8	46	69.7
Last test	57	83.5	39	83.6	46	76.8

Bender Gestalt. The Bender Gestalt was yet another instrument with which to determine changes in the degree of pathology with time and between groups. Without presenting an inordinate amount of detail it was found that there were no significant differences among the three study categories at the outset or at the final testing. However, each of the three groups showed significant improvement which occurred primarily from intake to the sixth month. These findings are displayed in Table 6-12.

Porteus Mazes. The last of the psychological tests was the Porteus Mazes test from which both an IQ score and an error quotient (QE), indicative of degree of pathology, were derived. Using the QE square root transformations, the three groups did not differ significantly at the onset of the study, nor at the final testing. On this, the only one of the tests in which such a result was obtained, there was no significant gain with time. In short, the QE measure failed to show any differences at any time. On the IQ, however, there were no differences at the beginning or the end between the groups, but there was significant patient improvement from the first to the last test period (see Table 6-13).

Psychological Tests and Home Care Success and Failure. Using the psychological test scores of the drug and placebo patients at the time of admission to the project, there was a well defined tendency for suc-

Table 6-12. Bender Gestalt Reciprocal Transformation Z Scores of Drug, Placebo, and Hospital Control Patients at Various Points in Time

	Drug		*Placebo*		*Hospital Control*	
	N	*Z**	*N*	*Z**	*N*	*Z**
Admission	57	105.7	40	99.9	54	97.1
Admission	57	105.7	38	99.8	46	95.2
6 months	57	112.8	38	108.9	46	102.5
Admission	34	105.2	24	104.0	29	98.9
6 months	34	110.8	24	114.8	29	101.3
18 months	34	113.1	24	114.5	29	101.6
First test	57	105.7	39	99.8	46	95.2
Last test	57	114.1	39	109.7	46	102.7

*Reciprocal transformation of Z.

cessful patients to have scored somewhat better than future failures in both study categories. There were, of course, some notable exceptions in this regard that only served to highlight the more general trend. The successful drug patients tended to score better, but not significantly so at the outset, on the WAIS, the Bender, and on both Porteus Mazes scales. Only the reaction time scores failed to distinguish as might have been expected. The successful placebo patients, on the other hand, showed significant initial superiority over the failures on three of the five scales—reaction time, Bender Gestalt, and the Porteus Mazes IQ. The WAIS IQ score was some 10 points higher. Even the QE scale scores conformed to this trend line although only modestly.

These findings are interpreted to mean that barring treatment intervention the psychological test scores are reasonably predictive of success and failure. Patients with the greater pathology, in the normal course of events, tend to fail more often than those with less pathology. This was indicated by the tests given the placebo patients. Treatment intervention, however, improves the chances of all for success thereby blunting the predictability of the various assessments, both psychological and psychiatric.

Table 6-13. Porteus Mazes IQ and QE Scores of Drug, Placebo, and Hospital Control Patients at Various Points in Time

	Drug			*Placebo*			*Hospital Control*		
	N	*QE**	*IQ*	*N*	*QE**	*IQ*	*N*	*QE**	*IQ*
Admission	57	61.0	80.7	40	58.4	80.8	54	55.7	68.0
Admission	56	60.9	80.8	38	58.0	78.7	46	55.4	65.4
6 months	56	63.8	88.1	38	56.8	87.6	46	58.5	80.8
Admission	34	60.7	81.7	24	55.9	82.4	29	55.1	64.9
6 months	34	62.9	84.1	24	56.3	87.7	29	56.5	78.6
18 months	34	59.9	80.8	24	57.7	86.0	29	61.5	74.9
First test	56	60.9	80.8	39	57.8	79.9	47	55.3	66.3
Last test	56	62.0	86.1	39	57.7	86.3	47	61.9	78.3

*Square root transformation mean score.

Table 6-14. Psychological Mean Test Scores of Success and Failure Patients at Admission

	Reaction Time	WAIS	Bender Z	Porteus Mazes	
Drug	*Mean*	*Mean*	*Mean*	*Mean QE*	*Mean IQ*
Success	3.2947	81.3	107.1	60.8	83.3
Failure	3.2575	80.6	100.9	62.0	71.7
Placebo					
Success	3.2165	87.3	112.2	57.5	96.8
Failure	3.3365*	73.6	93.9*	58.8	73.1*

*Denotes statistical significance.

Source: Dinitz, Scarpitti, Albini, Lefton, and Pasamanick, "An Experimental Study in the Prevention of Hospitalization of Schizophrenics: Thirty Months Experience," *Amer. J. Orthopsychiat.*, 35 (January, 1965), 7.

Patients as Problems

The perceptions of significant others about the burdensomeness of the patients were obtained by the social worker at the time of the patient's entry into the project and while still waiting at the Institute Treatment Center where arrangements were being made for the patient to be returned home, and at 3, 6, 9, 12, 18, and 24 months later by the nurses. The data derived from the 22-item problem subscale tend to corroborate, in every major respect, the findings on the more objective measures such as the psychological and psychiatric ratings. First, the relatives indicated a very significant improvement in the problems posed by the patients from intake to the sixth month on the project. After the sixth month, there was no significant lessening of the problems with additional time on the project. It seems obvious that once the more acute symptoms and signs, which primarily contributed to the perception of the patient in the household as a burden, were relieved, not much more gain was possible. After all, these patients had functioned at a low level for a long time before intake into the project, and a return to their prepsychotic episode status was all that reasonably could be anticipated. These general findings can be demonstrated by comparing the initial percentages presented in Table XIII in Appendix B, with the contrasting percentages at 6 months (see Table 6-15). The significant decreases in problems are readily apparent. At 6 months, unlike the situation at intake, the placebo patients seem to be a much greater problem for relatives than the drug patients. Of the 22 problem items, 19 favor the drug patients, 2 the placebo, and 1 favors neither group.

Table 6-15. Percentage of Drug and Placebo Patients Evidencing Each of 22 Behaviors

	At 6 Months	
Patient is Burdensome Because	*Drug (N = 50)**	*Placebo (N = 30)**
Trouble at night	4.3	33.3
Nursing problem	–	–
Source of worry	6.3	10.7
Worry about safety of others	4.2	32.1
Uncooperative	4.1	28.6
Strain on others	18.4	34.5
Patient's behavior is upsetting	8.5	33.3
Bodily symptoms cause concern	20.8	6.9
Sexual problem	2.1	10.7
Odd speech and ideas	8.3	32.1
Causes trouble with neighbors	2.1	3.6
Upsets household work and routine	15.2	26.9
Interferes with social activities	18.2	19.2
Forced to stay away from work because of patient	2.6	4.8
Forced to stay away from school because of patient	4.5	5.6
Caused you concern generally	34.0	55.6
Physical strain on significant other	18.8	39.3
Requires excessive amount of attention	21.3	17.9
Children ashamed of patient	3.7	11.1
Children afraid of patient	6.7	22.2
Significant other ashamed of patient	2.1	6.7
Significant other afraid of patient	2.1	13.3

*N varies by activity to some extent.

Domestic Performance (Females)

Adequate role performance, while perhaps not the single most critical measure of successful outcome, is indisputably important. The data obtained from the responsible relative on the domestic performance of the female patients indicated that this type of instrumental functioning in the drug group, like the other measures, significantly improved at the start and then leveled out with time. In numerical terms, the drug patients increased their mean scores on domestic functioning from 13.8 at admission to 15.0 at 3 months and 16.4 at 6 months. The comparable means for the placebo patients varied from this pattern. Their mean functioning score at intake was 15.9, which fell to 13.1 at 3 months and recovered to 15.2 at 6 months. At none of the three points were these differences between drug and placebo patients significantly different.

Nevertheless, there was still a substantial percentage of female patients who were partially or wholly unable or unwilling to handle customary household duties after 6 months on the project. Depending on the specific activity, from 16 to 40 percent of the drug patients and 17 to about 38 percent of the placebo cases were experiencing some difficulty in performing various tasks. These data are shown in Table 6-16. In looking at these functioning findings it is important to remem-

Table 6-16. Percentage of Female Drug and Placebo Patients Wholly or Partly Unable to Perform Specified Household Activities

	At 6 Months	
	*Drug (N = 33)**	*Placebo (N = 20)**
Attend to housecleaning chores	34.5	37.5
Prepare meals	25.9	35.7
Attend to laundry and cleaning	29.6	37.5
Shop for groceries	36.0	35.7
Do other shopping (clothing, etc.)	23.1	35.7
Budget for household	40.0	30.0
Plan daily activities	16.1	22.2
Solve daily problems	23.3	17.6

*N varies by activity to some extent.

ber that a larger percentage of drug than of placebo or control female patients, were at home and therefore were available for evaluation. Presumably the hospitalized patients would have performed at a lower level still.

Not only were the relatives periodically requested to provide this information on performance, but the patients themselves were also asked to indicate the quality of their performance. As a previous study also showed, patients and significant others tend to reflect each other's assessment on the specifics of patient performance. At the sixth months' testing, about one-third of the drug patients and somewhat fewer of the placebo patients indicated their total or partial inability to perform these eight specific and more or less routine duties.

Employment (Males)

The ITC program worked no greater miracles for the employment and employability of the male patients than for the domestic performance of the females. Since the number of male patients is so small that statistical data would hardly be appropriate, the actual and brief work history of each of the male drug and placebo patients during the course of home care is presented descriptively from the nurses' notes. To facilitate the reading of these descriptive statements, it might be useful to indicate that about a third of the home care patients held stable employment throughout the study while nearly as many more exhibited sporadic and poor work patterns punctuated by temporary or permanent lay-offs and dismissals. The remainder continues to be unemployed and by reason of illness, unemployable.

WORK EXPERIENCE OF MALE DRUG AND PLACEBO PATIENTS

DRUG

#106 (Failure)—Returned to hospital same day as admission to program. Did not work.

#111 (Failure)—Drives jeep truck for delivery purposes at present. Formerly drove car for salesman, but lost this job because of his poor work pattern due to illness. He was, however, recommended for his present job by former employer.

#122 (At home)—Patient has worked for a long time as government employee in Post Office as a postal clerk. Also has Master's Degree and does substitute teaching.

#132 (At home)—Divorced. Never has worked—too sick physically and mentally.

#141 (Failure)—No job. Too sick to work.

#153 (At home)—Went to work day after release from hospital as laborer in stock room of chair factory. Worked for 3 months. Said he lost his job due to seasonal lay-off. Helped brother paint houses, but has had no job in past year.

#164 (At home)—Railroad car oiler.

#176 (At home)—The degree to which this patient supports himself would be hard to determine. Since ITC intake, his wife has been working and he has received disability payments from Social Security. He does maintain his own sign-painting business and works at it at his own pace. Because of trouble with alcoholism, plus paranoid hostility, it is doubtful that he could hold a steady job as an employee of another person.

#181 (At home)—This patient came to ITC with little or no work record and with some training in a vocational high school. Throughout most of ITC care he did not work, although he was a referral to the Bureau of Vocational Rehabilitation in April, 1963. I am certain he did not get employment through the State Bureau, but he may have worked temporarily or may be working now as a result of his own incentive. He was considered too slow and too poorly motivated to hold a job.

#195 (At home)—This patient was just about to lose his job as a manual laborer in a granary (a job he had held for a number of years prior to ITC care) when he came on our program. Through this worker's intervention with the employer, and in particular with union help, he held his job. The employer wanted to fire him because of absenteeism due to drinking. While under our care, this problem appears to have been solved.

#209 (At home)—Patient finally lost the job he held prior to hospitalization and to which he returned while under our care. He worked for Kentucky Industries for the Blind and was released because he was slowed down to the extent that he couldn't do assembly line work. (We later discovered that the patient was overly medicated.)

Patient worked at a seasonal job for City Park Recreation and was released in winter due to seasonal lay-off. Finally secured a job with local paper selling newspapers on a street corner. His salary is supplemented by City Welfare checks. He likes this "lone dog" work. Referrals to work placement agencies never have helped this patient.

#211 (At home)—Patient returned to same job (assembly work) that he had held for a number of years prior to his hospitalization. Appears to be doing well.

#216 (Failure)—Patient continued to work at the same job he held at ITC intake—one that he had for a number of years. He was still working at the time of failure. He was his own boss and complained about a lack of motivation in getting about his job (subcontracting —construction work), but managed to do a passable job.

#230 (Failure)—This patient has worked on his own farm and has also worked as a tenant farmer. He returned to this same existence after hospitalization. Although he did some farm work, it is very difficult to assess the quality or extent of his self-support.

#233 (Failure)—This patient returned to a maintenance job at a factory. He had had this job for years prior to hospitalization. No news of severe difficulties on the job ever reached ITC and the patient was working steadily at the time we recommended hospitalization.

#246 (At home)—This patient lost his job at a factory where he had been employed for quite some time. Despite cooperation from the employer, we were never able to get patient to the point that he could cope with even the least demanding work (janitorial) that the company could offer. He now receives Social Security disability.

#269 (At home)—This patient lost the job (baker) he had held prior to his hospitalization. He was released from this position because the employer received no notification or explanation from the patient, his wife, or hospital personnel regarding the patient's two-week period of absence from the job. The patient was referred to State Vocational Rehabilitation Service, received no assistance, but secured a job on his own. He quit this job for a better paying one which turned out to be temporary and he was laid off. He is currently unemployed.

#289 (At home)—Works in yard at home. Shovels snow for neighbors.

#299 (At home)—Formerly worked in father's beer depot, but did not like this. Recently worked as orderly in private nursing home, but lost this job because his work was unsatisfactory.

#320 (Failure)—Single. Did not work.

PLACEBO

#102 (At home)—Ambition is to play drums with top band. Work pattern not too good due to lack of opportunities in area. Has sporadic employment with various orchestras to play in local night clubs. Patient also gives drum lessons. Patient falls for ads on how to make money in spare time; recently tried to sell hose and picture albums door-to-door.

#140 (At home)—Single. Never has worked. Too sick mentally.

#144 (Failure)—Married. Did not work. Do not know what he is doing now.

#147 (Failure)—Don't know what he is doing now.

#168 (Failure)—Did not work prior to hospitalization. Too ill mentally. Was a "failure." Since discharge from hospital, has been employed as a bricklayer.

#182 (Failure)—Patient was unemployed when ITC started treatment. He had lost a job after 7 year tenure (prior to hospitalization) because he could not "keep up" with assembly line production. After a few months under our care he got a job as a cab driver and was fired for sleeping on the job. He was never subsequently employed and is still hospitalized.

#228 (At home)—No jobs. Too sick to work.

#244 (Failure)—Did not work.

#257 (At home)— This patient had a good work record prior to hospitalization and was able to secure employment following ITC intake. He continues to hold this job (factory assembly line) and manages satisfactorily.

#260 (At home)—No job. Too sick to work.

#279 (Failure)—Not working at intake. After failure from ITC and return from hospital, patient has returned to job as laborer in factory.

#288 (Failure)—No job. Vagabond type.

#313 (Failure)—No information since hospital discharge.

Children

At Home. Despite a concerted effort to obtain systematic and reliable data on the influence on the children, the data collected in this area of functioning are the least adequate of all. For one thing many of the families had no children at home. For another, in some of the families children moved in and out and stayed in other households some of the time. Finally, it is not known what the impact would have been had the status of the patient as home care or hospital been reversed. Our findings disclose that without intervention such as that of ITC, these patients are usually in and out of the hospital. Is it better to have intermittent exposure to a schizophrenic parent or is consistent contact preferable? Our data cannot answer this question. Also, how can the influence of the sick patient be separated from the entire matrix of disorganization and deviancy so often characteristic of the homes from which state hospital patients are drawn?

For these reasons, a tabular presentation would endow the data with seemingly greater confidence than is deserved. Instead, the nurses' remarks about the effect of the patient on the children are reported here. These came from 16 of the 23 drug home care cases with children in the home.

#118 (Mother)[6]—One son aged 15 at home until institutionalized for delinquency (glue sniffing, stealing, truancy). Son's delinquency probable reason why patient became acutely ill. Mother (patient) fearful of son but still covers for him.

#122 (Father)—Children aged 19, 14, 13, 12, and 3. Father's illness and his being at home has had no effect on children.

#125 (Mother)—Children aged 15, 13, 12, 10, 8, 7, and 6. Because of father's occupation, the patient is almost solely responsible for the children. He sees his wife as being "normal" and as taking care of the kids.

#139 (Mother)—Children aged 15 and 13. No effect on kids. Son (13) was picked up by the police for glue sniffing (1st offense). Daughter 15 was picked up for drinking and being with a 50 year old man (1st offense). Patient attributes troubles of children to husband's drinking and meanness to children. Husband says Dr. ________ knows nothing and whiskey would help his wife (patient) more than anything.

#164 (Father)—Children aged 8, 5, and 2. No noticeable effect on children of having patient at home.

#176 (Father)—Children aged 17 and 15. Effect on them of having patient home has been negative. Would prefer him in hospital. Children are ashamed and fearful of father at times. Mother has cancer and this, too, may be a contributing factor to their problem. I feel that counseling with the children about mental illness at the beginning would have helped them.

#178 (Mother)—Son aged 11. Effect on him of having mother at home seems positive now. During early part of her illness, son was truant

[6] Indicates patient.

and complained that he would "just as soon be dead." Since going into 7th grade in new school the boy appears to be adjusting well.

#202 (Mother)—Children aged 18, 13, and 11. Children were understanding and helpful and wanted mother to remain at home. However, patient does not seem able to discipline children. Allows them to come and go as they please.

#209 (Father)—Children aged 10, 7, and 6. Father's presence in home no negative influence on children. The 3 children are not well behaved and are rather rude. Daughter (7) held back in school but I don't feel this was due to patient's illness. Believe children will have problems. Social level (of family) quite low. Receiving poor home training from both parents.

#211 (Father)—Child aged 14. Positive influence on son. Patient interested in son's work and accomplishments.

#246 (Father)—Children aged 17 and 13. Patient gets on daughter's nerves because of his slowness. He has always been a passive father. Children look to mother for decisions.

#261 (Mother)—Children aged 18, 16, 12, 11, 7 and 5. No special effect of patient on children. They like to be with her now (since treatment began). There seems to be a lot of love between parents and towards children in this home.

#269 (Father)—Children aged 3 and 1. Patient was just quieter than usual and children so young that nothing was noticed and apparently no effect on children.

#271 (Mother)—Three grandchildren 7, 6, and 5 and three children, 15, 11, and 10 at home with patient. Effect on them seems positive. Children continue to want to be around her and help her.

#285 (Mother)—Children aged 3 and 19 months. The patient's children were farmed out with various relatives on a week to week and sometimes day to day basis. The children were very upset and the ITC social worker made arrangements for specific family members to keep the children until the patient was able to care for them herself. The patient resumed the care of her children approximately two months after admission to ITC. Her children gradually became less fearful—after family was together again in their own home. The baby wasn't affected too much. The older child cried and begged for his mother and he wanted to go home to sleep in his own bed.

#295 (Mother)—Daughter aged 12 years. The child was upset by mother's hospitalization and was referred to Child Guidance Clinic by ITC social worker. The patient and the child would have been better off if they had gone right back into their home instead of having the child live with her married sister.

Education of Children. The quantity of data collected on the school performance of the children of our cases was even more meager than the effect on them of having a sick parent at home or hospitalized.

As originally outlined, permanent record file data would be gathered from the schools on the children before and after the admission of the parent to the ITC program. Additionally, these records were to be compared child for child with two control students of the same sex, race, and classroom. The controls were to be selected so that one alphabetically preceded the case and the other immediately followed.

This design itself was reasonably straightforward. The difficulty came in its implementation. For one thing, there were several school systems involved—city, metropolitan, county, township, and private—and the degree of cooperation eventually achieved ranged from none at all to complete cooperation. For another, the records in some of the schools which did cooperate were frequently incomplete even for such important details as absences and grades. For a third, some of the incompleteness of records followed from the intermittent school enrollment and attendance of the index cases and of their controls. In contrast, almost no difficulty was encountered in obtaining parental permission to examine the school records of their children.

Despite these handicaps, grade and attendance data were obtained on 27 children in 11 families in the drug cohort, and on 28 children in 9 placebo families. Assuming the probable selectivity of these cases, a descriptive analysis is all that seems warranted. In general, the study cases did no more poorly than their controls either before or after the admission of a parent to the program. Also, the before and after data on the index cases seemed to vary randomly. There was neither consistent improvement in grades and attendance nor systematic decline in these respects.

Social Participation

One final area of patient functioning deserves mention. Less important perhaps than the performance of either domestic or work roles, social participation is nevertheless a useful, if "soft" measure of patient functioning.

At the time of admission to the ITC project, the significant other was asked to indicate the extent to which the patients had participated in leisure activities and in social groups during the month preceding hospitalization at Central State. The degree of this interaction and involvement in leisure pursuits varied from a very few who attended meetings of social or other types of organizations to about three-fifths who visited relatives and friends.

Systematic data were gathered on both male and female social participation with length of time on the project. This information, unlike that presented in the preceding chapter, was obtained from the patients themselves and is consequently not directly comparable. Based on the more numerous female drug and placebo patients, the results indicated a slight lead by the drug group, and a modest increase with time for both categories of patients. Neither of these trends was statistically significant. They did indicate, however, the same pattern as the other indices of functioning. At the end of 6 months, the activities of the female drug patients varied from 85 percent who visited relatives since the last home visit to 15 percent who had given a party. None of the placebo cases had given a party, but about the same percentage of placebo cases as drug cases had been able to visit relatives and friends.

SUMMARY

This chapter has dealt with the results—objective and subjective—obtained in this home care study. The first section was devoted to the presentation of findings comparing the outcome of treatment in the three cohorts—drug, placebo, and hospital controls. It was shown that over 77 percent of the drug home care cases and just 34 percent of the placebo patients remained continuously at home during the program. All controls were, of course, hospitalized. This success story was translated into actual hospital bed-days saved as a result of home care with the conclusion that the virtue of home care is not merely the reduction in bed-patient time but also that scarce hospital personnel can treat more intensively the fewer patients who need hospitalization.

Excursions were also taken into other areas of outcome. A number of questions were posed, such as, how much attrition took place in the success rate with time? Also, who failed on home care, at what point in time, and why? What happened to the home care failures who required hospitalization? What happened to the controls during and after hospitalization?

Some very fascinating findings were obtained in answering these important questions. For example, every control patient was actually released from the hospital during the study. Hospitalization was not a one-way street. But, equally interesting, posthospital failure was greater for the controls than initial hospitalization for the drug patients.

In the second section, the more obvious demographic variables—age, sex, race, and education—were related to success and failure in outcome with the result that education alone was found to be associated with outcome.

In the third section, the data on the psychiatric and psychological evaluations were presented. Patient improvement was found in all groups on nearly every one of the instruments. These gains were achieved between the initial and 6 months' testing periods with only minor improvement thereafter. The home care patients did as well as the hospital controls on all the comparable tests and measures.

The last section dealt with domestic performance of females, the employment histories of the males and the effect of home care on children. Here again, some interesting findings were obtained.

7

THE COMMUNITY REFERRED PATIENTS

When it appeared that Central State Hospital would be unable to refer a sufficiently large number of patients to ITC to keep the staff completely occupied, it will be recalled that a concerted effort was made to locate patients elsewhere in the community who could benefit from the home care program. This decision to seek and include such cases was deemed justifiable on several grounds. For one thing, every community has a considerable number of schizophrenics who somehow manage to avoid hospitalization even though functioning at a less than adequate level. In the Baltimore study, for example, such nonhospitalized schizophrenics accounted for fully half of all schizophrenics in the Baltimore population. Although these disturbed persons have many attributes in common with schizophrenic patients admitted to state hospitals, a central and critical difference well worth examining is their ability to remain in the community. From our point of view, because these disturbed persons were not acutely or floridly ill, they represented an interesting and different population on which to evaluate the efficacy of the psychoactive drugs. Their inclusion also obviously permitted a comparison of the effectiveness of home care with the more acutely disturbed patients drawn from the state hospital. Clearly, since community mental health centers must plan for the treatment of all types of patients, the inclusion of these ambulatory[1] patients seemed very desirable.

[1] The word *ambulatory* is used throughout to identify those patients who were referred to ITC through various community sources and agencies rather than coming from Central State Hospital. Interchangeable terms include *community*, *community referred*, and *private* patients.

Physicians, welfare and other social agencies, and clinics were therefore asked to refer their *schizophrenic* patients to ITC. A mere trickle at first, but in increasing numbers with time, many such patients eventually came to the Treatment Center on referral. On examination, some of these community referred cases were not schizophrenic; others failed to qualify by virtue of age, residence location, or lack of a supervised family situation. Nevertheless, a considerable number of these ambulatory schizophrenics were uncovered, and when their illness was evaluated as severe enough to warrant hospitalization and when they also met the other criteria, acceptance into the treatment program followed.

These nonhospitalized (ambulatory) schizophrenics, many of whom had been under care on an outpatient basis at local clinics or had received treatment from local physicians and psychiatrists, could not be assigned to the study groups in the same way as the state hospital referred cases. They were understandably not willing to be hospitalized and in this their families concurred. Rather than lose these referrals, a separate deck of random cards was used specifying only two assignments: home on drugs and home on placebo.

Except for this one difference, these community patients were treated identically with the Central State Hospital patients. All of the tests, measures, and evaluations were the same and as routinely and vigorously applied. As with the state hospital patients, only the study director who made the initial study assignment knew which of the community referrals were receiving drug or placebo medication.

During the 30-month course of ITC patient intake, 36 ambulatory drug and 27 ambulatory placebo cases were accepted in the program. Seven drug and four placebo patients later became study dropouts. These dropout rates of 19.4 and 14.8 percent do not really indicate the extreme difficulty encountered in trying to conserve these community referred patients. Unlike the others, there was no state hospital threat over them. Consequently cooperation was exceedingly difficult to sustain over time. Of the 11 dropouts, 6 refused to cooperate after no less than but most often far more than 6 months on the project. Four others left the community or the state. The eleventh patient sought private care. Thus, the presentation which follows deals with 29 and 23 community referred drug and placebo cases respectively.

AMBULATORY PATIENT CHARACTERISTICS: DEMOGRAPHIC

Age, Sex, and Race

Whereas the Central State patients averaged 36.6 years of age with a range of 18 to 56 years, the ambulatory cases were approximately 2 years younger on the average at 34.2 mean years of age. The community drug cases had a mean of 34.7 years and the placebos of 33.5 years. This not quite statistically significant lower average age probably accounts for some of the differences to be described between the state hospital and the ambulatory patients, particularly in the area of previous hospitalizations and on related variables dependent upon life exposure.

The private patients were primarily females. This was also equally true of their state hospital counterparts. Over 69 percent of all ambulatory patients were females. Again, it is probable that the smaller number of males in the group is chiefly a function of the greater willingness to tolerate the deviant and sick female in the family group and in the community and to provide the requisite supervision.

Ambulatory patients were almost identical to the state hospital patients in their racial composition. Nearly 7 out of 10 community referred patients were white with a like percentage in both the drug and placebo groups. White patients constituted 67.1 percent of the CSH study population.

Socioeconomic Status

Education, Occupation, and the Hollingshead Index. In addition to being younger, the ambulatory patients were significantly better educated as a group. Over 46 percent had completed high school compared with only about 28 percent of the CSH patients. This difference, however, was chiefly attributable to the influence of the hospital controls in lowering the educational attainment level of the state hospital patients. Of the 52 community cases, one-tenth had a sixth grade education or less, and more than half had less than a high school diploma. Over 46 percent were high school graduates. There were no distinctions between the ambulatory drug and placebo cases on this variable of education.

The two sets of patients—state hospital and ambulatory—are a little harder to compare on the dimension of occupation. One reason is that 69 percent were females, and of these a considerable number were housewives. A second reason is that occupation is not a very clean variable, being neither wholly continuous nor wholly discrete. In any event, analysis indicated that the occupations of the male patients, and of the husbands or fathers of the females, were very heavily clustered in the blue-collar occupations. About three-fourths of the effective breadwinners were at the machine operative, semi-skilled, or unskilled levels.

A more stable measure of social class position than either education or occupation alone is the Hollingshead Index (HI) of Social Position. The scores on this index can range from a score 11 indicating high status to 77, the lowest possible score. The CSH patients, as indicated in Chapter 5, had a mean Hollingshead Index score of 62.2 while the drug cases were at 60.5 and the placebo cases at 58.8. The ambulatory patients had very similar scores. The overall average was 58.5 with 57.2 and 60.2 being the mean values of the drug and placebo patients respectively. Both the CSH and the community patients had the same score range, 11–77. About the same proportions had the top score of 11, while 5 others were at the very bottom with scores of 77. With respect to the Hollingshead Index, then, the Central State Hospital and the community referred patients were not significantly different from one another.

As with the state hospital patients, the low annual family incomes of the community cases were both a reflection and a concomitant of their low socioeconomic status. Over 28 percent of the ambulatory patients came from families whose annual incomes did not exceed $3500 a year. Median family income was about $4500. Only four families indicated earnings of over $7500 per year.

To round out this socioeconomic status description of the community patients, and purely as an interesting excursion into the area of status self-perceptions, the relatives of the patients overwhelmingly viewed themselves and their families as working class. Three-fourths identified themselves as working rather than middle class in status. Since in American society there is and has always been the tendency to perceive oneself as middle class, this self-definition as working class merely reinforces the objective facts, and in a sense also helps validate the contention that the ambulatory patients, despite somewhat higher education, were not very different from the state hospital patients in socioeconomic status.

Residence

As with the CSH cases, the ambulatory patients, with one exception, were native born, and so also were their fathers and mothers, again with but one exception. About three-fourths of the patients and their parents were born in Kentucky. About two-fifths of the patients, but a considerably larger percentage of their parents, were of rural or small town origin. At the time of study intake, however, all but two of the ambulatory cases were residing in the Louisville area.

In the 5 years preceding study intake, the community patients were even less well rooted than the CSH cases. Only 16 percent of the former had maintained the same residence address in the past 5 years while nearly a quarter had shifted their residence location 5 or more times in that period. The average number of changes of address was 3.1, and the drug and placebo patients did not significantly differ in this respect. By the same token, over 36 percent of the patients had resided in the present residence for less than 1 year and only 13.5 percent for 10 years or more.

Marital Status, Satisfaction, and Children

At the point of intake into the ITC program over 63 percent of the community patients were married (one-third of the married patients had been married at least once previously), 19 percent had never been married, and the remainder were separated, divorced, and widowed. Although a higher percentage of the ambulatory than of the CSH patients (50.7 percent) were married, this difference was not statistically significant.

As to type and duration of the most recent marriage, all were legally contracted and some had remained intact for a considerable period. While 8 of the 42 married patients had been wed for less than 5 years, 17 had been married for more than 5 but less than 10 years, and 17 had been wed for 10 or more years. This seeming stability in marital status is comparable to the data obtained for the CSH cases and may have been a function of the criteria of patient selection including having a family willing to accept, keep, and supervise the patient at home.

The softer, more subjective responses, confirm these more objective findings. According to the spouses, both they and the patients were overwhelmingly in favor of continuing the existing marriages. Their sexual relationships were portrayed as most often being satisfactory, and extramarital affairs were listed as highly infrequent. The most telling point in this respect was the positive feelings expressed by nearly all the spouses, about caring for the patients at home despite the fact that about 38 percent felt that the patient required more attention (watching) than other people.

Although 2 years younger, on the average, the average number of children born to the ambulatory patients was almost identical to the mean number born to the married CSH patients. The overall mean for the former was 2.9 and for the latter 2.8. In both cohorts, nearly 17 percent of the married patients were childless.

The descriptive demographic data discussed thus far are summarized in Table 7-1. Two conclusions can be drawn at this point. First, there is remarkable similarity in the social background characteristics of the state hospital and the ambulatory patients. These two sets of patients are largely indistinguishable from one another. Except for the age difference, which was noteworthy but not statistically significant, and the difference in education which was both noteworthy and statistically significant, analysis of the remaining varaibles failed to produce anything even remotely favoring or biasing one or the other cohort. Retrospectively, this does not seem unexpected or surprising, but at the outset of the program, when it became apparent that it would be desirable and even necessary to include community agency and private physician referrals, the expectation was that the ambulatory patients would almost surely be of higher socioeconomic status and self-selected from less complicated and problematic family settings.

Second, even a cursory look at the percentages or mean scores of the placebo and drug patients on some or all of the background variables provides reasonably good evidence that the random group assignment worked well. No differences of any kind were found between these two classes of ambulatory cases.

PSYCHIATRIC TREATMENT HISTORIES

The Central State Hospital and the community referred patients, while almost identical socioculturally, were significantly different in terms of their previous psychiatric treatment histories. Put simply, the

Table 7-1. Selected Characteristics of Community Referred Patients, by Study Group

	*Total State Hospital**	*Total Community*	*Community Drug*	*Community Placebo*
Mean age	36.6	34.2	34.7	33.5
Percent female	67.8	69.2	69.0	69.5
Percent white	67.1	69.2	69.0	69.5
Percent grade school diploma or less	14.2	9.6	13.8	4.3
Percent high school graduates	28.4	46.2	48.3	43.4
Hollingshead Index of Social Position	62.2	58.5	57.2	60.2
Percent residing at same address for last 5 years	28.0	16.0	14.8	17.4
Percent married	50.7	63.5	68.9	56.5
Percent never married	22.4	19.2	17.2	21.7
Mean number of children born to married patients	2.8	2.9	3.0	2.7

*See Table 1, Chapter 5. See also Appendix B, Tables XVII-XXIV for specific distributions of these characteristics.

community patients had approximately half as many previous hospitalizations as the state hospital patients. Additionally, twice as many ambulatory cases had never before been in a mental hospital as a patient. In quantitative terms, the ambulatory cases averaged 1.2 previous hospitalizations. Some 39 percent had never been institutionalized. Finally, no ambulatory patient had been hospitalized more than 5 times although this should be tempered with the observation that fully one-fifth of the referrals had been patients in a hospital on at least 3 prior occasions.

Translated into hospital bed-patient time, some 40 percent never spent a day in a mental hospital, and 22.4 percent more were hospitalized less than a month all together. Very few, 6.1 percent, had experienced extensive institutionalization of a year or more. These data are not directly comparable to the previous hospital bed-days information which was presented for the CSH patients since all of the latter had been hospitalized, even if only for a very short time such as a day or two before their ITC intake.

In addition to the hospitalization experienced on one or more occasions by nearly 62 percent of the ambulatory patients, most of the other patients had also had some previous psychiatric treatment. For them, however, this was provided in an outpatient setting. An interesting sidelight here is that while over 14 percent of the CSH cases had never received psychiatric care—either inpatient or outpatient—only slightly more ambulatory patients (21 percent) had never received psychiatric treatment before entering the ITC program.

From this evidence it seems reasonable to assume that the ambulatory patients were and had been sufficiently ill to warrant and command treatment and care. This illness, however, was either not as florid, or for other reasons was more tolerable in the family setting, so that a great many of these patients had not as yet been hospitalized. Because of this, the community patients provide an even better example of what a systematic program might do to prevent initial hospitalization. The ambulatory patients also more closely conform to the original design which called for the intake of first admission cases only.

On the treatment level, there are only a limited number of therapeutic practices and procedures. As far as could be determined, there was little or no difference in the type of treatment received by the two cohorts—community and state hospital. Inpatient psychotherapy was, of course, as rare for these cases as for the CSH patients. It was certainly

Table 7-2. Psychiatric Histories of Community Drug and Placebo Patients*

	Drug		*Placebo*		*Total*	
No hospital or outpatient care	5	(17.2)	6	(26.1)	11	(21.2)
Both hospital and outpatient care	14	(48.3)	8	(34.8)	22	(42.3)
Hospital only	4	(13.8)	6	(26.1)	10	(19.2)
Outpatient only	6	(20.7)	3	(13.0)	9	(17.3)
	29		23		52	

*See Table 2, Chapter 5 for comparable data on the CSH patients.

more common, however, as a form of outpatient care. The average duration of such treatment was under 1 year for patients having access to this form of care. Group psychotherapy—inpatient or outpatient—was received by no more than four of the ambulatory cases. More common was electro-shock therapy, consisting of from 1 to over 60 treatments, received by 14 patients either in the hospital or as outpatients. Five drug and two placebo cases received insulin shock as inpatients. Most common of all, was the prescription of ataractic drugs. Nearly all of the hospitalized patients had been on drug medication and the same applied to those on outpatient care. In all, 69 percent of the patients had received drug treatment. The ITC program, emphasizing drug care as a major part of community treatment, was therefore not any more unique to these referrals, than to the CSH cases.

One final aspect of the previous psychiatric treatment histories merits comment. This concerns the nature of the onset of the illness which eventually led to ITC treatment. There was a tendency, which approached statistical significance, for the ambulatory patients to have endured psychiatric symptoms leading to the home care program for a longer period of time. The onset of the psychiatric episode was acute in one-fourth of the cases, intermediate (2 to 6 months) in one-fifth of the patients, and insidious (of 6 months or longer duration) in 55 percent. Thus, greater chronicity and a lower level of acuteness of signs and symptoms seemed to distinguish the illnesses of the ambulatory from the state hospital patients. It is probably this more prolonged but lesser intensity of symptoms and impairment which accounted for the ambulatory status of the community referrals.

Table 7-3. Previous Care and Treatment of Community Drug and Placebo Patients

	Drug	*Placebo*	*Total*
Mean number of previous hospitalizations	1.3	1.1	1.2
Percent never hospitalized	37.9	39.1	38.5
Percent hospitalized for less than 1 month total	25.0	19.0	22.4
Percent hospitalized a year or more total	7.1	4.8	6.1
Percent with previous psychotherapy	37.9	13.0	26.9
Percent with previous group psychotherapy	13.8	13.0	13.5
Percent with previous EST	24.1	30.4	26.9
Percent with previous drug treatment	72.4	65.7	69.2
Percent insidious onset of present illness	51.7	59.1	54.9

FUNCTIONING: MENTAL STATUS

Psychiatrist's, Nurses', and SO Evaluations

Two major comparisons were made using the initial psychiatric evaluations of the patients by the ITC staff psychiatrist, the nurses, and the relatives. First, the ambulatory drug and placebo patients were contrasted with their state hospital counterparts. Second, the community referred drug and placebo patients were compared with each other. On the first count, the ambulatory patients were systematically rated as less impaired than the state hospital cases. This trend was consistent enough to preclude the possibility of chance variation. On all eight comparisons using the psychiatrist's ratings, the CSH patients had higher means scores signifying greater pathology. The same held on six of the eight nurses' ratings and on four of the eight ratings of the significant others. Additionally, many of the comparisons were very close, one way or the other, to statistical significance. Still, the ambulatory home care patients were rated by the psychiatrist as being as greatly impaired as the norm hospitalized group on which the IMPS was standardized. On the second point, the ambulatory drug and placebo patients were not very different from each other. The edge, however, belonged to the drug cases who were rated slightly lower on the morbidity measures. Only the significant others varied from this pattern. Table 7-4 contains these mean scores. For a comparison with the state hospital cases see Table 5-3.

Psychological Test Scores

The psychological test scores shown in Table 7-5 corroborate the results of the initial psychiatric evaluations. Again, two findings are most evident. First, the community referred patients scored higher or in the direction of better functioning on all five measures; on three of them the mean scores were significantly better. Community referrals were much faster on the sequential reaction time trials and were also significantly higher on both the WAIS IQ, and on the IQ score derived from the Porteus Mazes. The mean difference between the two groups of patients—referral and state hospital—was of the order of 10 points on the WAIS and 16 to 20 points on the Porteus Mazes IQ.

Table 7-4. Summary of Initial Evaluations of Community Drug and Placebo Patients

	Drug (*N* = 29)		*Placebo* (*N* = 23)	
	Mean	*σ*	*Mean*	*σ*
Psychiatrist's Ratings				
Total weighted score	74.8	30.9	79.6	31.9
Excitement – retardation	–1.9	21.3	–2.9	24.1
Perceptual and thinking distortion	9.8	18.0	10.3	15.2
Schizophrenic disorganization	30.9	19.2	36.8	18.0
Nurses' Ratings				
Total weighted score	40.7	29.9	56.3	32.1
Excitement – retardation	+5.6	14.4	+10.9	25.1
Perceptual and thinking distortion	4.7	9.6	7.3	8.3
Schizophrenic disorganization	10.2	10.2	15.9	14.7
Significant Other Ratings				
Total weighted score	33.4	33.5	33.7	29.0
Excitement – retardation	2.5	3.4	2.6	3.8
Perceptual and thinking distortion	16.4	21.8	14.3	17.2
Schizophrenic disorganization	6.7	6.7	9.2	7.9

On the two tests of pathology, the ambulatory patients did considerably better, too. They were at least 5 points ahead of their drug and placebo counterparts on the Bender Gestalt, and the drug patients scored 2 to 3 points better on the QE dimension of the Porteus Mazes. As if to confirm the rule of the exception, the state hospital placebo cases performed better on the QE measure.

Second, although the ambulatory drug patients were superior to the placebo patients on four of the five psychological measures, these differences were quite small and not statistically significant.

Patients as Problems

In terms of mean scores on the 22-item problems score, there were no significant differences between the two categories of patients—ambu-

Table 7-5. Psychological Test Scores of Community Drug and Placebo Patients

	Drug (N = 29)		Placebo (N = 23)	
	Mean	σ	Mean	σ
Reaction time (log transformations)*	3.1621	0.1	3.2105	0.1
WAIS	89.2	16.9	90.0	17.8
Bender Gestalt**	112.8	29.2	115.7	28.7
Porteus Mazes				
QE***	59.7	13.1	61.4	18.9
IQ	101.6	33.7	96.1	29.0

*Composite of 20 blocks, five trials per block.
**Reciprocal of Z.
***Square root transformation of QE.

latory and state hospital—nor within the community group between the drug and placebo cases. The mean scores were 31.7 for the drug and 33.7 for the placebo ambulatory cases contrasted to 33.2 and 32.8 for the counterpart state hospital patients.

The significant others on an item by item basis indicated that they were hard pressed by the demands of having a sick patient at home—and principally so in the areas of general concern about the welfare of the patient and household, the physical strain imposed, the patient's need of an excessive amount of attention, the bodily symptoms and complaints of the patient, and his odd ideas and speech. As in the instance of the state hospital cases, the significant others did not very often specify fear or shame—their own or that of the children—as especially problematic (see Table XXV in Appendix B).

Domestic Performance (Females)

The 20 ambulatory female drug and the 16 female placebo patients were only a bit more adequate in the performance of their routine domestic activities than the state hospital female patients. The ambulatory drug and placebo patients had mean scores of 17.0 and 16.8 on the eight-item domestic functioning subscale compared to 13.8 and 15.9 for the respective CSH cases. In general, this mean score difference was a function of two items involving the ability to plan daily activities and solve everyday problems. The community patients were clearly superior in this regard. Even so a third or more of the community referrals were partly or wholly unable or unwilling to perform many of the simple and customary household functions (see Table XXVI in Appendix B).

Employment (Males)

The work histories of the nine male drug and seven male placebo patients do not lend themselves to much quantitative analysis. Prior to their ITC intake six of the nine drug and three of the seven placebo cases were not employed. Of these unemployed, two had been out of a job for less than 3 months and the remainder for at least a year. In general, the employment data on these patients are no different from that of the state hospital males.

Social Participation

The community patients compared to the state hospital group were slightly superior in their social participation and involvement in leisure pursuits. They were somewhat more active on nearly all of the 15 items measuring social participation. This participation and involvement was principally in the more solitary activities and these patients were neither joiners nor activists (see Table XXVII in Appendix B).

Considering the relative softness of the functioning measures—the psychiatric evaluations, psychological tests scores, and others—the consistency of the data is certainly noteworthy if not quite remarkable. In nearly every comparison the ambulatory patients were rated as somewhat better functioners than the state hospital cases. Not the least interesting observation is that the relatives of the patients did about as good a job of reflecting this difference in their responses as did the professionals. Perhaps more attention ought to be paid, as stated previously, to the reports and evaluations of relatives and friends in making decisions about treatment and disposition, providing reliable instruments are systematically and uniformly used.

RESULTS

Although it became evident very soon after the inception of the study that community referral patients would be included as part of the

ITC program, their actual intake did not reach any sizeable number until several months later. Their average length of time on the project at its conclusion was consequently less than that of the state hospital patients. For this reason, the outcome of home care in the community cases will be contrasted with that of the state hospital patients at the end of 24 rather than the full 30 months of the study. In this way, the exposure of the two groups of patients will be more nearly equalized.

Prevention of Hospitalization

Ambulatory patients were in the study for 227 to 847 days with 445 being the mean number of days at risk. This was approximately 100 days less than the average length of time on the program of the state hospital cases. In the course of the study 22 of the 29 drug patients (75.9 percent) and 14 of the 23 placebo cases (60.9 percent) remained continuously at home. This compares with 83.3 percent of the state hospital drug and 35.7 percent of the state hospital placebo patients who succeeded during the first 24 months of the study. These respective percentages are shown in Fig. 7-1. Even though the success rate was 1.7 times as great for the community as the state hospital placebo patients, this difference did not quite attain statistical significance.

Converting these rates into the amount of time spent at home or as a mental hospital patient revealed that the community referred drug cases spent 95.2 percent of the time at home while the placebo cases spent 92.9 percent of their days at risk at home. These high figures contrast with percentages of 91.1 and 77.5 for the state hospital drug and placebo patients after 24 months of the program. These results are presented in Fig. 7-2.

These findings are wholly reasonable and quite expected in view of the characteristics of the ambulatory as opposed to the state hospital patients. Systematic evidence was presented to the effect that the latter were indeed sicker. Nevertheless, with the judicious prescription of medication plus the attention of the public health nurses and the other staff members, these initially sicker state hospital drug patients did as well or better than the less disturbed community referred drug patients. The medication, then, tends to level out variations in the degree of illness, at least insofar as success in remaining at home is concerned. This general observation is considerably strengthened by the placebo comparison. In the absence of active and effective medication, the sicker

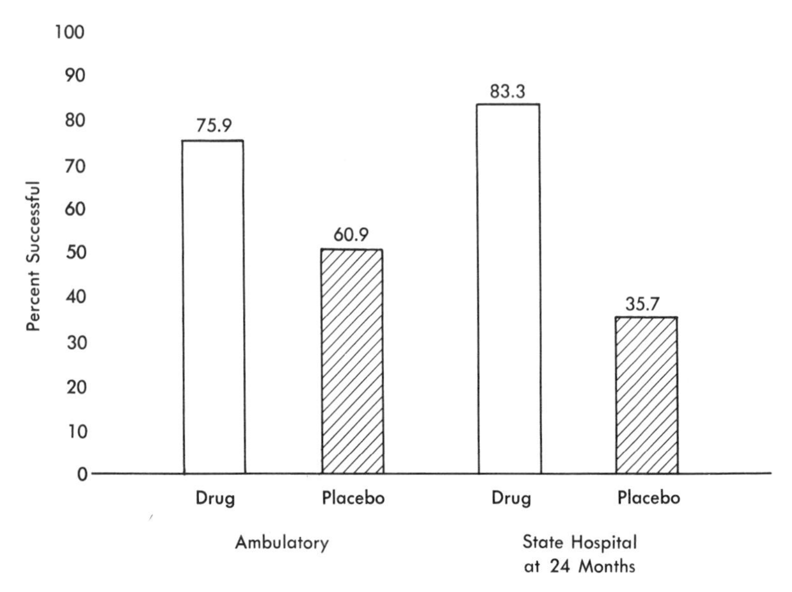

Figure 7–1. Drug and Placebo Success Rates in Community and State Hospital Groups

state hospital patients failed far more often than their less ill ambulatory counterparts. The difference was striking—60.9 percent success for the ambulatory and only 35.7 percent for the state hospital patients. Despite its magnitude, this difference was not statistically significant. Nevertheless, the direction and magnitude are convincing.

Another aspect of this general conclusion also merits mention. These results tend to show that psychoactive drugs were proportionately more effective the sicker the patient was. What is meant is that the less grossly disturbed ambulatory patients did about as well with or without the active drug. Their functioning, being better to begin with, remained tolerable whether or not they received medication. Since even at their worst, that is just before entering the ITC project, they were able to maintain themselves in the community, drug medication was less necessary and seemingly less effective.

On the other hand, the more highly impaired patients drawn from CSH could not as readily be tolerated in the community unless their functioning improved markedly. For those receiving effective medica-

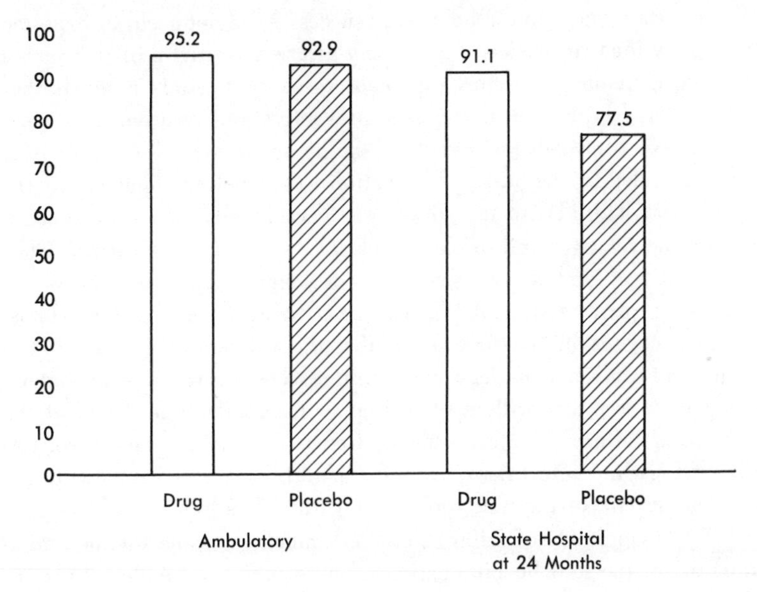

Figure 7–2. Percentage of Total Risk Days Spent at Home by Drug and Placebo Patients in Community and State Hospital Groups

tion, this improvement was much more likely to occur. This explains the much greater rate of success in the state hospital drug group as against the placebo group. Without attempting to generalize beyond these findings, although there is other evidence of this nature available, it is certainly reasonable to conclude that within certain limits, the sicker the patient, the greater the impact of the drug.

Success and Failure

Since the ambulatory patients were managing at home before their enrollment in the ITC project, the problem of failure and of hospitalization was even more important for this group than for the state hospital patients. Nevertheless, the specifics of success and failure were very much the same in the two cohorts. To begin with, there was very little attrition in the success rate with time. The success rate of patients in the program for 18, 21, or even 24 months was very nearly the same as for patients in the study for only 6 or 9 months.

Increasing attrition in home care successes did not occur as expected principally for two reasons. First, being aware and fearful of just such a prospect, a tremendous effort was made to conserve study cases. Rather than wait for failure to materialize, preventive and positive steps were taken to avert it. Additional visits to the home, or to the Center or both were scheduled by the nurses. Medication was sometimes changed by the psychiatrist. The ITC social worker was occasionally called on to counsel with the relatives and to obtain special services for the patient. Once or twice it was even necessary to find a new significant other who would continue to provide supervision for our patient. Second, failure almost always occurred in the first 6 months of treatment. Once the initial adjustment was made, patients and families seemed better able to contend with later crises and without resorting to hospitalization. Thus, of the seven drug failures, five came in the first 6 months, and, of these, two occurred within a fortnight. All nine placebo failures came within 6 months, and six of the nine took place within 3 months.

The precipitants of failure were very much the same for the ambulatory as for the state hospital patients. These conditions included bizarre or aggressive or similarly disturbing acts by the patient, changes in the family situation, and the inability of family members to tolerate, manage, or care for the patient because of the feeling that there was too little improvement in the patient's condition or that inpatient care was required. These precipitants are fairly well illustrated in the failure reports of the nurses. A sampling of these accounts follow:

#186 (Female, placebo)—Patient responded poorly to ITC treatment. Took medication with no apparent relief. Required on two occasions a "shot" for rest and sleep. This shot was administered by local physician.

Patient refused to assume any household responsibilities and was dependent on sister and husband. Spent most of her time in bed. Complained constantly about physical symptoms. Had frequent crying spells. In the past month became extremely hostile toward husband and sister—felt they were unsympathetic.

Patient was seen about a month ago by Dr. (at ITC) who suggested hospitalization. Husband refused at that time. (Later) patient and husband made decision about her going to hospital. Both realized she wasn't improving and required hospital attention. Patient was voluntarily committed.

#227 (Male, drug)—Patient responded poorly to ITC treatment. He was unable to adjust to his medication which was changed several times. He became extremely depressed and fearful and it was suggested he take a leave of absence from his work which he did. He was home approximately two weeks during which time he became progressively worse.

Patient and wife discussed hospitalization as they felt he required more intensive treatment. He was admitted to OLP (private psychiatric hospital).

#301 (Female, placebo)—Husband said patient awakened about 1:30 A.M., was very nervous and upset, talked constantly about the people at work talking about her and said he didn't realize (that) they really did talk about her.

He thought his wife went back to sleep finally but wasn't sure as he went in (to be) with their 8-year-old son who had awakened. (In the morning) when patient normally prepared to go to work, she cut her wrists and when husband saw the blood he called police who took patient to Louisville General Hospital. Wounds were superficial and doctors there said patient was in too good contact to admit to psychiatric service.

Husband called a friend of the family who took patient to Bridgehaven Hospital as (ITC) Dr. was out of town. Dr. at Bridgehaven sent her to Central State Hospital.

#303 (Male, drug)—Patient was returned to Louisville General Hospital. Mother states patient was extremely restless, noisy, hostile during the night, so at 3:30 A.M. he was taken to the hospital by the father.

Patient (had) responded poorly to home treatment. Did not feel medicine was helping him—later refusing to take any. (He) became very depressed, with suicidal thoughts. Could not sleep. Was very hostile toward his parents. They decided on hospitalization because they felt they could no longer manage him at home.

The seven drug and nine placebo patients who failed on home care spent 293 and 425 days in the hospital following failure. The mean number of inpatient days was 41.9 and 47.2 respectively. These means are only fractionally as high as those of the state hospital patients. The state hospital drug and placebo cases stayed an average of 172 and 133 days in the hospital subsequent to failure. This indicates, in still another way, the relatively less serious nature of the illness of the community referred patients.

While some of the state hospital failures had been hospitalized as often as five times before the end of the study, no ambulatory patient was institutionalized more than three times. Two drug and four placebo failures were hospitalized twice and three placebo failures as many as three times. All but one of the failure patients were at home when the ITC project ended.

Success and Failure: Population Characteristics

There were so few ambulatory failures that any definitive conclusions about their similarities and differences from the successes would be unwarranted. The facts, however, are these. The 22 drug successes were 35.9 years of age on the average while the seven failures were only 30.9 years. In comparison, the 14 placebo successes and 9 failures were 33.3 and 33.9 years of age on the average. In the state hospital group, the drug successes were also older than the failures, but the placebo successes were a little younger than the failures.

Neither sex nor race seemed to play much of a role in differentiating successes from failures. In the drug group, 5 out of the 9 males succeeded as did 17 of the 20 females. In the placebo group, all 7 males remained in the community but only 7 of the 16 females were equally successful. Obviously these data are inadequate as a test of the hypothesis concerning the willingness of the family and community to more readily accept the female as opposed to the male patient. In terms of race, 17 of 21 whites succeeded in the drug group compared to 5 of 8 Negroes who also remained at home. Among the placebos, 10 of the 16 whites and 6 of the 9 Negroes succeeded.

Previous outcome studies to the contrary, married patients were about as successful as the nonmarried in avoiding hospitalization. In the drug group, 16 of 20 married patients and 6 of the 9 nonmarried cases remained home; in the placebo group, 8 of 13 married patients and 6 of the 10 nonmarried succeeded.

The major departure from the results obtained for the state hospital patients occurred in the area of socioeconomic status. In the state hospital group, home care success appeared to be selective of the better educated patients. In the ambulatory cohort, the reverse seemed to be the case. Both the drug and the placebo successful home care patients were of lower socioeconomic status than the failure patients. On the two-factor

Hollingshead Index, the ambulatory successes—drug and placebo—had mean scores of 57.3 and 64.5 while the failures had the lower mean scores (higher socioeconomic status) of 48.8 and 53.6 respectively. It may be, of course, that socioeconomic status is largely unrelated to outcome. Or more likely, in view of previous studies dealing with socioeconomic status and case outcome, this difference is in fact attributable as alleged to the greater tolerance for deviation at the lower socioeconomic levels. All other things being equal, including the severity of impairment, lower-class families will presumably more readily tolerate sick members at home than will families of higher socioeconomic status. This explanation does not, of course, reconcile the reversal between the state hospital and ambulatory findings. Why the state hospital patients did not conform to the tolerance of deviance hypothesis remains a moot question. An alternative explanation was offered in the section dealing with the state hospital patients. The issue remains unresolved, however, at this point.

Finally, there seemed to be little relationship between previous hospitalization and success and failure on home care. This was contrary, at least in direction, to the results in the state hospital population. Of the never previously hospitalized ambulatory cases, 8 of the 11 drug and 7 of the 9 placebo patients succeeded on home care. In contrast, 14 of 18 previously hospitalized drug and 7 of 14 placebo patients succeeded in the program. The most probable explanation for the relative unimportance of previous hospital admissions in determining or at least being a correlate of success, was the generally lesser impairment of the ambulatory patients. Their previous hospitalizations, badly skewed in distribution, were not particularly reliable clues to functioning at admission to the study. Previous hospitalization, being more normally distributed, was a much better index of severity of illness and of success and failure in the state hospital population of drug patients.

FUNCTIONING AND OUTCOME

Mental Status

The same findings which emerged in the analysis of the CSH patients also occurred for the ambulatory cases. First, the community referred patients, both drug and placebo, were much improved with time according to the evaluations of the psychiatrists, nurses, and significant others. Second, the degree of improvement was not significantly different for the drug and placebo groups although the drug patients showed the greater gain as a rule. Third, nearly all of the gain occurred within 6 months of project intake. On the morbidity scales of the IMPS as rated by the psychiatrist, the drug patients reduced their mean weighted score from 76.1 to 29.2 in the first 6 months, the mean perceptual and thinking distortion score from 10.6 to 1.0, and the mean schizophrenic disorganization score from 31.3 to 13.6. On the same scales the placebo patients improved from 79.6 to 44.0 in the mean weighted score, from 10.3 to 5.0 in the mean perceptual and thinking distortion score, and from a mean 36.8 to 21.9 on the schizophrenic disorganization morbidity scale. Analysis of variance showed this improvement in both sets of patients to be statistically significant on all measures. There was no additional gain of any consequence at the 18 months' testing. These repeated measurement results are presented in Table 7-6.

The nurses's ratings, though indicating lesser pathology at the outset, also showed considerable but not statistically significant improvement with time. On the total weighted mean score the drug and placebo

Table 7-6. Mean IMPS Morbidity Scores Based on Psychiatrist's Ratings of Community Drug and Placebo Patients

	Drug				*Placebo*			
Time	*N*	*Mean**	*Mean***	*Mean****	*N*	*Mean**	*Mean***	*Mean****
Admission	29	74.8	9.9	30.9	23	79.6	10.3	36.8
Admission	27	76.1	10.6	31.3	23	79.6	10.3	36.8
6 months	27	29.2	1.0	13.6	23	44.0	5.0	21.9
Admission	20	76.3	12.5	26.8	12	80.0	11.3	34.8
6 months	20	30.5	1.2	13.4	12	35.1	1.8	18.5
18 months	20	29.1	2.8	12.2	12	27.5	2.7	12.2
First evaluation	29	74.8	9.9	30.9	23	79.6	10.3	36.8
Last evaluation	29	28.4	1.7	14.6	23	25.0	.3	12.9

*Total weighted
**Perceptual and thinking distortion
***Schizophrenic disorganization

patients improved from 41.3 to 29.2 and from 55.1 to 39.1 respectively from the admission to the 6-month testing periods. In the area of perceptual and thinking distortion, the respective drug and placebo gains were from 5.0 to 2.1 and 6.4 to 6.2. And on the schizophrenic disorganization measure the mean scores reduced from 10.4 to 9.2 for the drug and from 15.5 to 9.7 for the placebo patients. Significantly, three of the six mean scores rose from the 6 to the 18-month testing periods indicating again that improvement occurs reasonably early in the home care setting, if at all. These repeated measurement mean scores are displayed in Table 7-7.

Table 7-7. Mean Morbidity Scores Based on Nurses' Ratings of Community Drug and Placebo Patients

	Drug				*Placebo*			
Time	*N*	*Mean**	*Mean***	*Mean****	*N*	*Mean**	*Mean***	*Mean****
Admission	29	40.7	4.7	10.2	23	56.3	7.3	15.9
Admission	27	41.3	5.0	10.4	17	55.1	6.4	15.5
6 months	27	29.2	2.1	9.2	17	39.1	6.2	9.7
Admission	22	42.5	5.4	10.2	14	49.5	6.3	9.6
6 months	22	28.5	2.3	8.3	14	31.1	4.4	6.6
18 months	22	27.4	2.1	7.0	14	36.0	6.4	8.8
First evaluation	27	41.3	5.0	10.4	17	55.1	6.4	15.5
Last evaluation	27	30.2	2.5	9.0	17	47.5	9.2	11.2

*Total weighted
**Perceptual and thinking distortion
***Schizophrenic disorganization

The significant others also rated the patients in the same consistent manner as both the psychiatrist and nurses. In fact, the greatest patient improvement occurred in the assessments of the significant others. The minimum gain in the first 6 months of both the drug and placebo patients was a halving of the mean scores. On most of the measures, the mean scores fell to an even greater extent. Needless to say, the F ratios were statistically significant indicating that the improvement could not readily be attributed to chance alone. Indeed, the evidence is such that it is difficult to even seriously entertain the hypothesis that these findings are simply a function of chance or of repeated testing. All six mean scores, as a matter of fact, rose from the 6- to the 18-month testing periods (see Table 7-8).

Table 7-8. Mean Morbidity Scores Based on Ratings of the Significant Others of the Community Drug and Placebo Patients

Time	Drug				Placebo			
	N	Mean*	Mean**	Mean***	N	Mean*	Mean**	Mean***
Admission	29	33.4	16.4	6.7	23	33.7	14.3	9.2
Admission	27	34.7	17.0	7.0	17	37.5	16.5	10.3
6 months	27	9.1	2.3	2.6	17	17.6	7.7	4.0
Admission	22	36.4	18.1	7.4	14	38.7	16.9	10.6
6 months	22	9.0	2.3	2.5	14	14.4	6.5	2.6
18 months	22	10.4	4.4	2.8	14	17.7	6.7	4.9
First evaluation	27	34.7	17.0	7.0	17	37.5	16.5	10.3
Last evaluation	27	10.7	4.3	3.1	17	21.2	8.8	6.0

*Total weighted
**Perceptual and thinking distortion
***Schizophrenic disorganization

Initial Psychiatric Assessment and Outcome

Although there were too few failure cases, both drug and placebo, to deserve intensive quantitative analysis, it was evident that the same general trend prevailed for the ambulatory as for the CSH patients. Again, utilizing the three scales of total weighted score, perceptual and thinking distortion, and schizophrenic disorganization, the 22 drug *successes* were rated as sicker at study intake by the psychiatrist, nurses, and significant others than were the 7 patients who later failed. Obviously, other factors besides degree of illness played some role in case outcome. On the other side, the psychiatrist and nurses but not the significant others rated the placebo successes as less impaired than the later placebo failures at the point of admission to the ITC program (see Table 7-9).

Table 7-9. Initial Psychiatric Ratings and Success and Failure in Community Cases

	Psychiatrist's Ratings			*Nurses' Ratings*			*Significant Others' Ratings*		
Drug	*Mean**	*Mean***	*Mean****	*Mean**	*Mean***	*Mean****	*Mean**	*Mean***	*Mean****
Success	77.6	11.9	32.3	42.5	5.0	11.0	34.8	16.7	7.7
Failure	66.0	3.4	26.6	35.0	3.4	7.7	29.3	15.4	3.6
Placebo									
Success	77.6	9.7	34.8	49.5	6.3	9.6	38.7	16.9	10.6
Failure	82.6	11.1	40.0	66.8	8.9	25.7	25.8	10.2	7.0

*Total weighted
**Perceptual and thinking distortion
***Schizophrenic disorganization

Table 7-10. Psychological Mean Test Scores of Community Drug and Placebo Patients at Various Points in Time

	Drug					*Placebo*				
	*Reaction Time**	*WAIS IQ*	*Bender Z***	*Maze QE****	*Maze IQ*	*Reaction Time**	*WAIS IQ*	*Bender Z***	*Maze QE****	*Maze IQ*
Admission	3.1933	89.2	112.8	59.7	106.6	3.2105	90.0	115.7	61.4	96.1
Admission	3.1952	89.2	112.8	59.7	101.6	3.2105	90.0	115.7	61.4	96.1
6 months	3.1871	92.6	120.3	57.8	108.6	3.1846	93.1	118.5	57.1	107.7
Admission	3.1787	94.4	120.4	54.0	106.5	3.2303	87.3	115.4	54.7	83.7
6 months	3.1749	95.3	123.3	58.2	113.8	3.1950	86.1	118.7	62.3	94.7
18 months	3.1881	93.8	128.8	61.4	102.7	3.1919	89.7	117.4	61.0	105.6
First test	3.1933	89.2	112.8	59.7	101.6	3.2105	90.0	115.7	61.4	96.1
Last test	3.1905	92.0	122.6	59.1	104.0	3.1836	94.2	118.1	56.7	111.2

*Scores are log transformations.
**Reciprocal transformation of Z.
***Square root transformation mean score.

Psychological Test Results

The psychological test scores confirm in nearly every particular the findings obtained from the psychiatric assessments. In both the drug and the placebo groups the test results showed patient improvement from admission to the 6 months' testing and no gain and an occasional loss thereafter. In both categories—drug and placebo—patient reaction time speeded up considerably in the 6 months' evaluation but some of this improvement was lost in the 18 months' testing. The WAIS IQ score improved about three points for both categories of cases at the 6 months' testing. The Bender Z scores also showed marked improvement in the same time period as did the Porteus Mazes IQ and QE test scores.

On the other issue, that of predicting success or failure from the initial test scores, there was again a high degree of corroboration of the psychiatric evaluations. Thus, the drug successes scored more poorly than the later drug failures. For example, their reaction time was much slower than that of the failures, and the IQ scores were consistently lower. On the other hand, the later placebo failures were characteristically more impaired at admission than the successes. Thus, in the absence of drug medication, the degree of severity of illness at intake was a fine indicator of successful or unsuccessful case outcome. With drugs, however, the variable of initial impairment was no longer a major factor in predicting case outcome.

Table 7-11. Psychological Mean Test Scores of Community Success and Failure Patients at Admission

Drug	*Reaction Time Mean**	*WAIS Mean*	*Bender Z Mean***	*Porteus Mazes Mean QE****	*Porteus Mazes Mean IQ*
Success	3.2065	86.5	108.0	59.0	100.0
Failure	3.1517	97.7	128.1	61.7	106.3
Placebo					
Success	3.1621	94.9	115.3	61.9	101.2
Failure	3.2858	82.4	116.2	60.8	88.2

*Scores are log transformations.
**Reciprocal transformation of Z.
***Square root transformation mean score.

OTHER FUNCTIONING

Although the ambulatory patients were very successful in remaining home and while they improved significantly in their functioning, especially during the early part of their ITC experience, some were still not performing at more than a minimal level in various spheres of daily life. On the 22-item problem checklist scale, the mean scores fell for both the drug and placebo patients indicating a lessening of disruptive and prob-

Table 7-12. Percentage of Community Patients Evidencing Each of 22 Behaviors

	At 6 Months	
Patient is Burdensome Because	*Drug (N = 27)**	*Placebo (N = 18)**
Trouble at night	3.7	16.7
Nursing problem	–	–
Source of worry	18.5	5.6
Worry about safety of others	11.1	11.1
Uncooperative	37.0	33.3
Strain on others	40.7	27.8
Patient's behavior is upsetting	25.9	33.3
Bodily symptoms cause concern	33.3	23.5
Sexual problem	14.8	11.1
Odd speech and ideas	11.1	27.8
Causes trouble with neighbors	–	–
Upsets household work and routine	25.9	16.7
Interferes with social activities	30.4	5.9
Forced to stay away from work because of patient	4.5	8.3
Forced to stay away from school because of patient	6.7	–
Caused you concern generally	66.7	41.2
Physical strain on significant others	33.3	27.8
Requires excessive amount of attention	55.5	38.9
Children ashamed of patient	–	8.3
Children afraid of patient	11.8	8.3
Significant other ashamed of patient	11.5	11.1
Significant other afraid of patient	7.7	5.6

**N* varies by item to some extent.

lematic behavior. Nearly all of this improvement occurred in the first 3 to 6 months after ITC program induction. In specific terms, both the drug and placebo patients were viewed by the significant others as being less burdensome in nearly all areas of daily functioning. Still, to a large percentage of significant others, caring for the patients even after 6 months on the project was a strain and caused concern and anxiety to those responsible for their supervision.

Further, many of the female patients, though performing better than at intake were still wholly or partly unable to function adequately as housewives. As many as 35 percent of the female drug patients and a somewhat higher percentage of female placebo patients were having difficulty doing some of the routine household chores without assistance after 6 months in the study.

Table 7-13. Percentage of Female Ambulatory Patients Wholly or Partly Unable to Perform Specified Household Activities

	At 6 Months	
	*Drug (N = 20)**	*Placebo (N = 11)**
Attend to housecleaning chores	22.2	37.5
Prepare meals	5.9	37.5
Attend to laundry and cleaning	16.7	37.5
Shop for groceries	31.3	42.9
Do other shopping (clothing, etc.)	35.3	42.9
Budget for household	33.3	25.0
Plan daily activities	15.0	22.2
Solve daily problems	20.0	22.2

**N* varies by activity to some extent.

The work histories of the men were about on a par with the domestic functioning of the females and also little better than those of the CSH patients. A very small number of male patients were continuously employed and functioning adequately on the job while most had trouble getting and holding a job. A case-by-case summary of the work histories of the ambulatory male patients follows.

WORK EXPERIENCE OF MALE AMBULATORY DRUG AND PLACEBO PATIENTS

DRUG

#148 During the year and a half that we have known this patient he has continued to hold the same job as night clerk but has experienced difficulties severe enough that his job was in jeopardy. The problem involved answering the telephone to take night messages for Western Union (patient has phobia regarding telephones). Occasionally the patient tries to sell products door to door on a part-time basis.

#206 Patient has a history of losing many jobs because of absenteeism due to drinking. He was unemployed at the beginning of care under ITC and continued as such despite a referral to the State Department of Vocational Rehabilitation. Patient got his own job when, because of his wife's illness, it became necessary. It has been "touch and go" due to a couple of days off for drinking, but he has held this assembly line job to date.

#225 On admission, the patient was employed as a factory worker. He quit this job because he couldn't tolerate the heat from the furnaces and because of his phobia about writing in front of others. Later he wanted the job back, but due to belligerence over unemployment benefits was not rehired. At present he is working for an employment agency that sends him out on short term jobs. He seems to like this work.

#227 Works as an assistant shipping clerk in a paint manufacturing company.

#241 No job. Too sick to work.

#276 This patient secured a job after ITC intake and is still holding it. He came very close to losing it but only because his poor eyesight interfered with his ability to do his work (painting cars); however, after our assistance in obtaining glasses for the patient, this problem appears to have been solved. The patient is performing satisfactorily on the job and is well liked.

#303 Did not work—too sick mentally.

#310 Patient lost job as apprentice meat cutter because of paranoid episode. Failed on treatment after 3 weeks. Returned to hospital. Is presently not working..

#324 Dr. _______ considers patient in need of and capable of employment. He has been referred to the State Department of Vocational

Rehabilitation, but I do not believe he is trainable or placeable because of no education, no skill, plus cerebral palsy.

PLACEBO

#203 No job. Too sick to work.

#256 This patient had either just lost or was just about to lose his night watchman's job when he came on our program. It seems that the reason he lost the job was due to his paranoid thinking; he believed he needed a gun because people were after him.

#272 Apparently unable to work. Never held other than part-time job. Recently worked one day as stock boy in supermarket but was unable to hold job.

#274 Patient continues at same job he held before ITC intake. No work difficulties ever mentioned to ITC.

#286 Generator operator. Has held this job for a long time. Work pattern good.

#293 No job.

#319 This patient continues to hold the job he held prior to ITC care. He has not been threatened with job loss, but he has expressed worry about being fired if he should continue a pattern of absence from work due to drinking and the court appearances which result from it.

In the less important but nonetheless interesting area of social participation, significant others were asked to indicate the extent of the patients' involvement before ITC care and periodically thereafter. The results indicated a reasonably high degree of participation to begin with, relative that is to the activities of the CSH patients, and only a slight increase in this degree of participation with time. The chief leisure activities continued to be largely passive although there was a considerable amount of visiting and entertaining of relatives and friends. The most consistent activity, however, was watching TV.

One final note deserves mention. It will be recalled that the CSH patients, by almost all standards and measurements, were rated as more severely ill at ITC intake than the community referred patients. This initial difference in functioning tended to disappear with time. At the end of 6 months and thereafter the two sets of patients—state hospital and ambulatory—were virtually indistinguishable from one another in all but one respect. The IQ scores, although improved in both groups, remained much higher for the ambulatory patients. On all other measures and evaluations including those of the psychiatrist, nurses, and significant others, and in terms of their domestic, work, and other functioning, the two populations had become very nearly identical in character.

SUMMARY

This chapter has presented a description of the community referred patients and the results achieved by the ITC program with them. The 52 community referred patients were young (34.2 years of age), predominantly white (69.2 percent), and female (69.2 percent). They were a little better educated than the state hospital patients and of slightly higher socioeconomic status. Moreover, three in five were married and these patients averaged 2.9 children each. Their psychiatric treatment histories indicated an average of 1.2 previous hospitalizations and about 60 percent had been hospitalized at least once before. The initial evaluations by the psychiatrist, nurses, and significant others, and the initial psychological examinations plus the functioning scale scores indicated considerable pathology but less acute and florid signs and symptoms than evidenced by the state hospital patients.

The results of home care intervention were about as expected. Some 76 percent of the drug and 61 percent of the placebo patients remained continuously at home throughout the study. This represented some 95 and 93 percent, respectively, of the days at risk by these population groups. Other findings pertained to failure and to the degree and type of improvement among the successful patients. Generally, hospitalization, when required, occurred early (within 6 months) in the patients' tenure in the program. Hospitalized cases spent very little time as inhospital patients and were released much more quickly than their state hospital counterparts.

The successful patients, both drug and placebo, improved in all areas in which measurements were available during the course of the program. Most of these gains, and all of the significant ones, in mental status, psychological test scores, and in everyday functioning, occurred within the first 6 months. Not much change in these measures occurred thereafter.

Finally, although less ill to begin with, the community referred patients were, with only the major exception of IQ, doing no better than the state hospital cases either 6 months after intake into the ITC study or at the last evaluation.

8

CASE HISTORY DOCUMENTS

INTRODUCTION

The preceding chapters on the findings of the study presented quantitative and group pictures tending to obscure the individuals involved, the details of their illness, and the daily difficulties encountered.

To illustrate these individual problems, public health nursing methods of approach, and care and outcome, a number of typical cases were selected from the case registry. As much as possible they were diversified by success and failure, state hospital and ambulatory origin, drug and placebo, male and female, white and nonwhite, middle- and lower-class status, and in type of problem presented.

These patients are largely chronically ill with little dramatic change in status except for some of those who failed to remain in the community. External "social problems" play obvious and important roles in the capacity of the patient to adjust to illness and to the environmental demands and stresses. It is equally apparent that relatively little was or could be done to alleviate these social problems. In many respects the depth of the problems, the behavioral aberrations, and the nurses' responses and activities are concealed by the summary treatment given them in their notes but the difficult and often dreary work involved is distinctly shown by quoting the case materials in their entirety. In addition a table of each patient's performance on the various psychological tests and a chart of the ratings on some of the functional instruments are offered to complete the picture and to indicate how these correlated with the nurses' descriptions of clinical and social performance.

HOME CARE—PLACEBO SUCCESS

Case #102, an 18-year-old white male was admitted to the home care study on December 6, 1961. After an initial 7-day period of hospitalization at Louisville General Hospital the patient was transferred to Central State Hospital where he was diagnosed as schizophrenic and referred to the Institute Treatment Center.

The parents reported that after the patient learned that his girl friend was pregnant, he became extremely depressed and withdrawn. The patient's erratic behavior caused his parents to become concerned and to take him to General Hospital where he was admitted to the psychiatric unit.

The patient is a recent high school graduate, unmarried, and living with his mother and 7-year-old brother. His parents are divorced but the father visits the home often and lives nearby. The mother works sporadically, and with the husband's support payments and rent received from a boarder, reports a yearly income of approximately $5000. The patient had been employed as a drummer in a band for nearly a year but left this job because of the present illness 1 month before his hospitalization.

At the time of his examination by the ITC psychiatrist, the patient exhibited the following prominent symptoms: very marked anxiety, difficulty concentrating, fatigue, withdrawal, phobias, insomnia, obsessive-compulsive symptoms, marked depression, slow and stuporous behavior, definitely inappropriate affect, clear and definite thinking disorder, unsystematized paranoid delusions, and auditory and visual hallucinations to a major and disturbing degree. The examining psychiatrist felt the patient had some insight into his illness, and was concerned but unable to give any explanation. The diagnosis was schizophrenic reaction, acute undifferentiated type, and his prognosis was "should improve, total adjustment same or some better, with stress may return." Prescription: chlorpromazine (Thorazine), 50 milligrams. two times a day and trifluoperazine (Stelazine) three times a day. Study assignment: home on placebo.

The initial psychological testing session was terminated after approximately 30 minutes because of the patient's unresponsive, inattentive, and preoccupied condition. The material obtained was so erratic that it was unscorable. The home treatment of this patient began immediately and can be followed chiefly through the reports of the visiting Public Health Nurse assigned to this case:

12/7/61. Patient seemed less confused than 12/6/61 in office. Was very slow and usually answered "yes" or "no." Volunteered very few comments. Seemed to understand. Parents are divorced but apparently have friendly relationship. Father was there. Parents seem to treat patient like a sick child and seemed to be fearful that patient may do bodily harm to himself.

Two days after this home visit the patient's mother telephoned ITC and excitedly reported that the patient was in the basement of their home playing his drums in a "wild" manner. She was advised to permit him to continue to play and to call back later if his condition deteriorated. Mother never called back.

On December 13, 1961, the patient returned to the ITC in order to take the psychological tests that he was unable to take the week before. At this time he was a polite, cooperative, neatly groomed young man. He was cheerful and seemed to accept the tests as a challenge; a good working relationship was established easily. The patient followed instructions well and was generally attentive to the tasks before him. His verbal ability was adequate, although on some tasks where clear, controlled deduction was needed, he had difficulty. At these times, he would become indecisive, change responses, slow down in response time, become vague, ramble, and seem unable to say "I don't know." He often used personal, rambling analogies apparently in an attempt to clarify. At times there were some fairly marked mood fluctuations that were contrary to his usual cheerfulness. With these exceptions, he appeared overtly calm, confident, and controlled.

12/14/61. Patient seems fully oriented today. Very suspicious and curious. Talks freely. Appears disturbed about sex. Priest says one thing, doctor another. Talked with priest 12/13/61 who apparently disturbed him. Priest discussed possibility of parents re-uniting, masturbation was wrong, etc. Patient very hostile toward girlfriend's other alleged boyfriend. Still confused about original problem. Seems to feel this "breakdown" could happen again so would like to understand and know how to prevent it if possible. Medication given.

12/21/61. Patient oriented. Upset over mother and girlfriend's mother who had words over phone. Girl's mother apparently intoxicated. Wants girl to come to his house to stay. Mother says no. Girl's mother also verbally abusive toward daughter. Feel that patient will marry soon. Suggested that patient's girlfriend and his mother talk with social worker. Mother working now and left letter for nurse. Feel that family wants ITC to solve problem for them. Medication given.

12/28/61. Feel that patient is not doing as well. Seems quite nervous. Mother called Institute and came in to see social worker during nurse's home visit. Suggested girlfriend make appointment with social worker and psychiatrist. There seems to be too much friction. Patient still working and driving. Feel concerned. Patient seems to talk freely and almost excessively. Medication given.

1/3/62. Girlfriend is going to (X) Clinic this week. Patient seems a little suspicious of his medicine—states he doesn't like to take medicine at all. Patient's mother phoned during visit and wanted to know if patient needed nerve medicine.

1/11/62. Patient seems improved since home visit of 1/3/62. Not as concerned about basic problem. Very conceited and egotistical about ability to play drums and success with women. Rapport good. Patient not working now and very restless. Doesn't seem particularly concerned. Discusses illness freely. Tried out for job as drummer approximately one week before illness and played miserably. Patient asked nurse to listen to him play drums. Accidently skipped 2 doses of medicine since last week. Medication given.

1/18/62. No particular change in patient's condition apparently. Still very restless. Mother was wondering about patient's "IQ." Says she has noticed recently that patient will laugh when they laugh at something on TV but several times has said "I don't get it" afterwards. Patient had burr haircut recently for 1st time. Seems rather shallow, self-centered, and conceited. Patient's girlfriend to call psychiatrist 1/19/62 for appointment. Feel that mother to a certain extent is a disturbing influence.

1/25/62. No apparent change. Still restless. Patient was in fight in school yard July 1961. Face bruised considerably at that time and was suspended from school for 3 days after having perfect attendance record. Patient's parents said it was unjust and took matter before Board of Education. There was quite a write-up in the local paper. This family seems to have little control over their emotions. Express them quite freely.

1/31/62. Talking about going into the Army. Thinks he could go in and get into the band immediately. Doesn't realize that this illness might prevent him from going into service. Did not talk about girlfriend except to say her baby was due in May when the nurse asked about her.

2/8/62. Patient seemed cheerful and happy. Working at bar as drummer. Likes making the salary. Feels he is well now. The girlfriend has not called him since talking with psychiatrist. Medication given. Patient told RN about traffic ticket received last week but has not told his mother. Apparently trusts RN. Still talks about going into service or being a detective. Thinks parents may remarry.

2/15/62. Patient's condition seemed improved. Sleeping too much, however. Has different job now. Wonder if patient doesn't have difficulty in keeping jobs. Did not seem upset when he found out that he would not be allowed to go into service if drafted.

2/22/62. Social worker made home visit with RN. Patient appeared cheerful, happy. Played drums for us. Still seems conceited. Talked about going to New York for jazz tour with a group from University of Louisville. Also talked about joining Marines to play in band in a year or so. Seems immature in many ways but after all he was just 19 a few days ago. Medication given. States he feels better just taking 2 pills per day. Sleeps approximately 10 hours per day but says this is not unusual.

3/1/62. Still restless. Bored and conceited. Wants a job but only playing drums. Playing drums and shooting pool seem main interests. Still talks about going into the service in the future but believe he does this mostly to disturb his mother. Medication given.

3/8/62. Patient seemed improved. Needs letter from psychiatrist for employment office about work capability. Seemed sorry that nurse would only be calling every other week. Was very talkative. Had been to see Dave Brubeck and talked with drummer backstage and wanted to tell about it. Medication given.

3/23/62. Patient seems happy and cheerful. Seems to enjoy particularly teasing and picking on his mother. Still seems conceited and immature. Was very curious about questions nurse asked mother. Does not talk about girlfriend or her pregnancy now. Knows he was mentally ill but feels he is well now. Apparently very conscientious about taking medicine. Playing in band 6 nights a week at $10 per night.

4/5/62. Patient working and seems happy and normal. Was friendly and answered questions freely. Seems to be glad he didn't marry girl who became pregnant. Says when he marries he plans to stay married. Not be like his parents. Unable to see mother this visit. Mother working.

4/19/62. Patient seemed cheerful, happy and industrious today. Had no complaints or apparent unusual symptoms. Still playing drums in band at night clubs. Likes progressive jazz. Planning on working on another job also to make more money. This is apparently more the norm for patient. In the past before present illness he has always been interested in working. Likes to earn money. Says he is taking medicine regularly. Mother was working, so nurse was unable to fill out SO (significant other) rating scale.

5/3/62. Patient seemed a little more restless today. Pregnant girlfriend is due this month and patient is wondering how she is getting along. Feel there may be some problem with him or regression after baby arrives.

5/18/62. Patient working approximately 12 hrs. per day now. Plays drums at night club and is lifeguard at pool. Patient seemed more alert and happier today. Likes to make money. Has not heard from girlfriend.

6/1/62. Patient seemed a little disturbed this morning. Mother told PHN in presence of patient that she had told PHN the day before that he had spent the night in a girl's apartment. Patient was quite ashamed and embarrassed. Rapport poor today. Still working both jobs. Former girlfriend has had baby but didn't have the opportunity to talk with patient privately this home visit.

6/15/62. Patient seen at office today since he had appointment with psychiatrist for 6 mos. check. Seemed more nervous than usual but is usually this way when he comes to office. Refuses to discuss former girlfriend—evades. Seems to have fairly good insight into his illness.

6/28/62. Patient seemed rather agitated today. Quit job at night club because he was told to send home girlfriend who was underage. Seems overly preoccupied with girls. Mother on vacation. Grandparents, who don't wait on him as much as mother does, staying with patient. Present and past history of patient shows that he has a great drive to excel at whatever he tries. Also, quite conceited—"Best drummer in Louisville." Believes in a healthy body and certainly gives the impression he is "God's gift to women." Does not mention ex-girlfriend or his (?) child.

7/3/62. Discussed with psychiatrist that patient seems to be on cloud nine most of the time and also seems to be overly preoccupied with girls and sex. Medication to be changed to Thorazine 50 mg., tid. New medicine taken to patient. Told him to cut medicine to bid. if he became too sleepy.

7/12/62. Patient appears to be functioning normally. Suggests no problems or complaints. Cheerful mood.

7/24/62. Patient seemed improved under new drug. Definitely not as "high." SO report obtained from father this visit. Mother at work. Mother and father both think patient improved last few weeks. Seems to have settled down more. Patient seems happier to nurse. In many ways, patient seems almost closer to grandmother than mother. Does not get along with father too well. Has only lifeguard job at present. Wants to play with band after pool closes. Filled in for drummer at nightclub recently. Still quite thrifty (has saved almost $1000 since going back to work and still quite interested in physical health and body development).

8/15/62. Patient seemed in good spirits. Still has lifeguard job and is to start playing in orchestra at night club 5 nights a week. Mother was upset over bickering between patient and his father. Patient apparently has very little respect or love for father or father toward son. Father and son threaten each other at times. Have noticed hostility on former visits. From history of family feel that patient's disrespect is justified. Patient is going to take only 2 doses of medicine per day because he states he is too sleepy.

9/12/62. Patient seemed quite restless and bored. Seemed to have quite a flight of ideas. Not working now. Talked about getting a job in a band, going to New York to school, and entering the service. Had difficulty getting patient to be serious about questions asked. Patient talked so much it was hard to get a word in edgewise. Appointment given for patient to see psychiatrist at 1 P.M. 9/14/62 for 9 mos. evaluation.

10/11/62. Patient's condition seems good. Went to New York recently to visit brother who lives there. Was impressed with patient's apparent behavior during trip. Did a great deal of sight-seeing and picture-taking. Brother drinks a lot; patient did not. Patient wants to go in the service and play in the band. Wants psychiatrist's O.K. Told him to call ITC for appointment which he did. Patient feels a great need to get away from home. I believe this is a good idea. There is a lot of quarrelling and this disturbs patient. Not working now, and this is also hard on patient since he has always been the eager-beaver type. Patient seems to believe implicitly in ITC program.

11/7/62. Patient seems rather "high." Not very co-operative today due, I feel, to the treatment patient feels he received last time he stopped in at ITC. Seems rather bitter and hostile about this. Does not always take medicine 3Xday but 2Xday. Says it slows him down. Urged him to take it as prescribed. Working part-time. Says no drummers needed in Marines. Still a lot of friction in home. SO quite disturbed today about entire family. Says she has about reached a breaking point. Feels, among other things, that she must be more firm with patient regardless of what it would do to him. Says patient inconsiderate, argumentative, will not help around house or pay board. Says many characteristics are those of his father. Older brother is to come home to stay Thanksgiving. This brother drinks a great deal and becomes belligerent.

12/6/62. Patient seems quite exhilarated today. Patient and brother went to a party (party of 4) last night and stayed out all night. Feel that he may be a little jealous of brother. Working in band 2 nights a week, still taking drum lessons and spends most of the day at the "Y." Still on body-building kick. Feels he can get any girl he wants and he seems to want them. Very egotistical. Says he only takes 2 doses of medicine a day because the

3rd one slows him down too much. Doubt if he always takes 2. Did not feel patient was too well and hope visit helped.

1/3/63. Mother called nurse at home 12/29/62 to state patient seemed not as well. Was afraid he would become acutely ill again. Recommended medication 3Xday and more attention until patient could see Dr. 1/2/63. Mother said patient was better today; however, he still seems rather high. Talking rapidly and in excess. More argumentative than usual and rather rude. Felt and still feel part of patient's present episode is due to older brother who is living in home now. Older brother is nicer looking, very polite and helps around house which patient does not and will not do. Attention of mother divided now. Patient only working 1 or 2 nights a week. Says he is going to take a course in Psychology at the University of Louisville. Talk is very immature.

One year after the patient came into the home care study the formal psychiatric evaluation was repeated. The patient was considerably improved, and most of the prominent features of his illness of the year before were measurably reduced or had disappeared. At this time the patient showed only mild anxiety and agitation, ordinary facial expressions, voluable speech, demonstrative and appropriate affect, mild suspiciousness, and no hallucinations. The examining psychiatrist felt that the patient's insight was not quite as good, but his prognosis improved.

1/29/63. Stopped by patient's home to change appointment and found he had stopped by ITC earlier to see nurse because he was going out of town for 1 or 2 weeks and would not be home to keep appointment. Still working just 1 night a week. Did not seem as high today or as rude and boisterous.

2/28/63. Not too much change noted. Playing in band in low-class night club 4 nights per week. Trying to find a job. Much friction and arguing at home, as usual. Still girl crazy. Patient seems improved when he has been away from home but yet he seems drawn to home.

3/12/63. Patient called ITC to tell nurse he was going on the road with a band. Would be home occasionally and would keep in touch. Said he was going to take medicine 2Xday instead of 3. Appointment given for patient to see psychiatrist 3/16 at 8:30 A.M. for 15 mos. evaluation.

3/16/63. Stopped by patient's home to do 15 mos. evaluation. Patient said he did not keep appointment this A.M. with doctor because he played last night and did not get to bed until 4 A.M. Mother phoned ITC. Patient seems happy about new job but yet realizes band might not succeed.

4/4/63. Patient seemed a little high and exuberant today but this seems to be more or less usual with him. Orchestra job lasted one week, but reasons for failure were good. Starts lifeguard job at park next week. Bought new car and quite happy about this. Mother fusses over son so very much.

4/30/63. Stopped by patient's home to set time for appointment 5/2 and found that patient is out of town, traveling with an orchestra. This job set-up seems to be a better one than past engagements. Mother says patient may be gone for some time, but he wants to stay on the program. He feels the medicine is necessary. I will try to keep in touch with patient by letter if possible and will contact mother occasionally.

5/22/63. Patient phoned RN at ITC 5/21/63 to say he was in town. Appointment made for home visit 5/22 and 5/23 to come to ITC for 18 mos. check. Plans to leave again 5/23 or 5/24. Says orchestra has booking at Rock Island, Ill. for the summer. Says he likes job fairly well. That he is not ready yet for type band he would like to play in. Seemed high, restless, and boisterous, but actually no more than usual. Seemed glad to be home and happy. I am concerned about blood pressure. Says he has only been taking 1 capsule daily. Suggested he take dose prescribed. Apparently wants to stay on ITC program.

6/20/63. Patient not playing with band on the road now. Unemployed at present. Patient said he quit job for 3 reasons: (1) band would never get anyplace and he wants to be drummer in a top band; (2) bored when not on job—rest of band drank a lot and patient did not; (3) homesick. Patient quite engrossed in book written by MD on "How to Live 365 Days" or something similar to this. Patient seems to be trying to mature. Feel that like so many young people patient does a lot of blustering to try and hide his true feelings.

7/19/63. Patient seems to be functioning well. No problems. Working as lifeguard at pool. Has rather grandiose ideas about the band he wants to have when he becomes 21. Doesn't seem entirely impossible because he certainly has the desire, energy, and apparently some ability. Stated he wants to stay in Louisville and expressed a great deal of affection for mother today. Dosen't seem to care for father. Rather fearful of marriage. There is quite a divorce pattern in family. Believes still in keeping body healthy.

8/16/63. Patient seems to be doing unusually well. Still working as lifeguard. Has another job starting next week playing in orchestra. Studying for college entrance exams. Has music scholarship at University of Louisville if he passes exams. Plans to have a tutor if he fails. Seems quite sincere.

Case #102. Psychological Test Results

Test	Direction of Change	1st Testing Initial	2nd Testing 6 Mo.	3rd Testing 18 Mo.	4th Testing 24 Mo.
Reaction time	+	3057	2954	2924	2892
Maze QE	+	035	066	068	048
Maze IQ	+	122	122	126	129
WAIS, verbal IQ	+	099	097	110	117
WAIS, performance IQ	+	094	105	103	115
WAIS, full IQ	+	097	101	108	119
Bender Z	+	182	182	192	244

\+ Improvement
\- No improvement
= No consistent change

Case #102. Medications

12/6/61. Chlorpromazine–50 milligrams, twice a day
Trifluoperazine– 5 milligrams, three times a day

2/16/62. Trifluoperazine– 5 milligrams, twice a day
7/12/62. Chlorpromazine–50 milligrams, twice a day
9/14/62. Chlorpromazine–50 milligrams, three times a day
12/10/63. Chlorpromazine–50 milligrams, twice a day
1/1/64. Chlorpromazine–50 milligrams, twice a day
1/30/64. Discontinue all medication

9/12/63. No particular change. Patient seems to show a little more insight and seems to be maturing some. Did not pass college entrance exams. Giving private drum lessons and playing drums 6 and 7 nights per week. Argued about seeing records at ITC.

10/10/63. No change noted. Seems to be functioning well. Was not belligerent today.

11/14/63. Patient seemed a little high today. Very positive opinions. Talked about how parents have always quarrelled. Said as a child he always thought it was father's fault, but now thinks mother is also to blame. Patient says he manipulates mother. Feels that women are competing too much with men. Believes ITC medication is a fooler. Said he took 4 pills and had no effect.

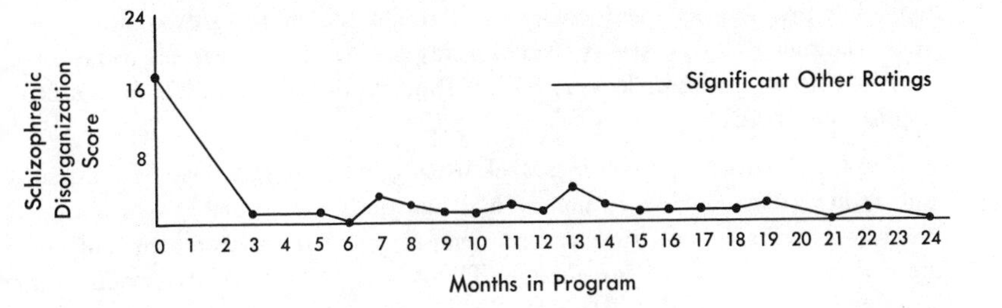

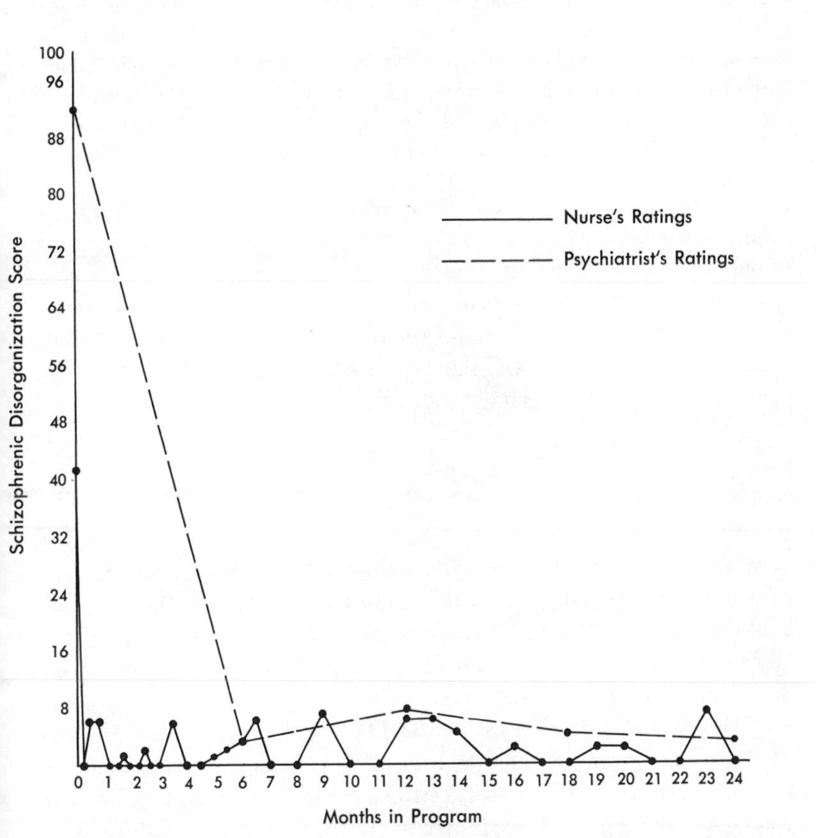

Patient #102. Schizophrenic Disorganization Ratings by Psychiatrist, Nurse, and Significant Other

12/13/63. No particular change noted. Patient argumentative and a little high, but this is usual. Did not seem to resent that nurse will continue to visit even though 2 yrs. are up. Not working steady, but this seems usual for patient. Still on health kick. Very boastful and show-off. Patient has decreased medication greatly.

1/16/64. Talked with patient last week when in home to talk with SO Patient and father (does not live in home) had had quite an argument and almost came to physical blows. In 2 yrs., no change noted in environment and believe there is no chance for change. There is a great deal of turmoil and arguing in home and this seems to disturb patient. He became so disgusted that he threw medicine away. Patient called RN at home last night to say he would be unable to keep appointment today. Seemed rather high. Believe he realizes he needs medicine after being without. This month he is enthused over job selling picture albums; not long ago it was hose. Still convinced he will become famous as a drummer. Relationship has been very gratifying.

Twenty-five months after being admitted to home care study, the patient was examined by the staff psychiatrist who could detect evidence of only mild anxiety. At this time he felt that the patient had some emotional insight into his problem and was beginning to understand the importance of emotional factors. Again, prognosis was good. All medication was discontinued, and the patient was discharged from the treatment program.

HOME CARE—PLACEBO FAILURE

Case #109, a 48-year-old white housewife was admitted to the ITC program on January 10, 1962. The patient, a high school graduate, lives on a farm in Nelson County with her husband, an 18-year-old son, and a 10-year-old daughter. A 17-year-old married daughter lives away from home. The husband is a tenant farmer and reports an income of less than $3500 a year.

The patient was referred to the ITC from Central State Hospital where she had been admitted as a result of a medical certificate signed by two physicians. The medical certificate had been sought by her husband after the patient became extremely delusional and hallucinatory. The patient's history of mental hospitalization goes back to 1956.

The interview with the ITC staff psychiatrist indicated that the prominent features of the patient's present illness were as follows: very marked anxiety, difficulty concentrating, fatigue, withdrawal, marked depression, agitation, slowed and stuporous behavior, anxious and tense facial expression, isolation, major ideas of influence by others, threats of assault or destruction, bland and definitely inappropriate affect, systematized paranoid delusions, and auditory hallucinations present to a major and disturbing degree. The patient appeared to have no insight into her illness, denying the existence of any problem. Her diagnosis was schizophrenic reaction, paranoid type. The prognosis was for improvement with the possibility of stress symptoms recurring. Prescription: trifluoperazine (Stelazine), 5 milligrams three times a day. Study assignment: home on placebo.

The initial attempt to administer the psychological tests to the patient was terminated when she went into a tirade after completing only a small portion of the battery. Her behavior was bizarre, explosive, and tyrannical during the entire 25-minute session—cursing and expounding scripture in a confused disassociated manner. The patient was delusional and seemed to be hallucinating. Finally, she refused to continue and left the room.

Home treatment began that day when the patient returned to her farm with her husband. The nurse made her first visit the next day.

1/11/62. Patient was cordial and seemed pleased to see nurse. Responded well to routine blood pressure, temperature, and other tests. She refused to talk about herself or her problems but would talk about farm chores and younger daughter. Then husband decided to go to Central State Hospital to get patient's clothes. The moment he left she became extremely hostile and angry—cursing and quoting the Bible. Said nurse was hearing voices and that nurse had no right to force herself on patient.

1/18/62. Patient was taking in coal. She said hello to nurse, then turned around and went in house and closed the door. Still very hostile, but was not talkative today. Husband says she is very restless and nervous after she gets up and until about noon; then she seems to quiet down. She keeps telling nurse she is doing the best she can.

1/25/62. Patient in good mood today. States she enjoys her food. Will not talk about any personal problems. Husband had been drinking and was hardly able to stand, but he was very jovial. Patient taking medicine and keeps saying she is doing O.K. Asked son to have husband bring patient to office for Psychological Exam next Monday or Tuesday. Could hardly get back home as lane was so muddy; got stuck and had to be pushed out.

2/1/62. Patient will talk if you ask questions but will not carry on conversation. Continues to say she is doing all right. States she is doing all right over and over, but refuses to answer when you ask about problems. Husband states that patient gets "all riled up" each morning—curses and accuses him of running around. Then he says she calms down around 12 or 1 P.M. and seems to be pretty good the rest of the day. (Patient's husband) has been under care of doctor. He appears quite ill and upset. Asked him to bring (patient) to ITC for Psychological Exam. He will when able.

2/8/62. As I came around patient's house I could hear her talking a mile a minute. She opened the door and walked into the next room. She will not offer to converse with nurse. Still she does not object to having temperature and routine blood pressure check. Will not admit to being nervous. Says she is doing just fine and that nothing is wrong with her. Also she insists that nurse knows all about her so she doesn't intend to tell me anything about herself. Says she doesn't care if I come back or not, but I told her I would visit her next week. I talked with her husband. He says she thinks everyone knows all about her so she refuses to talk very much to anyone. After asking patient about her husband, she said she did care how he was. Later she said he's sucking on the bottle and she didn't care what happened to him and she would be better off if he was dead. Talked with the owners of the farm. Evidently (patient's husband) does quite a bit of drinking and they feel that is why (patient) is sick. They also said (patient's husband) had been to the doctor and that he had very bad hemorrhoids due to drinking. Asked (patient's husband) to bring wife to ITC for psychological tests. I do not feel that patient is improving, but seems as if she is functioning in the home at her own level. Does not seem to disrupt the home too much. Husband says some nights she sleeps like a baby and other times she is awake by midnight and doesn't sleep after that. She is usually in bed by 7 P.M. Started medicine four times a day today.

2/15/62. Husband said he received letter yesterday from ITC asking to bring patient in for psychologicals. When he told patient he was going to take her in, he said she flew into a rage, cursing and yelling, and that she didn't stop carrying on all night. Said he didn't get 15 minutes sleep. She was her usual self when I visited. She denies all illness. Keeps saying she is doing fine and is taking her medicine. Husband says she only takes it if he insists. I suggested she take her fourth capsule around midnight, as it seems as that is when she awakens (according to her husband) and begins to chatter. Husband asked that I not mention going into the Center today as he said he couldn't go through this ordeal another night. (Husband) seems quite upset himself—very nervous, hands shaking. 19-year-old son was asleep on the couch when I arrived. He made no attempt to leave the room while I talked to his parents. Evidently he refuses to help his father at all and spends most of his nights out. This upsets the father, but doesn't seem to bother the patient. She covers up, so it is hard to say if it affects her.

2/22/62. Patient was hiding in cellar and refused to answer when nurse called her. Husband searched premises then looked all through house before finding her. She said it was none of nurse's business what she did. She was extremely hostile, talked constantly, cursing and quoting the Bible. Said nurse was born out of wedlock and all knew this and that I was damned to hell. She said the Lord God helped her put her new linoleum down in her bedroom. She would spring from her chair and run out into the kitchen waving her arms and cursing and talking so fast and what seemed to be such double-talk you could not understand her. When I walked out the back door she began banging chairs and cursing up a storm.

Husband said patient will go on as long as a week and things will be fine. Then she will start on one of these rampages—accusing him of being unfaithful. States she talks to one sister whom she hates and would kill her if she could. He said she hears voices at these times. He is giving her the medicine, but she doesn't take it regularly. He also said the doctor at the hospital before said Thorazine did not help her and he doesn't feel as if the medicine she is taking now is taking hold. He said he would try to bring her back to ITC, but would not try to do so while she is in this humor (I agree).

3/1/62. Patient was ironing and quiet when nurse entered home. In a short time she became overtly hostile and verbalized her hallucinations and delusional ideas. The patient's husband advised that patient's anticipation of nurse's visit precipitates overt hostility and nurse's presence in the home antagonizes her extremely. She remains emotionally upset and agitated from an hour to all day following the visit. (Husband) feels the medication is helping her. She failed to take it 2 days and she became considerably worse. He said he gives it to her now. If it remained for her to take it she would throw the capsules into the fire. She functions very well as a homemaker—cooks 3 meals a day, puts out 2 washings per week, and makes a fair attempt to keep the house clean. Patient's trend of thought was rambling and scattered. She referred to her conversaton with God and most of verbalizing was not understandable to observers. She was in contact with reality because she gave sensible responses to a few questions. PHN's presence definitely antagonized and disturbed patient. Visit was terminated early for this reason.

3/8/62. Patient extremely hostile, talking constantly, quoting Bible, accusing nurse of all kinds of things. Very agitated, impossible to carry on a conversation with her. When we left the house she ran out the door, screaming at us using obscene language. Husband says she has been calm all week, but that she carried on after nurse left last week. Husband promises to bring patient into Clinic next week.

On March 12 the patient returned to the ITC to take the psychological examination. Again she was bizarre and explosive, cursing, and quoting the Bible. She continuously moved her hands, almost rubbed her forehead raw, moved anxiously about her chair, and attempted to break the equipment used on all motor tasks. Her attention, interest, and effort on all tasks were very poor.

3/15/62. Patient extremely hostile. Openly accused nurse of having affair with her husband and having children. Also said the nurse was the devil and patient chased her black cat around the house and put it out so nurse could not be near to it. Verbally threatening nurse with biblical quotations and passages relating to adultery, damnation and punishment. Had door locked and yelled out "You are not welcome." Patient threw her glasses into the fire last week and states she sees better without glasses. Patient came to ITC Monday 3/12 for psychological exams. This did not seem to upset her after she returned home.

3/19/62. Made home visit to get patient to sign release papers for Central State. Patient signed (an alias) which she insists is her right name. She refused to sign (her proper surname) and would have destroyed papers if they had not been removed. Patient extremely hostile and accusing. After signing papers she became very jittery and her hands shook. She appeared as if she were going to burst out in tears, but she didn't. She told nurse positively she wasn't welcome or wanted in her home. I told her I would return 3/29, next Thursday.

3/29/62. Patient was extremely hostile and rude from the moment she saw me coming around the house. She permitted me to take her blood pressure, etc., but said I was forcing her to do it. She continually talks about sin and damnation, constantly accusing nurse, stating she has no right to enter her home and ask her anything. She became very angry and threw a large glass of water in nurse's face when I implied that she may be hearing voices. She said it was none of the nurse's business—anything she did. Husband said that wife has been very hostile for past 3 days. Has been accusing him and cursing him. He warned me I would probably get a good cussing when I went to the door, which I did.

4/12/62. (Husband) did not want nurse to visit patient. She had taken screw driver and pounded it into the wall, saying that is what the nurse would get when she came in. (Husband) was afraid she would injure the nurse. He stated she knew her older daughter Sunday and was very glad to see her and talked very sensibly for a while, then went into her tirade of cursing, etc., saying she was (alias)and never was (real name). Husband said she was worse at her period time. She said he had died, then she said he was going to die, that the tractor was going to run over him. He said she did a good job of keeping the younger child's clothing clean and that she can sit down and work arithmetic problems; that she will play games and laugh and seems to have a good time with the 10-year-old daughter. Made appointment for patient to see psychiatrist on 4/20/62.

On April 20th the ITC staff psychiatrist saw the patient and wrote the following report:

(Patient) was brought into the Institute Treatment Center by her husband for a follow-up evaluation. At this time she was quite verbal and abusive, quite preoccupied. She had periods of silence alternating with outbursts which lasted for several minutes. She apparently hallucinates, is quite delusional, quotes the Bible. The medication does not seem to be holding her as this behavior seems to be almost continuous, whether or not the nurse visits on that particular day. She repeats words. She has so far not been destructive or assaultive although she has a screwdriver in her possession and her husband does not know where this is hidden. She is quite controlling of the interview. However, she seems to be suffering a great deal and on one occasion said, "I hurt." She calls various people by name including the Governor, a person by the name of Nell, Clinics—"they should tear them down." She has sharp mood swings. She is quite powerful and says that "(her name) is right." She has identified with the Lord and with right and has depersonalized and talks to herself in the form of a third person.

For the most part she did not talk directly to me but directed her remarks towards the corner of the room or towards the well opposite me. She was not looking at me through a good part of the interview. She looks at her hands quite closely as if she is looking through them.

She is much worse than when I saw her on the other occasion. However, she will at times catch herself, look up and say, "Are we finished?" She talks to a third party and states that she is telling the truth. She states, "I am not afraid of you for very long. I am not afraid of what a man may do to me."

Her condition has worsened since our last interview and her husband is by this time quite frightened of her presence in the home. Therefore, it was advised that (he) return his wife to Central State Hospital and that she be admitted this afternoon. In talking with (him) he gave the information that medication was not holding and that this woman was being continually upset from day to day. Her condition has grown steadily worse. At this time (he) was told that his wife constituted too much of a risk at home and it was strongly advised that he return his wife to the hospital.

The Admissions Office at Central State Hospital was contacted that (patient's husband) would be there with his wife this afternoon. (He) agreed to return his wife to the hospital.

After 3 months and 10 days of home care, this patient was returned to the hospital because of her inability to function at home. Since the patient was given placebo, the acute nature of her present illness was not alleviated by medication. Without medication her symptoms continued unchecked, and the fact that she was able to stay out of the hospital as long as she did is a tribute only to the tolerance of her family.

Case #109. Psychological Test Results

Test	*Direction of Change*	*1st Testing Initial*	*2nd Testing 6 Mo.*	*3rd Testing 18 Mo.*	*4th Testing 24 Mo.*
Reaction time	+	3401	3236	3210	3342
Maze QE	+	050	073	057	064
Maze IQ	+	058	066	058	062
WAIS, verbal IQ	+	068	094	094	118
WAIS, performance IQ	+	053	086	099	099
WAIS, full IQ	+	058	089	096	110
Bender Z	+	053	128	122	114

+ Improvement
− No improvement
= No consistent change

Case #109. Medications

1/11/62. Trifluoperazine— 5 milligrams, three times a day
1/17/62. Chlorpromazine—100 milligrams, three times a day
2/ 2/62. Chlorpromazine—100 milligrams, four times a day

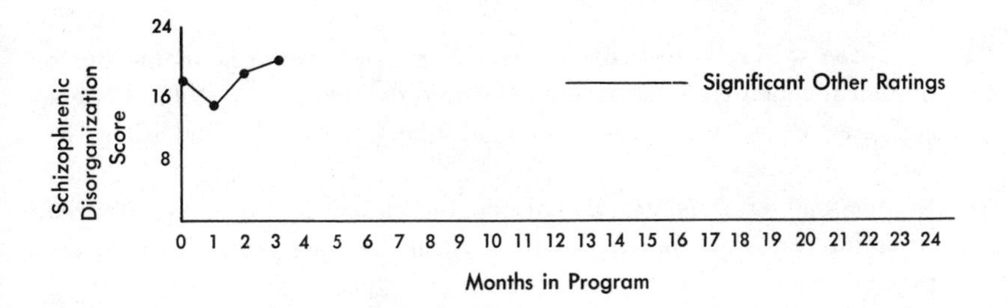

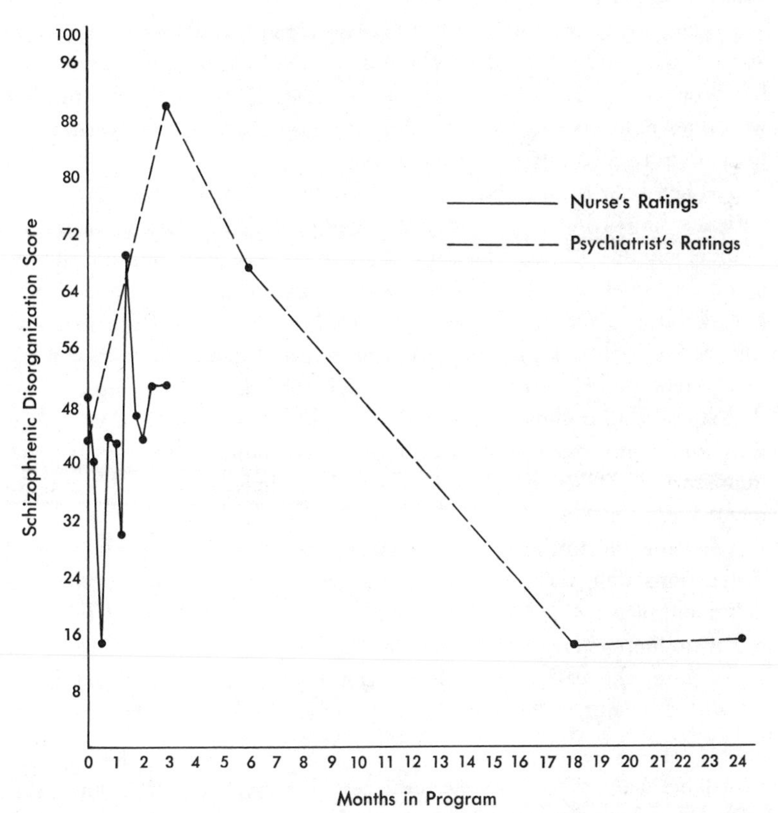

Patient #109. Schizophrenic Disorganization Ratings by Psychiatrist, Nurse, and Significant Other

HOME CARE—DRUG FAILURE

Case #111, a 20-year-old male Negro was referred to the home treatment center by Central State Hospital on January 12, 1962. Patient had previously been retained at Louisville General Hospital where he had been taken by the police after threatening a man and acting in a strange manner. Prior to this episode, the patient had been hospitalized twice for very short periods of time within the past year. However, the patient's mother reported that the present illness had been developing over a long period of time.

The patient is single and has been working sporadically for several years as a chauffeur. He left school at the end of the ninth grade and has been the family's chief breadwinner since. There is an older brother who does not live at home. In 1961 a younger brother drowned while the patient tried vainly to rescue him.

When seen by the staff psychiatrist, the prominent features of the patient's illness included moderate anxiety, difficulty in concentrating, fatigue, withdrawal, some feelings of worthlessness, guilt, and inferiority, agitation, quiet depression, slow speech, mild ideas of influence, completely flat and definitely inappropriate affect, and some suspiciousness. The patient's illness was diagnosed as schizophrenic reaction, chronic undifferentiated type. His insight was fair, feeling that the cause of his illness was within himself, but unable to give any explanation. Prognosis was for improvement but with minor complaints. Prescription: trifluoperazine (Stelazine), 2 milligrams, three times a day. Study assignment: home on drugs.

During the initial psychological examination the patient followed instructions well, was cooperative, and seemed eager to please. He was polite and pleasant. No mood fluctuations were observed during this time nor were there signs of excessive overt anxiety.

Again, the patient's condition can be followed best through the reports of the nurse who made her first home visit the next day.

1/13/62. I was greeted cordially at the door by the patient. He took my coat, hung it up, then asked me to be seated. Patient and his mother were very nice and seemed pleased to have me in their home. Patient was a little upset when he realized that I hadn't brought more medicine with me. He accepted my explanation gracefully and was relieved when I reassured him that I would come back and bring him more medicine.

1/15/62. Mother and patient living in 3-room, well furnished, neat apartment. Mother and patient apparently sleep in same room, but have separate beds. Patient states his illness stems from drowning of younger bother. Feels much better. Not restless and doesn't feel people are against him now. Wants to go back to work as soon as possible. Advised patient not to drive car. Apparently complains of stomach frequently. Reassured that "pills" would not hurt stomach. Medication given. Rapport good.

1/19/62. Patient called ITC in A.M. stating 1 capsule of medicine came apart and he would not have enough to last until home visit. Did not object to PHN bringing him medicine at work. Delivered capsule. Patient states he is feeling better.

1/22/62. Home condition same. Patient feeling much better. Working. Breakdown apparently caused by disappointing love affair and patient started brooding. Wants to start driving 1/24/62. Promised to ask psychiatrist and call patient's home 1/24 to give decision. Patient seems to be hostile toward police, but this may be justified. Would like to have something to do with his free time. (1/24/62—psychiatrist gave permission for patient to drive. Called patient's home and gave message to mother.)

1/29/62. Patient talked freely and during the course of conversation stated "My mother doesn't want me to go out. She's afraid I'll get in trouble. I think she's afraid that I might commit suicide. She doesn't like for me to go out with the boys I used to run around with because she's afraid I'll get into trouble." Patient denied having any desire to commit suicide. Also patient stated that his mother didn't want him to live his own life and that he was thinking about getting an apartment for himself. He followed this statement with "But you just can't walk off and leave your mother."

Patient asked if he could get a 2-week supply of medicine this coming Wednesday because he was supposed to go out of town for 2 weeks on the job. I explained that I would have to talk with psychiatrist about this and that I would let him know.

2/3/62. Patient was running an errand for his boss this A.M. and was driving the boss' new car on the River Road. The police stopped him and accused him of stealing the car. They were apparently rude and obnoxious to patient. This upset him and probably he talked back to them. He also told police he was taking medicine. They told him he had no right to be driving a car. He explained he had permission from the doctor. They took him to the station and he was released in an hour through the arrangement of his boss' son-in-law who is a lawyer. He is scheduled to appear in court Monday at 9:30 A.M.

2/4/62. Mother phoned answering service and asked to get in touch with nurse. Explained (patient's) trouble with police and said he was acting about the same as he did on admission to ITC. Suggested she give him another capsule about 2 A.M. and reassure patient. Phoned psychiatrist to receive O.K. about medication and any suggestions.

2/5/62. Phoned patient's home. Patient feels better this A.M. Patient to appear in court at 9:00 A.M. Will phone ITC when he gets home for nurse to make home visit.

2/5/62. Patient seemed in good spirits. Police had apparently been a little nasty to him. Brother posted $100 bond and boss' lawyer was in police court with him this A.M. Hearing to be Feb. 27. Told story with gestures but saw nothing unusual in this. Patient definitely hostile toward police, but as I stated before I see nothing unusual in this. Is not hearing voice nor does he think everyone is against him. Has told me on last 2 home visits about someone he was at CSH with who was found dead on the road (he was told). Apparently this is preying on his mind. Medication given.

2/12/62. RN phoned psychiatrist to check prescription. Said to take (patient) extra pills and have him continue taking qid. if necessary. Patient seemed quite depressed, hostile, uncommunicative, sad and brooding today. Favorite aunt died last night and mother did not tell him she was critical nor tell him of her death right away. Patient said he lost his temper and feels justified. There seems to be a great deal of hostility building between patient and mother. States she nags him. Social worker will visit home next week also. Told patient to take pills qid. and I would bring him more 2/14/62. Feel that patient has regressed greatly the last 2 weeks.

2/19/62. Patient still seems quite hostile. Seems concerned about money. Volunteers little information. Answers mostly with "yes" or "no" and does not elucidate. Says he is going to Dental College for partial plate. Is going to try to take just 3 caps. a day this week. Social worker made home visit with RN this week and did an SO. Patient seemed rather belligerent.

2/26/62. Patient seemed in much better spirits today; in fact, seemed a little high, a sense of well being. Plans to buy a car. Cautioned him about driving carefully and for some indefinable reason felt the need to warn again about consuming alcohol on ITC medication. Has only been taking 3 doses daily this past week, so only left him enough for 3/day. Said 4 was making him drowsy. Well being may change rapidly and hostility begin again if for financial reason he can't buy car.

3/2/62. Patient called that he was getting out of jail (for traffic offense) and they (at the jail) couldn't find his medicine. Patient very hostile and wants to go to CSH. Told him to come in to see psychiatrist and get some medicine. Patient did so. Prescribed cap. qid. (capsule, four times a day).

3/3/62. Patient alone in apartment. Very hostile. Held his head between his hands, would not look at nurse and gave delayed answers. Would volunteer no remarks. Usually answered "yes" or "no" or "I don't know." Said there would be no use to visit him 3/5/62, because he would be in jail over a $5 ticket which he wasn't going to pay. Still says he wants to go to CSH. Was not courteous as usual. Felt that neither of us received much satisfaction from the H.V. (home visit).

3/5/62. 10 A.M. Phoned to see if patient home. No one answered phone. Called sister who said mother was working and she didn't know where (he) could be. Also stated he was fired Sat. Older brother will probably take job which will not help matters.

3/7/62. Patient called ITC. Didn't know when he would be home, so suggested he come to office. Asked him if he felt better. He said "yes," "no," "I don't know."

Later—Patient much more talkative today. Apparently trying to tease nurse. Said he was leaving town. Didn't know when or where and would steal money to go. Said he was too smart to get caught. Filed for unemployment this A.M. Said he has to get a job or go to CSH. That his mother can't support him. Wants O.K. from psychiatrist to see former boss' brother for a job. Told him to have man call psychiatrist. Said he didn't have ITC phone number. Reminded him he called office this A.M. Patient has to attend Traffic School. Said nurse did not come to see him Sat., but know he really knew better. Apparently wanted nurse to give him bus fare or drive him home. Tax returns being questioned. Said he didn't have money for notary public (had fresh pack of cigarettes, however). Gave him address of Legal Aid Soc. Also gave him appointment to see him at his home 10 A.M. 2/12/62 and for him to call ITC if he won't be at home. *Very immature.* No medication given since he had picked up enough medicine at jail Monday.

3/12/62. Patient rather uncommunicative. Talked very little. Still unemployed. Says he would like a job. States he has been going out and seeing people. Still hostile. Didn't say anything more today about leaving town. Rapport poor today. Medication given.

3/19/62. Rapport very poor. Patient volunteered few remarks. Answered "yes," "no," or "I don't know" and looked at the floor. A friend was there when I arrived and he made no effort to introduce me which he would have done at the beginning of the home care program. Patient said he lost his billfold but didn't know when or where. Wasn't sure what day mother would be off to obtain SO. Very hostile. Short H.V. made. Medication given.

3/28/62. Had appointment with patient and mother at 8:30 A.M., 3/27/62. Not home. Left note for patient to call ITC, which he did not do. Called patient A.M. 3/28 and made appointment for 1 P.M. Significant other evaluation and Nurse's psychiatric evaluation done. Mother feels patient much improved. Was very quiet after being let out of jail and she did not expect this. Patient seemed much improved to nurse today. Said he quit job because he was only making 70¢/hr. Mother said he told her he was fired. Patient was looking for job he heard about yesterday and did not get back in time for home visit. Talked and laughed more today. Still says "I don't know" when he doesn't want to answer. Says he doesn't feel as bitter about brother's death. Would rather take 3 capsules per day so told him to try it. Apparently has friends. Wants a job. Has gained weight.

4/3/62. Patient seems improved. Does not talk much, but this is patient's usual behavior. Did not seem sullen or hostile as he has been recently. Still looking for a job. Has been doing some part-time work. Taking 3 capsules daily. Appointment with psychiatrist given for 4/13/62. 3 mos. check-up due.

4/16/62. Patient has no special complaints. Now working part-time and states he's going out of town with his boss. May return Friday or Monday.

5/2/62. PHN tried innumerable times to contact patient. Patient finally called ITC 4/30/62 and appointment made for patient to come to office to see psychiatrist and PHN 5/2/62. Patient had no complaints and appears to feel well. Working part time now. Home visits to be made every 2 weeks now and patient to take medicine three times a day. Importance of keeping on ITC program stressed.

5/21/62. Patient seems to be progressing well. No complaints. Working part time driving for furniture salesman. Driving and mostly out of town. Cautioned patient about not running out of medicine as he did this time.

6/4/62. Patient had no complaints. As usual talked very little. Working part time. Has had large weight gain and blood pressure is elevated. Suggested lose some weight.

6/18/62. Patient seemed improved this A.M. Has job now and seemed quite happy and cheerful. Was even talkative for this patient. Blood pressure high, however, and patient still quite heavy. Recommended that he slow down on eating and explained that high blood pressure may make him more irritable and he wouldn't want to lose his temper and as a result his job perhaps.

7/2/62. Patient working and appears well and happy. Talking more. No particular problems.

7/23/62. Patient was out of town when last home visit due 7/16/62. Said he didn't have quite enough medicine. Progress report made on patient today and appointment for 6 mos. check at ITC made for Aug. 8 at 1:00 P.M. Stressed importance. No problems and no symptoms noted. Patient working at old job again and driving out of town. Next home visit to be Aug. 20.

8/20/62. Patient seemed happier today than usual. Was very polite and seemed glad he was improved. Still working. No problems. Told patient he would be visited monthly hereafter, but nurse would call on phone between visits. Left medicine for 3X/day. Patient said psychiatrist told him twice a day. Said I would check with psychiatrist 8/22, but in meantime take three times a day.

9/24/62. Called Mother. Patient called her 9/23/62 and stated he would be gone for another week. Mother said patient inquired if nurse had been there and was sorry he missed her. Mother said patient sounded all right and would send patient his medicine this morning.

9/30/62. Patient appears emotionally stable. Denies complaints, problems or nervous symptoms. Conversation is limited and brief answers in reply to questions asked.

11/26/62. No apparent change. Patient seems well. Works regularly and seems happy. Says he has no particular problems. Due for a raise in pay soon.

12/21/62. Patient has lost approximately 20 lbs. Said he had been watching his diet. Had a cold 1st of week and went to Louisville General Hospital for penicillin. Seems O.K. now. Will watch weight loss. Patient seemed much friendlier and more communicative. Is usually very reticent. Seems happy and no problems. Working regularly. Likes job.

1/18/63. Patient feels well. Seems happy. Said he may marry soon. Has changed jobs. Driving delivery truck now and makes more money. Asked when he could stop taking medicine. Seemed a little high but not abnormally so. Friendlier and talks more. Shows off a little.

2/15/63. Patient seems to be functioning well. No particular change apparent since last visit. Patient still likes to tease nurse. Told about man who was patient at CSH when he was there who has been dismissed. Said this man didn't have to come to ITC or take any medication. Asked how he was getting along and patient said this man not doing too well and got patient to admit that ITC program was good and it felt good to know somebody was interested and cared.

3/15/63. Patient came to ITC for visit on his lunch hour. No particular change noted. Plans to marry 3/22/63. Future wife has 2 small children. One child will live with couple. Patient said mother planning to marry and will give them the furniture in apartment and couple will stay there. Mother, however, did not say this. Unable to discern exactly what is to be done. Patient invited psychiatrist and nurse to reception. Says wife-to-be knows about his illness.

4/11/63. Patient seemed well and happy. Married recently and says he is very happy. Wife has 2 children. Younger (4 mo.) is with them. Patient's mother also still living with them. Apartment only has 3 rooms. Patient says everyone gets along well. Wife taking Nurse Aid Training.

5/17/63. Patient seemed rather uncommunicative today. Stated everything was fine and he was happy. Said job secure and he was quite happy in his marriage. Wasn't dressed as well as usual. I have heard that mother-in-law and daughter-in-law are having a few problems, mainly in regard to treatment of patient (by wife), but patient did not admit any of this.

6/28/63. Patient's appointment was for 6/21 but he forgot. Patient apparently not taking medicine or very little. Urged him to do so. Says he is very happy and feels well. Patient's mother still with couple and this is apparently causing some friction. Patient concerned having to report to draft board July 15. Neglected to get reclassified when he married. Told patient psychiatrist would write a letter to board. Patient still working full time.

7/25/63. Patient's condition seems good. Apparently has no unusual problems. "Forgets" medicine at times. Wanted to know when it would be discontinued. Seems to be functioning well. Still likes to tease nurse.

8/22/63. Patient semeed a little worried about money matters. Wife is pregnant and ill with kidney infection. Mother still living in 3 room apartment with couple and wife's 2 children. Mother and wife not getting along very well. Wife says mother to marry and leave soon, but patient doesn't know this yet. Stressed to wife again that patient not to have too much stress and tension.

9/25/63. No change noted. Seems to be functioning well.

10/22/63. Patient seems to be functioning better than ever. Talked quite a bit today which is unusual for him. Said he felt ITC program had helped him very much and talked about ways it had helped. Patient, wife and stepdaughters living alone now and patient seems happier than he ever has.

Showed a great deal more insight. Wife is due to have baby 1st part of November.

One month later, on November 20th, the patient was admitted to Louisville General Hospital and the next day was transferred to Central State Hospital. In her final report, the patient's nurse attempted to describe the circumstances leading up to this home care failure:

Patient seemed to be functioning well but less than a year ago married a woman with 2 illegitimate children and who became pregnant again before or immediately following marriage. Wife seemed unable to comprehend that too much pressure not be put on patient. Patient's mother lived with family in 3-room apartment and apparently did most of housework and gave financial support. Friction ensued. Patient had to get up with children at night. Mother remarried and moved out. Patient had full responsibility then. He was fearful of wife's impending delivery. The weekend of October 26th, patient was arrested after threatening same person as 22 months ago. Released. Seen by psychiatrist and prescription increased. Prescription then given to patient on weekly basis. Seemed to improve; then wife had baby. Patient had to borrow money, move to larger apartment while wife in hospital. Became angry because wife and infant not dismissed from hospital (Louisville General) the day he wanted them to be. Wife stated she had difficult labor and patient was apprehensive about trial coming up in December and was apparently not taking medicine as prescribed.

Patient picked up by police for threatening neighbor with knife and other bizarre behavior 11/20/63 and taken to Louisville General Hospital where it was necessary to put him in seclusion. He was transferred to Central State Hospital 11/21/63.

Wife says she has talked with patient and he will apparently be dismissed from Central State Hospital soon. Patient apparently being very ambivalent about this. Wants to come home and also likes security of hospital, I believe.

Wife also stated patient had told someone that a woman was taking him to Court for support of child she had by him some time ago. This seems a little improbable. Also said patient had been drinking the last few days.

This patient had been under the ITC care for 22 months at the time of his failure. He had adjusted quite well through the extensive efforts of his nurse. During the course of his care he had two encounters with the police and on both occasions ITC was able to carry him through. Despite his nurse's reservation about the advisability of marriage, patient married into a problematic situation.

The patient began to be faced with the added stress of marital responsibilities and children. He continued to work and made a relatively good adjustment up until the time his wife delivered their baby. When she was not able to return home from the hospital at the time he had expected, the patient created a public disturbance, threatened a neighbor, and demanded that the police hospitalize him. He was taken to the General Hospital and admitted to the psychiatric unit.

Case #111. Psychological Test Results

Tests	*Direction of Change*	*1st Testing Initial*	*2nd Testing 6 Mo.*	*3rd Testing 18 Mo.*	*4th Testing 24 Mo.*
Reaction time	+	3143	3190	3068	NSO
Maze QE	=	083	070	079	NSO
Maze IQ	+	066	074	083	NSO
WAIS, verbal IQ	−	089	083	081	NSO
WAIS, performance IQ	+	090	103	103	NSO
WAIS, full IQ	=	089	092	088	NSO
Bender Z	+	099	169	147	NSO

+ Improvement
− No improvement
= No consistent change
NSO No score obtained

Case #111. Medications

1/12/62. Trifluoperazine–2 milligrams, three times a day
2/16/62. Trifluoperazine–2 milligrams, four times a day
5/ 2/62. Trifluoperazine–2 milligrams, three times a day
8/22/62. Trifluoperazine–2 milligrams, twice a day

10/29/63. Chlorpromazine–100 milligrams, two capsules before retiring
Trifluoperazine–5 milligrams, three times a day

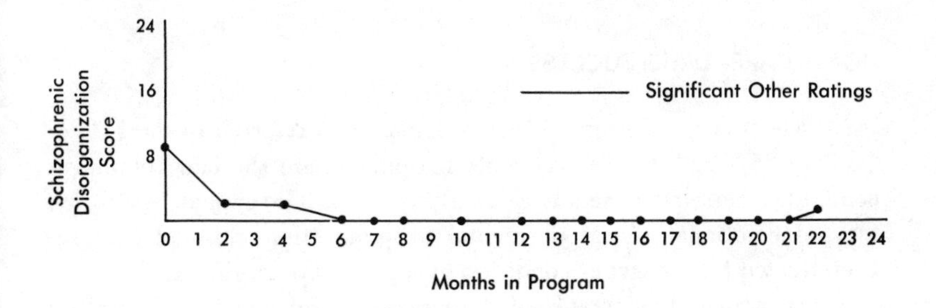

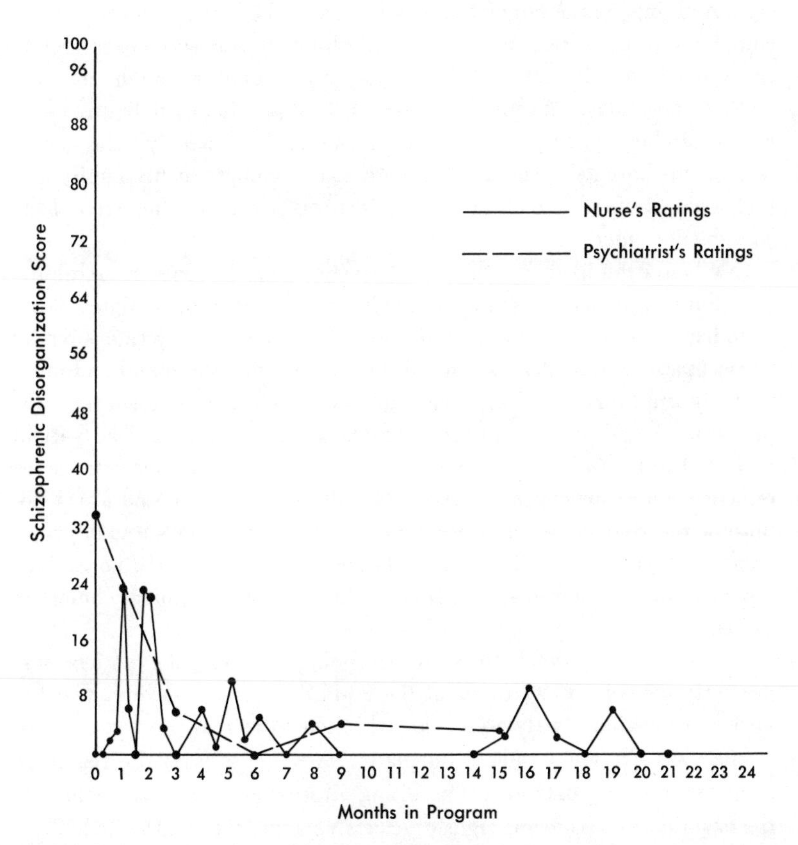

Patient #111. Schizophrenic Disorganization Ratings by Psychiatrist, Nurse, and Significant Other

HOME CARE—DRUG SUCCESS

Case #115, a 21-year-old white female was referred to the ITC on January 24, 1962, by Central State Hospital where she had voluntarily committed herself on the advice of a physician. The patient has no history of emotional illness or mental hospitalization although she has been treated for a nervous condition by a general practitioner.

The patient has completed 9 years of school and has never been employed outside the home. She has lived with her present husband in a common-law arrangement for 3 years although she was never legally separated from her first husband, a 60-year-old man whom she married while in her teens. The present husband, a high school graduate, works as a receiving clerk and reports an income of $115 weekly. The couple lives in his parents' 6-room house with four members of his family and their own 15-month-old child. The patient was pregnant when seen at the Treatment Center.

When examined by the staff psychiatrist, the patient exhibited symptoms of moderate anxiety, difficulty in concentrating, fatigue, hypochondriasis, phobias, withdrawal, slowed behavior, moderate suicidal preoccupation, some depression, mild ideas of influence, bland and questionably appropriate affect, clear and definite thinking disorder, suspiciousness, and major auditory and visual hallucinations. The patient appeared to be aware that she was ill but tended to consider extraneous or irrelevant problems as the cause. Her illness was diagnosed as schizophrenic reaction, acute undifferentiated type. The prognosis was improvement with continuing minor complaints. Prescription: trifluoperazine (Stelazine), 2 milligrams, four times a day. Study assignment: home on drugs.

While taking the battery of psychological tests, the patient was passively cooperative throughout the 80-minute testing period. She followed instructions fairly well, but exhibited little real interest in most of the tasks. No temperament fluctuations were observed; she remained calm, quiet, and controlled, exhibiting little emotional involvement in the examination. No overt signs of excessive anxiety were detected.

The first home visit by the nurse assigned to this patient occurred the next day.

1/25/62. Patient lives with her "in-laws"—a temporary arrangement. The house is a 6-room, 3-bedroom, 1-bath frame house, reasonably clean, furniture in fair condition. Mother-in-law was present during interview. Since it was my first visit, I did not suggest she leave.

2/2/62. Patient moved from her mother-in-law's house a few days ago, and is now living in a furnished lower flat. Consists of 4 rooms—2 bedrooms, one bath. Furnishings in fairly good condition and the general appearance is neat and orderly. Patient has a 15-month-old baby boy who was up and around, playing contentedly and seemed very well behaved. The interview was pleasant, atmosphere quiet and relaxing. Patient's greatest concern is over her first marriage from which she was never legally divorced.

2/5/62. Complains of slightly blurred vision on Saturday and today. No edema present. Patient has an appointment with a general practitioner Saturday, Feb. 10.

2/10/62. Was seen by general practitioner today. Nothing unusual to report.

2/23/62. Patient cheerful today. Optimistic about divorce.

3/2/62. Patient appears cheerful today. No special problems or complaints.

3/9/62. Patient cheerful. Looking forward to her "marriage."

3/16/62. No special complaints. No apparent change.

3/22/62. Patient upset because lawyer has not called her regarding divorce. She's very anxious to become legally married before birth of baby. "Husband" drank quite heavily last weekend which upset patient. She's afraid he might make a habit of it. Worries constantly that something might happen to him. For the past week patient has been tired and listless. Can't seem to interest herself in much of anything. Blames lawyer for her feelings and attitudes.

3/30/62. Condition appears the same. Nothing unusual to report.

4/6/62. No apparent change. Patient's main concern is divorce.

4/13/62. Condition appears the same.

4/19/62. Patient appears the same. Has no complaints.

4/27/62. Patient seen by psychiatrist for 3 month check-up. Medication increased to three times a day. Patient not sleeping well. Last month of pregnancy.

5/3/62. Patient visited at Norton's Infirmary. Apparently in false labor. Patient appears sad and depressed. Worries about everything. Is taking medication, administered by floor nurse.

5/11/62. Patient so pleased that divorce has been granted. Anxious now to become legally married. Worried about all the details. Patient now living in an apartment. Consists of 2 bedrooms, bath, living room, kitchen. Furnished sparsely, furniture in fair condition. Not too clean. Atmosphere musty, no screens on windows. Patient hesitates to open windows as child may tumble out. She is not too happy with apartment. Does not like the neighborhood.

5/18/62. Patient in an elated mood. Will be married by priest tonight.

5/24/62. Patient becoming restless and anxious to have baby. Confinement date May 23.

5/31/62. No special complaints.

6/7/62. Visit made in Norton's Infirmary. Patient delivered of 9 lb. 8 oz. baby boy June 2. Patient appears depressed, preoccupied today. States she dreamed last night that a man was trying to kill her. Awakened screaming. Nurse gave her a sleeping pill so that calmed her down. Appetite poor. Having difficulty voiding. Catheterized twice yesterday.

6/14/62. Patient states she has felt depressed this past week. Worried about baby because he cries a great deal. Complains of being tired all the time. Not getting enough sleep.

6/19/62. Patient fixing her evening meal. Home neat. Patient seemed in good spirit today; said she has been feeling pretty good. Stated her husband has been pretty good about helping her. Patient did not seem depressed. At times her face had a blank stare. She seemed pleased the nurse visited.

6/21/62. Patient complains of being tired all the time. Worried because she may be pregnant. Thinks if she becomes pregnant again, she'll die. Patient's husband's brother is living with them now. She is not too pleased about it as it means extra work for her and he is not helpful. Also feels he is a bad influence on her husband as they do quite a bit of drinking together.

6/28/62. Patient states she has slightly blurred vision and dizziness. Suggested she reduce medicine to 2 capsules daily rather than 3. Complains about apartment. Would like to move.

7/5/62. Patient upset and worried because she received a phone call from a man she dated several years ago. He was a married man, although patient denies knowledge of it at the time. Now she is afraid that her husband will find out about it. She states he threatened to kill her if she as much as looked at another man. Patient states she wrote her former "suitor" and his wife a note informing them of her baby's birth and that it what prompted the phone call.

7/12/62. Patient appears upset today. Husband's brother and child are now living with her and she feels the added work is too much for her. Neither man offers any assistance. She is unhappy with apartment because it is infested with roaches; they even get into the refrigerator. Husband refuses to move because he doesn't feel they can afford to. Patient resentful because the men drink over the weekend and the money spent could be used for paying bills. Suggested husband see social worker and will make arrangements.

7/18/62. Patient seems a little more cheerful today although is still upset over apartment and anxious to move. States roaches even got into her pill box and punctured capsules (this is not a delusion!) Nephew has left, so situation somewhat improved.

7/26/62. Patient complains of feeling tired today. No ambition or interest in anything. Worries constantly about her husband's weekend drinking sprees. Also afraid she might become pregnant again; would "drive me crazy if I did." States her obstetrician advised against having any more children. General appearance apathetic. Frowns frequently.

8/9/62. Complains of long periods of depression at various times since her baby was born. States she does not feel well; gives history of kidney trouble and other physical problems. Fatigued, unable to accomplish her homemaking duties. Her apartment is dirty and disorderly. Infested with roaches. She is apprehensive about possibility of being pregnant. She had sexual relations with husband 2 weeks after delivery. Environment condition offers very little to make her cheerful. Patient worries a great deal about the family debts. They still owe medical fee for delivery of older child. Her husband occasionally drinks on weekends and is verbally abusive to her. Apparently her husband has little insight or understanding of patient's mental condition. Patient states she has crying spells occasionally. She appeared on verge of weeping several times during interview.

8/23/62. Patient states she's been taking medication 4 X daily. Feels less nervous. Complains of lower back pain and "just not feeling good." Appears apathetic, little facial expression. Worries about becoming pregnant again.

9/5/62. Patient still unhappy with apartment and would like to move. Says she awakens during night hearing noises. Afraid someone is trying to break into apartment. Continues to worry about becoming pregnant.

9/21/62. Patient moved last week. Now lives on the first floor of a single house. Landlady lives upstairs. Consists of 2 bedrooms, living room, bathroom, kitchen. Furniture attractive and in good condition. Patient appeared cheerful and more content. Seems to be doing well.

10/4/62. Seems to be progressing well. Continues to have physical complaints. Has pain in side. Believes she'll eventually have to undergo surgery for removal of ovarian cyst.

10/19/62. Patient is worried that she might be pregnant! Doesn't really want another baby so soon as doesn't feel they can afford it. She is upset today because her mother and stepsisters have found out where she lives and she's afraid they will start "pestering" her. She visited her mother at the hospital a few days ago as mother called and said she was going to have surgery and would like to see patient. She still feels bitter toward mother for the way she was treated as a child.

11/1/62. No apparent change. Continues to worry about being pregnant. Hostile toward husband because he has started drinking again.

11/14/62. Patient complains of pain in chest and cardiac region. Also pain in stomach. Believes she has an ulcer. Complains also of nausea and lack of energy. Has an appointment with obstetrician next week. Worries that he may not accept her as a patient because she still owes him for the last baby.

11/29/62. Patient was seen by obstetrician last week. Is definitely pregnant. Patient seems to have accepted the fact that she is, and isn't too worried, although the thought of caring for three young children becomes overwhelming. Smiled inappropriately throughout interview. Did not have a great deal to say.

12/13/62. Patient states she is very tired and really looked it. Children whined and cried, coughed—both have colds—patient had elevation of temperature but said she did not have cold or sore throat. Gets up all hours of the night to give both children bottles; would rather do this than hear them cry. Has no schedule whatsoever with children. Small baby has not had immunizations. Reason for not doing so is they owe the doctor and she doesn't want to go back. Patient to see OB Dr. next week. Did SO with husband who was on vacation. He seems to think all is well—no problems, etc.

1/2/63. Patient called this A.M. Says for past few weeks she has been hearing voices and has been nervous and depressed. Psychiatrist (ITC) informed. Patient advised to increase medication to 2 capsules four times a day today and that medicine would be changed tomorrow when PHN makes home visit. Psychiatrist prescribed trifluoperazine (Stelazine) 5 mg. tid., tranylcypromine (Parnate) 10 mg., trihexyphenidyl (Artane) ½ tab. bid.

1/3/63. Patient appears depressed and upset today. Says for past few weeks she has been hearing voices, especially during night. Voices don't say anything in particular. Also hears people walking upstairs. Husband investigated, but found no one up there. Worries constantly about finances, and about her husband (he should have some cysts removed from face). Feels very discouraged. Children make her nervous. During interview she smiled inappropriately almost continuously. Appears listless and apathetic.

1/31/63. Patient states she is no longer bothered by noises or voices. Chief complaint is inability to sleep. Has a difficult time falling asleep and when she does, only sleeps about 2 hours. Becomes depressed occasionally. Grinned inappropriately throughout interview.

2/28/63. Patient appears about the same. Still not sleeping well although is taking Doriden as prescribed by obstetrician. Appears listless and apathetic—not much facial expression. Grins inappropriately.

3/28/63. Patient seems about the same. Says she's sleeping better. Not very conversive. Grins inappropriately. Worries a great deal.

4/25/63. Patient seems about the same. Says she has been depressed, but feeling better today. Was hospitalized for one day (past Tues.) for false labor. Appears apathetic. Not much facial expression.

5/23/63. Patient seems about the same. Little or no affect. Grins inappropriately. Sleeping better. Expects baby "any day."

6/27/63. (Since last visit patient has had child and been released from hospital.) Patient continues to appear listless and apathetic. Grins inappropriately, otherwise no facial expression. Many physical complaints.

7/23/63. Patient seems about the same. Says she hears voices at night (not talking directly to her) which frighten her. Somewhat depressed because she never goes anywhere. Tired all the time. Manages to take care of other small children fairly well. Continues to grin inappropriately.

9/16/63. Patient seems very listless and apathetic. Is depressed because she knows she's pregnant again. Upset also because they are moving again in December. Will be living in the "sticks" away from everyone.

10/16/63. Patient seems depressed today. Says she has the "flu," but husband doesn't think she's sick. Very discouraged because she never goes anywhere. Thinks she might have started to miscarry, as she had some bleeding last week. Was seen by OB. Says she sleeps poorly. Hears voices practically every night. They say bad things—like going to kill her or her house is on fire. Hears voices during day only occasionally. Continues to stare and grin inappropriately.

11/14/63. Patient states she is still nervous, disgusted, depressed. Due mainly to the fact that she never goes anywhere. Hostile toward husband for that reason. Says she still hears voices every night. They awaken her, frighten

Case #115. Psychological Test Results

Tests	*Direction of Change*	*1st Testing Initial*	*2nd Testing 6 Mo.*	*3rd Testing 18 Mo.*	*4th Testing 24 Mo.*
Reaction time	=	3297	3270	3346	3292
Maze QE	=	054	066	048	042
Maze IQ	=	058	058	053	058
WAIS, verbal IQ	=	067	065	067	067
WAIS, performance IQ	=	070	073	053	055
WAIS, full IQ	–	067	067	059	059
Bender Z	+	070	070	071	075

+ Improvement
– No improvement
= No consistent change

Case # 115. Medications

1/24/62. Trifluoperazine–2 milligrams, four times a day
5/ 1/62. Trifluoperazine–2 milligrams, three times a day

1/ 2/63. Trifluoperazine–5 milligrams, three times a day
Tranylcypromine–10 milligrams, one capsule before retiring
Trihexyphenidyl–2 milligrams, one-half capsule twice a day

2/ 4/63. Tranylcypromine–10 milligrams, three times a day
3/12/63. Trifluoperazine–5 milligrams, two capsules twice a day
8/ 8/63. Chlorpromazine–50 milligrams, one capsule before retiring

11/16/63. Trifluoperazine–5 milligrams, one capsule twice a day
Tranylcypromine–10 milligrams, twice a day

1/ 9/64. Chlorpromazine–50 milligrams, one capsule before retiring
Tranylcypromine–10 milligrams, one capsule twice a day
Trifluoperazine–5 milligrams, one capsule twice a day

her by saying "they" are going to kill her. Continues to grin inappropriately. Stares blankly.

12/13/63. No noticeable change. Says she still hears voices, but not as bad as before. Not as depressed.

1/10/64. No change. Still hears voices. Sleeps poorly. Depressed because she never goes anywhere.

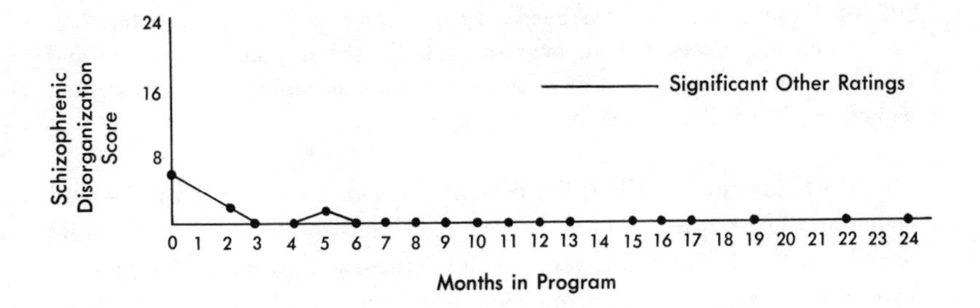

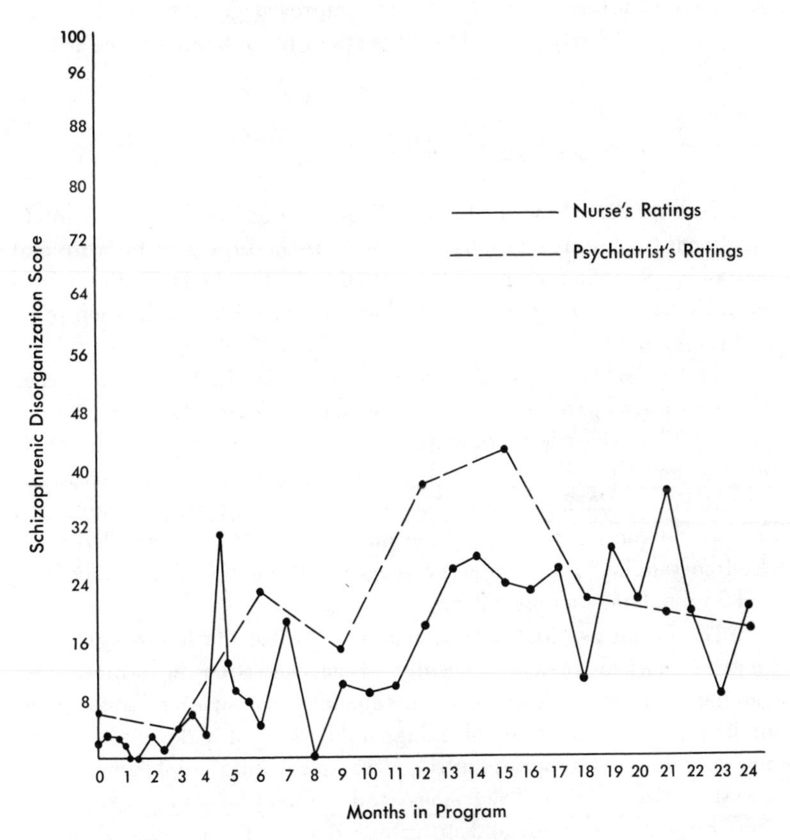

Patient #115. Schizophrenic Disorganization Ratings by Psychiatrist, Nurse, and Significant Other

2/7/64. Patient states she has been very ill. Was seen by a doctor who diagnosed stomach ulcers and an ovarian cyst. So she is taking medicine and feeling a little better. Continues to hear voices at night, but not as often as before. Otherwise, seems about the same.

On February 20, 1964, the patient was again examined by the staff psychiatrist. At this time the patient exhibited moderate anxiety, mild withdrawal and depression, tense facial expression, no ideas of influence, reserved, questionably appropriate affect, and auditory hallucinations questionably present. Her insight had improved greatly and the prognosis remained fairly good. After 2 years of home treatment the patient was released.

HOME CARE—DRUG SUCCESS

Case #122, a 46-year old male Negro was accepted by the Institute Treatment Center on February 14, 1962. At the urging of his wife and the family physician the patient admitted himself voluntarily to the hospital. He has no history of mental illness or mental hospitalization prior to this episode.

The patient is a college educated (Master's degree) schoolteacher who also works part time for the post office. He reports a monthly income of $762 which is supplemented by his wife who works as a substitute teacher. The wife is also college educated. The patient served in the Armed Forces during World War II and received an honorable discharge. He and his wife have been married for 18 years and have five children ranging in age from 17 years to 18 months. The family lives in a 5-room home that they own.

The initial psychiatric examination revealed the following: symptoms of marked anxiety, difficulty in concentrating, withdrawal, insomnia, depression, slowed speech, suicidal preoccupation, restlessness, anxious facial expression, blocking, mild ideas of influence, reserved and definitely inappropriate affect, clear and definite thinking disorder, unsystematized paranoid delusions, and auditory and visual hallucinations present to a major and disturbing degree. The amount of insight was moderate. The patient's illness was diagnosed as schizophrenic reaction, paranoid type, and the prognosis was for improvement with recurring minor complaints and difficulties. Prescription: trifluoperazine

(Stelazine), 2 milligrams, twice a day. Study assignment: home on drugs.

During the initial psychological examination, the patient was cooperative and appeared to be overtly calm and reserved. His attention, interest, and effort toward the tasks administered during the 100-minute testing period were good. Some hand tremor was observed. On verbal tests he expressed himself well even though he had a tendency to overelaborate.

As usual, the nurse assigned to this case visited the home the next day.

2/15/62. Family of 7 living in fairly neat and clean, adequately furnished frame cottage. Patient was scrubbing front porch. Patient friendly and receptive. Suggested he not work for at least another week. Denied most symptoms, but did say he became angry easily. Medication given.

2/22/62. Patient states he feels much better. Did not seem as hostile. Wants to go back to teaching Tues. 2/27, so told patient to come to ITC to see psychiatrist at 1 P.M., 2/23/62. Will not admit he has a mental illness. When asked what he tells friends he stated he says he's tired and nervous. Feels rested now and tries to give impression he is well. Medication given.

2/28/62. Patient states he has no complaints and did not admit to any symptoms. Still does not admit he has a mental illness. States he has enjoyed teaching this week and it has not bothered him. Says the childern at school have been unusually good and the other teachers are wonderful; however, wife states he has one teacher that is a dilly. Talked with wife and she feels that ITC has certainly helped him. He is not having hallucinations now she states. Patient has always denied this. Medication given.

3/7/62. Patient improved this week. More animated. Discussed juvenile delinquency. Talked about a program seen on TV the night before. Still does not admit any mental illness. Needs statement from ITC before going back to work at Post Office. Will call psychiatrist. Medication given.

3/14/62. Not too much change in patient. Does not seem as tense. Admitted there have been times when he felt that if he would let himself go he would explode.

3/21/62. Patient seemed a little more tense today, but could be because a significant other evaluation was done before he came home. In talking to the SO, I realized something I had failed to note in previous visits; *i.e.,* the patient does fix his face so you can't tell what he is thinking. He always smiles and doesn't meet your gaze too often. Is proud of oldest daughter who is graduating from high school. Seemed a little irritated because children kept coming into room. States he frequently smells gas fumes when others do not. Reveals little of his true feelings, but yet is friendly. Talked about his sister today and said that they were very close.

Impressions gained from significant other. Patient thinks he is well now, but has frequent temper tantrums mainly toward wife and is also suspicious. States they have not gotten along well for years. He gives her what money he wants her to have and she doesn't know what he does with the rest. SO dislikes patient's sister intensely and he has quite an attachment toward her. He plans to visit her soon.

3/28/62. No particular change in patient's condition apparent. Still thinks he smells gas occasionally. Admitted today for the 1st time that he heard voices that no one else heard, but not since he has been under ITC program. Says that he doesn't lose his temper as quickly.

4/3/62. Visit made in office at ITC today because patient had appointment with psychiatrist to sign some papers. No change noticed except that patient seemed happier today. Feel that mood change was due to visit being made at ITC rather than in home. The only emotion nurse notices about patient's feeling towards family is pride in oldest daughter's school grades and love for his sister.

4/11/62. Patient not home at time of home visit. Wife states he is doing very well. He occasionally has an emotional flare-up, but he seems calmer and rests better now. He has obtained a driver's permit and plans to learn to drive a car by June. Patient has no interest in recreational activities or hobbies and spends his leisure hours at home watching television. Wife is careful to avoid saying or doing anything that will antagonize patient.

4/18/62. Patient called ITC early P.M. to say he didn't teach today and nurse could visit earlier. Patient seemed to stutter and stammer more than usual. Stated it was due to his cold, but doubt this. Said that examiners from state visited school yesterday for grading purposes and that he knew in advance they were coming and it did not bother him. Doesn't know whether he can work at Post Office this summer or not. Seemed to be a little hostile about treatment received at Post Office. Had the feeling patient had regressed somewhat, but as usual, would not admit illness. Was confused about nurse's name when he called ITC. Patient realized he should have known and couldn't understand why he was mixed up.

4/25/62. Patient did not teach today. Had sick leave and wife worked. No noticeable change in patient. States he feels he is improving. He does apparently have periods of depression and some elation, but feels that events occur which make this justifiable. I left word for wife to call ITC to make appointment for SO form.

5/2/62. No apparent change in patient's condition.

5/9/62. Patient had no complaints. No apparent change.

5/16/62. No apparent change. Planning to work at Post Office this summer.

5/23/62. Very little change. Patient does seem a little improved. Patient working at Post Office now also and has been for almost a month. Has evaded answering this question. Apparently thought PHN would disapprove of 2 jobs. Wife has been teaching for him some days to help. Believe that wife's attitude toward patient has improved.

6/4/62. Visit made at office today since patient had appointment with psychiatrist today for 3 mos. check. No particular change noticed except patient always seems a little more tense after PHN has visited with wife. Has never admitted he is mentally ill.

6/13/62. No particular change in patient. States he feels better, thinks he has improved since coming to ITC. Still feel patient hides emotions from RN. Noted today that when RN probes, patient will switch and make flattering remarks concerning public health nurse.

6/22/62. Patient seems to be progressing well. Is studying to take exam at Post Office. He sorts and places mail in slots and is to be assigned to an area of approximately 595 cities in Kentucky. Was very talkative today and interested in telling and showing PHN about his job. Discussed possibility of his not passing exam the 1st time and patient stated he didn't feel it would bother or upset him too much.

7/6/62. Patient seems improved. More outgoing today. Talked more freely last 2 home visits about self, but still evades discussion of illness. Talked about experiences while in the Army, schooling and present job. States he likes to relax and be with others, but apparently patient and wife go out very little together. Social interests are apparently different. Very polite to nurse. PHN feels he must have taken a Dale Carnegie course at one time. For example, never fails to compliment RN about something during home visit. Patient says he is not as tense and does not appear to be. Does not plan to have 2 full time jobs this winter.

7/20/62. Patient seemed more relaxed today. Took exam at Post Office Monday, 7/16, and made a grade of 99. Feels much relieved. Managed to get SO today. Patient always seems rather suspicious and resentful when SO (significant other) interviewed.

8/3/62. Patient appeared in cheerful mood and friendly. Conversation limited, but readily answered questions. Feels medication is effective in keeping him relaxed so that he is able to get adequate rest. The children do not agitate him. He is taking driving lessons from his 18-year-old daughter. Enjoys driving now. Expects to work as substitute teacher this fall. States holding 2 full time jobs is too much for him. Denies problems or symptoms.

8/17/62. Patient was friendly and as talkative as he ever is. Never admits he is mentally ill and tries to give the impression everything is wonderful. Tells only what he wants to tell. Apparently patient is very reserved by nature. Reads a great deal and is rather anti-social. Has no close friends apparently.

9/14/62. Patient seemed happier than usual today and more contented. Is teaching temporarily in addition to Post Office job. Substituting for teacher who will probably be off for some time. No particular problems.

10/12/62. Patient still teaching as substitute and working at Post Office. Did not feel too well today. Felt patient was a little hostile and anxious to terminate interview. Never feel as if patient is really open and frank. SO states patient seems to be doing well. Patient says he takes his medicine.

11/9/62. No change in patient last few visits. Seems to be functioning well. Has had 2 jobs lately. Discussed over-working again with him. For the 1st time, patient admitted he was mentally ill. Feels he would recognize symptoms if he became ill again.

12/7/62. Did not do TPR (temperature), etc. today because patient got home at approximately 2:55 P.M. from teaching and had to punch in at Post Office at 3:30 P.M. Warned patient about working too many hours. Said he wasn't going to do any more teaching until after 1st of year. SO interview today. Rather bitter toward patient. Told of contracting gonorrhea from him after birth of 1st child. Patient and SO apparently have poor rapport. SO likes to party; patient doesn't. SO goes to taverns frequently and at present seems to like a certain man. Patient apparently unaware of this.

1/4/63. No particular change noted. Patient has tendency to work at 2 jobs too much. Became ill last year while working at Post Office and teaching. Cautioned him against this.

2/8/63. No particular change noted in patient. Smiles sweetly and you get the feeling that he relates very little. Does say he has improved over the past year and has more insight regarding his limitations.

3/4/63. Patient says everything getting along fine. I believe patient is working too hard however. Teaching most of the time now in addition to regular job at Post Office. Wonder if patient doesn't want to work rather than stay home. Wife has talked about cleaning house up since patient came on program and hasn't done so yet. Wife likes to party and apparently does so. Patient controls money. Rapport between patient and SO seems poor. Children seem to be closer to father than mother. Wife apparently resents this. Feel that she probably needs help also.

4/2/63. No apparent change.

4/29/63. No apparent change.

5/27/63. No change noted. Patient has worked as postal clerk from 4 P.M. to midnight and teaching school fairly regularly all winter and has seemed to do fairly well. Has seemed improved physically as well as mentally and has used very little of his annual leave. Says he takes his medicine.

6/24/63. No particular change noted. Wife seems rather hostile toward patient. Says he does not trust her with money and that patient is worried about bills. Patient very close and indulgent toward oldest daughter and wife resents this. Patient and wife apparently have poor rapport. Patient has always been very polite and friendly toward nurse, but I have never felt he expressed his true emotions to me. Wife seems to feel patient is like this toward her also. Patient seems to keep a tight control on himself. Doubt if patient is taking medication as prescribed. Will talk about his work, but not his illness.

7/22/63. No apparent change.

8/28/63. No particular change noted. Seems to be functioning well. Talked more than usual today. Patient taking tablets now and says they don't do him as much good as the capsules even though he has been told medicine is the same.

9/25/63. No change noted. Seems to be functioning well.

10/23/63. No particular change noted. Have the feeling patient takes very little of his medicine. Patient apparently seldom talks of his real feelings to anyone. Seems to have a tremendous drive to advance in job and do work above average. Studying to take supervisor's test at Post Office. Purchased books and applying himself. Likes to talk and explain about these things. Anxious for children to do well in school. Quite proud of daughter in college.

11/20/63. No particular change noted. Apparently takes very little medicine. Does not believe he is ill. Rapport between patient and wife still poor. Wife very hostile toward husband. States she stays with him so he will support children. She apparently has her fun on the side. Keeps this from patient. Is a little afraid of what he might do if he found out.

12/18/63. Patient not home. Working overtime at Post Office. Left medicine with wife who said patient doing about the same.

1/16/64. No change noted in patient. Talked quite a bit today. Seems to like being asked questions about his job and other things (not his illness). Enjoys taking yearly postal exam. Do not believe patient taking medicine regularly. Evades answering.

2/19/64. No particular change noted. Wife states patient loses temper readily. Apparently poor rapport between patient and wife. Patient doing quite a bit of substitute teaching in addition to regular job. Family has fairly good income, but little to show for it and during 2 yrs. patient has been with ITC he has always been concerned about bills. Patient manages and handles his income. Think he is relieved to be off the program.

On March 3, 1964, 2 years after being accepted on the home care study, the patient was seen for the last time by the psychiatrist. At this time he exhibited mild anxiety, no ideas of influence, reserved but appropriate affect, and only questionable suspiciousness. His insight had improved and his prognosis remained good. He was released from the program.

Case #122. Psychological Test Results

Test	*Direction of Change*	*1st Testing Initial*	*2nd Testing 6 Mo.*	*3rd Testing 18 Mo.*	*4th Testing 24 Mo.*
Reaction time	+	3350	3270	3258	3228
Maze QE	+	054	042	052	048
Maze IQ	+	114	129	129	129
WAIS, verbal IQ	=	122	110	110	148
WAIS, performance IQ	+	079	096	083	105
WAIS, full IQ	+	101	103	100	128
Bender Z	+	071	125	122	111

\+ Improvement
− No improvement
= No consistent change

Case #122. Medications

2/14/62. Trifluoperazine–5 milligrams, twice a day
1/9/64. Trifluoperazine–5 milligrams, twice a day
1/16/64. Trifluoperazine–5 milligrams, one capsule daily in A.M.

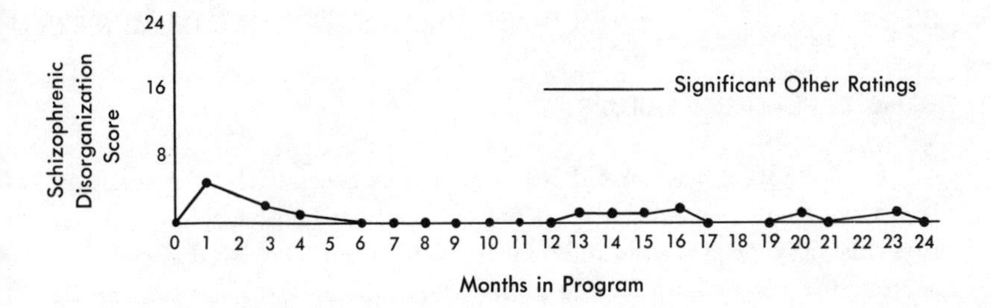

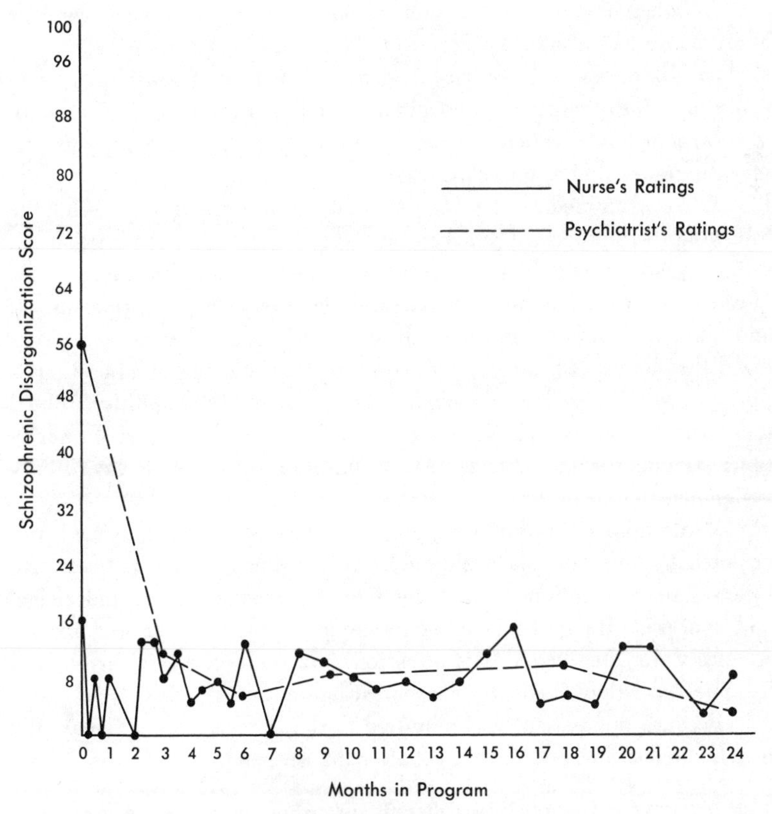

Patient #122. Schizophrenic Disorganization Ratings by Psychiatrist, Nurse, and Significant Other

HOME CARE—DRUG FAILURE

Case #136, a 34-year-old white male was accepted by the Institute Treatment Center on March 16, 1962. The patient had been hospitalized after his 60-year-old widowed mother with whom he lived secured a warrant for his pick-up by the police. The mother did this as a result of what she felt was the patient's deteriorating condition and unmanageability. The patient had been hospitalized at least four times since 1950 and has also received psychiatric care as an outpatient.

Although the patient has not worked steadily in a year, he is a house painter by trade. A veteran of the Armed Services, he received a medical discharge (psychiatric) and collects a monthly disability compensation. Both the patient and his mother live on this $122 per month in a 5-room house which the mother owns. The patient completed the seventh grade and has never married.

When examined at the ITC, the patient was found to exhibit the following: symptoms of marked anxiety, difficulty in concentrating, fatigue, phobias, withdrawal, insomnia, agitation, slowed behavior, mild ideas of influence, completely flat and definitely inappropriate affect, and clear and definite thinking disorder. Although the patient recognized that he was ill, he saw the cause as lying outside of himself. His illness was diagnosed as schizophrenic reaction, acute undifferentiated type. The prognosis was improvement with minor difficulties. Prescription: Trifluoperazine (Stelazine), 5 milligrams, twice a day. Study assignment: home on drugs.

While taking the initial psychological tests the patient seemed well oriented to time and place although he was almost mute at times. He followed the instructions without comment but seemed unsure, indecisive, and confused. He spoke in a monotonous slurred manner and his responses were often vague. His attention, interest, and effort varied, and he appeared to have difficulty concentrating on some tasks.

Because this patient was admitted to the program on a Friday, the first home visit did not occur until after the weekend.

3/20/62. Patient friendly and coherent throughout interview. Appeared to be in cheerful mood and cooperative. Taking medication as directed. He answered all questions willingly. He made no spontaneous comments and permitted nurse to direct the conversation. He said he was a painter by trade and would like to go back to work. He presents an unkempt and disordered appearance; however, he was not aware of this. From the condition of his home his appearance was in keeping with the environment. Patient lives in 5-room, ramshackle cottage with his aged mother. Extremely dirty and cluttered with broken down furniture. An odor of excreta permeated the place. There were piles of soiled clothes and trash scattered throughout. The general appearance of the home is deplorable.

Interview with patient's mother reveals patient is a member of (a small religious sect), and he feels he has the calling to preach. Religion is a major factor in his life.

3/27/62. Patient cheerful, friendly, and cooperative. Taking medication as prescribed. Has followed last week's suggestion about keeping busy and cleaning up the house. He appears receptive to advice. He asks that the doctor complete the VA form so that he may apply for pension until he is able to secure a full-time job. He drew a disability pension when he was discharged from the Air Force for nervousness.

4/3/62. Patient appeared friendly and in good contact. Cheerful mood. Is very pleased that he has part-time job with former employer as maintenance helper. Earning approximately $12/wk. Patient talked on various subjects —such as filing his income tax return, of planning to sell a lot he owns because he cannot afford to build on it, of his plans to buy a cottage similar to the one his mother owns for rental purposes. He is anxious to obtain his pension from the VA and asked if the doctor completed the form. He said that since we suggested he avoid places that are very noisy and over-stimulating such as the church meetings where there is handclapping and body motions, he thought he would attend another church where the services were quiet, such as the Catholic Church. He was very impressed with the Sisters at St. Anthony's Hospital when he was a patient there. He also commented that the people in the church where he went knew he had been a patient in a mental hospital and they watched him when he participated in the handclapping, etc., as though he may overdo it.

He sometimes drives his boss' car. He says he feels much better now that he has a little spending money.

4/10/62. Working as painter. In cheerful mood today. Enthusiastic and talking about his work and future plans today. States he is not driving automobile since we last talked to him. PHN emphasized danger of drinking. Patient did not admit drinking, but his mother said she saw him with a bottle of beer the other night. Patient expresses a series of ideas of what he wants to do, such as to take dancing lessons, to join the Masons in order to meet a more select group of people, to go into business for himself, etc., with apparently no consideration of the time involved in attaining these objectives. It's sort of random thinking at the period of time he is expressing them.

4/17/62. Patient in cheerful mood. Working full time with former employer as a painter and maintenance helper. Home is a mess. Patient is trying to paint and straighten up place, but gets no help from mother. He is also taking accordion lessons. States the tranylcypromine is effective. Getting his necessary rest at night and feels calmer during day.

4/24/62. Patient working regularly every day. Becomes restless when not employed. Feels medication is effective in keeping him calm. His mother states he was irritable when he returned from work yesterday evening. After taking his medicine, he settled down and went to sleep. He spends very little time at home except when he is sleeping. Mother states last week patient was talking about selling his lot. He knows he cannot do this without his mother's consent, which she will not give. He commented that since he can't sell his ground or do anything else, he might as well kill himself.

5/1/62. Denies complaints or problems. Continues working everyday. Appears in cheerful mood. Seems a little preoccupied in that he wants to be on the move away from his home and back to work. He comes home from work just long enough for nurse's visit. Taking medication as directed.

Mother feels he is considerably improved. Describes it as getting more like his former self. "Coming out of his mental illness."

Home is dirty and disorderly.

5/8/62. Patient appears in cheerful mood. Continues to work everyday. Becomes restless and dissatisfied when not working.

Home is very dirty and disorderly again. Patient apparently takes no interest in his home. He implies he spends all his time away from home except when he sleeps. He eats most of his meals in a neighborhood restaurant. States he is getting along better with his mother. Taking medication as prescribed.

5/15/62. Patient appears cheerful. Taciturn, answers questions. Conversation is not spontaneous. Denies problems or complaints. Replies he is feeling well physically and mentally. Working regularly every day.

5/22/62. Patient in cheerful mood. Continues to work every day. Participates in recreational activities. Taking dancing lessons once or twice a week. Goes fishing on Sundays. Plans to go swimming this summer. Patient is restless in that he wants to get a better paying job. Wants to go into business for himself as a painter for a real estate business.

Patient appears a little more secure in interpersonal relationships.

Says he feels people accept him now. He is not as sensitive and self-conscious as previously. His mother feels he is getting along well. Says he is more settled and relaxed.

5/29/62. Patient denies symptoms. Not working this week because employer is angry with him for not going fishing Sunday. Advised patient to inquire at employment agency for more desirable employment. Also gave him referral to State Vocational Rehabilitation. Patient becomes very restless and anxious when not working. Urine positive for dye.

6/5/62. No apparent change in patient. Agreeable and quiet. Working this week. Was irritable and restless last week when he was not working.

6/12/62. Patient had no complaints today. Appeared happy and admitted to no problems. Talked some about his work as a painter and other activities. Said he bowled, swam, danced, and played the accordion. Said he drank occasionally. Cautioned him against this and why. Said he was going to the Vocational Rehabilitation Center today.

6/19/62. Patient is presently employed by construction company. Doing same type work. He appears satisfied and enthusiastic in new job. Mother states he is more relaxed now. Taking medicine as prescribed. Patient occasionally appears preoccupied during the interview.

6/26/62. Patient oriented. Appears preoccupied during interview. Sometimes requires asking question twice to secure his attention. His answers to direct questions relating to his illness and treatment indicate some indifference in his attitude. He feels he would have done as well at home without the treatment he has received at home. He does not feel hospitalization would have been necessary or appropriate for him.

7/3/62. Patient continues to work regularly at part-time job. PHN suggests that patient apply to State Employment Office for more permanent job. He admits his present employer is too demanding, causing patient to be nervous and tense when he is working for him. Patient generally appears unemotional, with poverty of thought. His facial expression is quizzical and anxious throughout interview. When asked about his medication, he says he thinks it helps him.

7/10/62. Patient in apparent cheerful mood. Understands he has appointment with psychiatrist 7/11 at 1:30 P.M. Has job to paint houses. Appears pleased that he was given responsible job. Patient understands that nurse will visit him every 2 weeks in future.

7/24/62. Patient appears in apathetic mood. Has been without work for approximately 2 weeks. He is preoccupied with desire to find work. Has made contact with Voc. Rehab. Patient was denied pension from VA. He blames his mother for not "helping" him get the pension. He has been more irritable and restless. He feels capable of working full time if he could find a job he'd like to do. States he would like to drive a truck.

8/7/62. Patient appears in cheerful mood. Emotionally flat. No interest in his home environment. Has made no attempt to clean up rubbish in home or yard. No plans for future, but repeats he wants to get a regular job. Would like to be a truck driver. Patient is well oriented and has good memory for past events.

8/21/62. Patient is working irregularly. Has had no further contact with Voc. Rehab. since initial interview more than 2 weeks ago. States he is irritable and restless when not working. Feels he is getting along all right and could do without his medication. However, he is taking it as prescribed. He denies symptoms of emotional illness. Patient appears passively cooperative.

9/4/62. Patient working irregularly. When he is not working he is irritable, restless, and sometimes depressed. He has had no further communication from Voc. Rehab. since the initial interview. He is indifferent to surroundings and has made no attempt to clean up the debris in and around his home. He is taking his medicine, but thinks he could get along just as well without it.

9/18/62. Patient not working. Has not heard from Voc. Rehab. since initial interview approximately 1 mo. ago. Appears chereful and friendly. Answers questions with minimal responses. Denies symtpoms. Speech is limited to answering questions.

SO (significant other) states he seems more relaxed and contented at home than formerly when he was not working. He is attending a church and has been reading the Bible, although he does not seem to be preoccupied with religion.

10/2/62. Has been working regularly for past 2 weeks. Had evaluation at Voc. Rehab. yesterday. Patient has no complaints or problems. He is satisfied with progress. His facial expression showed pleasure when he was told nurse would come at intervals of 4 wks. now.

SO feels he is doing well.

10/30/62. Patient appears to be functioning at normal level. Working as painter's helper whenever jobs are available. He really wants a regular job. Denies symptoms. Appears relaxed and cheerful.

SO is pleased with patient's behavior and progress. Taking medicine as prescribed.

11/27/62. Patient states he is not taking his medicine. He is apparently experiencing a religious hysteria. Quoting Bible to back up answers for reason his attitude toward treatment has changed. He admits feeling this way for 2 or 3 weeks. He is attending church daily. Becomes very agitated and emotional when discussing religion. He claims he has the gift of speaking an unknown tongue. Pressed on this, he used some gibberish, ending with "Thank you, Jesus." He is of the opinion that he is healed by faith. He is praying for the power to drive out devils and be given the power to heal.

In discussing topics other than religion, he is meek and cooperative, although emphatic about not taking his medicine. He accepted an appointment to see the doctor tomorrow. He admits not wanting to return to hospital, but refused to take choice of hospitalization or taking medicine. His mother feels that refusal of Social Security may have triggered patient into this episode. Patient works irregularly, but has not had a regular job for years. He has had nothing to do recently, but attend the church. Patient was also apparently rejected by the Voc. Rehab. after initial interview.

When asked to leave the room so that nurse could interview mother, he became very hostile and refused, saying that since the questions were about him, he should be present to hear them. In order not to upset him further, the mother's interview was dropped. This is the first time he has refused this request. Patient denies hallucinations and depression.

Patient is delusional in that he believes he has special powers such as speaking unknown tongue. He does not hear commands from God; God speaks to him through the Bible. He expects to have the power to heal and to drive out devils sometime in the future.

12/3/62. Patient appears quiet and more relaxed. States he is taking his medicine now although it's against his will. He continues to remain at home and reads the Bible, except when he goes to church.

He is not working and apparently he hasn't anything else to do except read the Bible. It would be well if he could find employment.

Urine specimen obtained. Positive for drugs.

12/18/62. Patient is taking his medicine only to "please" the doctor. He denies he is ill now and feels he was cured through Jesus. He uses the Bible to affirm this. He is on a religious jag. He is calm and unemotional now. He is more cooperative and less suspicious than he was 3 weeks ago. General appearance and behavior are improved.

1/15/63. Patient appears cheerful and content. Offers no complaints. Denies emotional problems. Seems to have adjusted to staying at home. Takes medicine as directed. Apparently has no social activities. Goes to church for meetings. Does not visit relatives or friends. He appears relaxed and is quiet except for answering questions. When asked about his feelings relating to nurse's visit and taking medicine, he admits he would like to be discharged. States he would like his freedom. Continues to read the Bible.

Patient goes to unemployment office at intervals to find job. No success.

2/12/63. Patient seems to be on quite a religious kick yet. Wanted to know when nurse was "saved." Mother said when patient gets religious, he doesn't go to dances or taverns. Mother quite concerned about patient giving money and clothes to 2 religious friends. It seems unbelievable that patient can look so neat and seem so clean and live in such a dirty, messy hovel.

3/12/63. Patient in cheerful mood, in good contact. Appears relaxed and attentive. Answered questions easily. He does not converse spontaneously nor present any ideas. He is quiet except for his answering. The information elicited is that patient is grossly preoccupied with religion which he describes as an emotional type of worship consisting of loud singing, dancing, shouting, prophesying, clapping of hands and other forms of demonstrating. He attends these meetings 4 or 5 times per week. His only recreation at home is Bible reading. He admitted speaking, which he refers to as "preaching," on street corners several times in the past weeks. He said people generally are inattentive, but this is the only way to bring religion to the people. He quoted a few passages in the Bible to justify his reasons for this. He says he is content and happy although he admits he does worry about not working sometimes.

Throughout interview patient answered questions calmly and with little emotion—in contrast to his behavior during a previous interview, when he became very agitated and emotionally stimulated describing his religious experiences.

For his mental health patient should have some sort of employment.

Patient is taking his medication. The period he discontinued taking it, he frankly told us.

4/11/63. Patient is adamant in his refusal to take his prescription. He demands his release from Institute Treatment Center.

Patient's resistance is impregnable. He is solely dependent upon his fanatical religious beliefs that by faith alone he is cured and he has no need for medical assistance. His speech was well controlled, and his manner was calm.

Shortly after his home visit the patient's mother died. All attempts to get the patient into a supervised home failed since other family mem-

Case #136. Psychological Test Results

Tests	Direction of Change	1st Testing Initial	2nd Testing 6 Mo.	3rd Testing 18 Mo.	4th Testing 24 Mo.
Reaction time	+	3360	3176	3100	NSO
Maze QE	+	068	065	062	NSO
Maze IQ	+	070	122	122	NSO
WAIS, verbal IQ	+	087	095	104	NSO
WAIS, performance IQ	+	072	084	083	NSO
WAIS, full IQ	+	079	089	096	NSO
Bender Z	+	076	109	137	NSO

\+ Improvement
− No improvement
= No consistent change
NSO No score obtained

Case #136. Medications

3/19/62. Trifluoperazine–5 milligrams, twice a day
4/10/62. Tranylcypromine–10 milligrams, before retiring
12/12/62. Trifluoperazine–5 milligrams, twice a day

bers refused to take any responsibility. The final report on this patient was written by the staff social worker:

5/3/63. A few weeks prior to this date, the patient's mother died which left him unsupervised in the home. He came in shortly thereafter to be seen by the doctor and to be interviewed by both the nurse and me. The patient was on an extremely religious bent and refused to talk about taking medication, stating that God would take care of him. It was later learned that he is fasting and is not taking medication. He calmly asked the nurse that she not visit him in the future and politely turned down offers of help from us. We were able to secure from him the brother's telephone number, and I later got in touch with his brother's wife. The brother's wife told me that she did not know if her husband would take any action but suggested that I get in touch with the patient's sister.

The sister later called me, and I reiterated that it was essential that the patient live in a supervised home, be given his medication, and that it was up to the family members to do this. We stated, if such a situation could not be arranged, it would be necessary for the patient to be returned to the

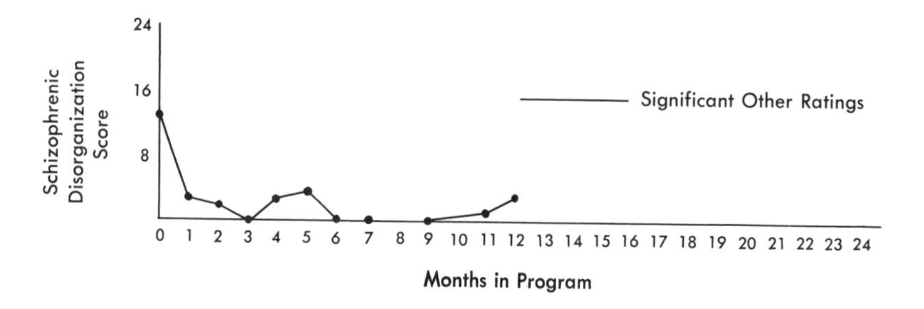

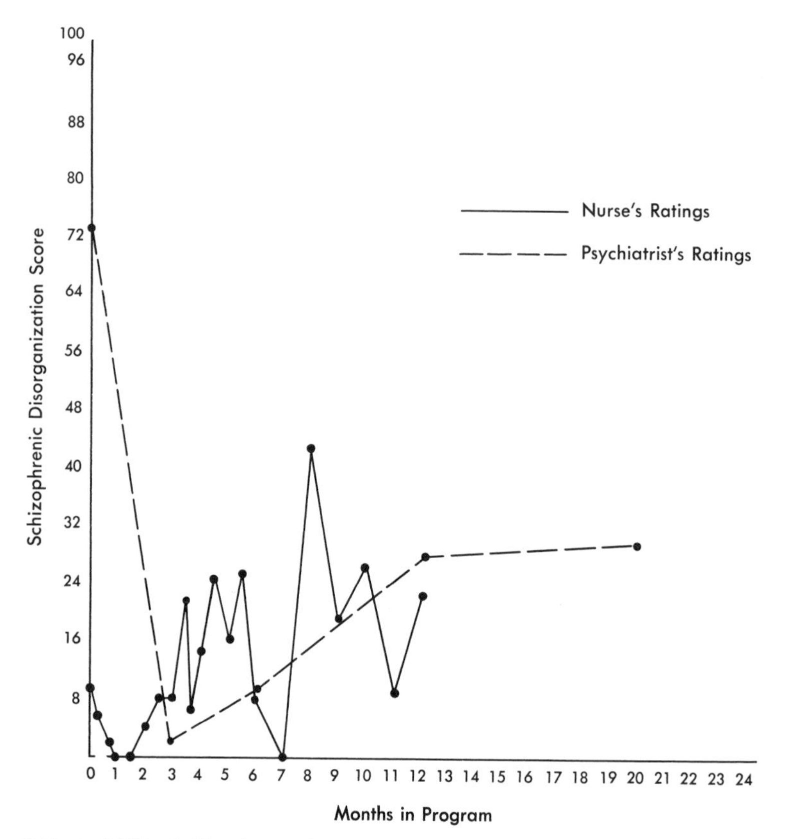

Patient #136. Schizophrenic Disorganization Ratings by Psychiatrist, Nurse, and Significant Other

hospital. I asked that the brother call me since the sister stated she did not have the time nor was she able to do anything for her brother. A few weeks passed and no word was heard from the brother and the patient continued to live alone in his mother's house.

A last letter was written by me to the patient's brother repeating the urgency of placing this patient in some supervised situation. An offer of help was again extended to helping the family in any way that we could. The same date this letter was mailed to the brother, the sister called, stating the patient's home was going to be sold and the patient would be "left out in the street." I told her that the remaining possibility then would be for the patient to be returned to the hospital. I gave her instructions on how to accomplish this, but she told me she did not know if she would have the time to follow through on it. Nevertheless I called Louisville General Hospital and told them there was the possibility that this lady would be in regarding the patient.

Although the patient had periodic difficulties while being treated at home, he may well have been able to weather the latest episode if there had been some home supervision. While he was taking his medication his behavior was acceptable. Once he stopped, he deteriorated. Since he obviously would not continue to take the prescribed medication without some supervision in the home, the family's refusal to be responsible for him forced ITC to recommend immediate hospitalization.

HOME CARE—DRUG FAILURE

Case #146, a 43-year-old white housewife was admitted to the home care study on April 13, 1962. After voluntarily admitting herself to Central State Hospital she was referred to the Institute Treatment Center. The patient had a history of 11 previous hospitalizations beginning when she was 24 years of age. The present episode developed over a short period of time, and the symptoms were severe enough to cause patient and her husband to seek hospital admission.

The patient, one of nine children, has a junior high school education and has been married for 20 years. She has given birth to seven children, four of whom (sons 6 and 16, daughters 14 and 18) live with the parents in a 3½-room house owned by the family. The patient's husband works as a grocery clerk and has a weekly income of $40.17.

At the time of the initial psychiatric examination by the ITC staff psychiatrist, the patient's symptoms included marked anxiety, difficulty in concentrating, fatigue, withdrawal, insomnia, marked depression, slowed and stuporous behavior, and bland and inappropriate affect. The psychiatrist felt that she had some insight into her illness but was unable to give any explanation of it. The diagnosis was schizophrenic reaction, schizo-affective type, and the prognosis was for improvement, but the additional statement was made that with stress the symptoms may recur. Prescription: trifluoperazine (Stelazine), 5 milligrams, three times a day. Study assignment: home on drugs.

During the initial psychological examinations the patient seemed oriented to time and place. She was polite but expressed opposition to some tasks. Her cooperation seemed to vacillate, and interest, attention, and effort were often lacking. She had little to say throughout the 65-minute testing period. Although her verbal quality was fair, her general lack of expression resulted in some responses being unclear and vague.

As usual, the home treatment of this patient began immediately with the nurse's first visit occurring the next day.

4/14/62. First interview. Patient pleased to see PHN and happy to be on ITC program. Appeared somewhat nervous and tense. States she feels depressed most of the time and broods over death of her 11-year-old son last year. Says medication seems to relax her.

4/19/62. Patient had been crying when nurse arrived. Emotionally disturbed—agitated, anxious, apprehensive because 18-year-old daughter remained away from home until 4 A.M. When she returned, (patient's husband) and daughter had an argument about this, and daughter said she was going to leave home. Parents do not know where she is or whether she plans to return. Patient's husband is concerned about effect this is having on his wife. Patient answered questions coherently and was in good contact throughout interview. She yawned frequently and said she was very sleepy. She feels the medicine is effective is calming her nerves. Her eyes were red and pupils contracted. Patient denies hallucinations and delusions.

Interview with patient's husband. He is aware of patient's complaints of nausea and upset stomach. She has been cooking the meals but neglects other household chores. Said she has always been careless about housekeeping. He is gravely concerned about effect daughter's leaving will have on his wife. When he is at work there is no one with patient except younger children. He said the children resent their mother—make fun of her and talk about her illness. She is aware of their attitude toward her. Husband said they do not do this when he is home.

4/26/62. Patient states she is sleepy most of the time. However, she feels she needs the medication *tid.* (three times a day) as prescribed. She said she noticed the difference (she was more nervous) when she took the medicine *bid.* (twice a day) for 2 days as psychiatrist advised last week. It did not make any difference with her A.M. nausea when she reduced the dosage. PHN suggested that patient eat several soda crackers upon arising and to eat a hard cooked egg an hour or so later instead of the fried egg she is used to eating. She may have better luck in keeping it on her stomach. Patient feels she is doing well at home. Has no complaints of being nervous or emotional. Has been doing the regular cooking, washing and some ironing. Is not able to do all the housekeeping chores alone. She has gone out in the car with her husband for short errands but does not wish to visit friends or relatives except her parents. Has no desire to take short walks in the neighborhood.

Interview with patient's husband. He feels patient is gradually showing some improvement. He verified what patient told nurse about herself. He feels pleased that she is able to do as much as she does. He says she is showing some interest in her environment. He states she is occasionally a little sassy which he feels is a good indication. The children are showing more understanding of their mother's condition and are willing to help with household duties.

5/3/62. Patient has no desire to get out in crowds or to take walks in neighborhood. She is doing the cooking, a little ironing, very little housework. Her major complaint is a quivering of her legs. It appears to be minor muscle contractions apparent to observer. She appears very drowsy.

5/6/62. (Patient's husband) called about 10:30 P.M. Sunday night and said he was going to take his wife back to Central State because she couldn't sleep and was keeping them all up and that we just didn't know how she acted. He said that usually after she had been taking medicine for a while this is the way she would act and wouldn't we advise him to take her back. I told him we would not be the ones to make that decision. He then said that he had a chance to get his old job back tomorrow and he would be holding down two jobs, and he couldn't cope with her. He felt that we had been very nice to him and his wife but thought he would go ahead and take her back to the hospital.

Patient was returned to hospital by husband on May 6, 1962. She was admitted and released 1 week later. On June 2, the patient's former ITC nurse visited the family and wrote the following report:

Patient's husband states that his wife became depressed, hyperactive, and sleepless after she visited her son's grave. These symptoms were present for 3 days following, and decided that his wife should have immediate medical treatment. He took her to Central State Hospital. After examination, patient's husband stated the doctor concluded the patient's medication was too strong for her. He described it as causing a "muscular stiffness." He prescribed Mellaril, two tablets at hour of sleep. After a week at Central State Hospital she was sent home on her present medication.

Patient appears cheerful, well oriented and interested in family and environment. She is functioning normally and managing and organizing all her daily activities. Patient and family are well satisfied with present treatment and situation (refers to State Hospital outpatient treatment).

Twenty-three days after being admitted to the program, this patient was returned to the hospital by her husband. The chronic nature of her illness and her history of numerous hospitalizations were difficult handicaps for the home treatment program to overcome. In addition, this case illustrates the effect that significant family members can have on patient success or failure. Both the ITC nurse and social worker felt that the patient was making some improvement on home care but that the attitude of her husband was not conducive to continued treatment in the home. He complained that the patient was lazy, "just wanted to stay in bed all of the time," and was not efficient in her household chores. Perhaps the patient could have functioned adequately on home care if the husband had been less demanding and more tolerant during the difficult period of adjustment.

Case #146. Psychological Test Results

Tests	*Direction of Change*	*1st Testing Initial*	*2nd Testing 6 Mo.*	*3rd Testing 18 Mo.*	*4th Testing 24 Mo.*
Reaction time	+	3258	3225	NSO	NSO
Maze QE	–	026	042	046	NSO
Maze IQ	=	042	058	042	NSO
WAIS, verbal IQ	+	076	078	078	NSO
WAIS, performance IQ	+	057	069	083	NSO
WAIS, full IQ	+	065	072	079	NSO
Bender Z	–	110	097	064	NSO

+ Improvement
– No improvement
= No consistent change
NSO No score obtained

Case #146. Medications

4/12/62. Trifluoperazine–5 milligrams, twice a day

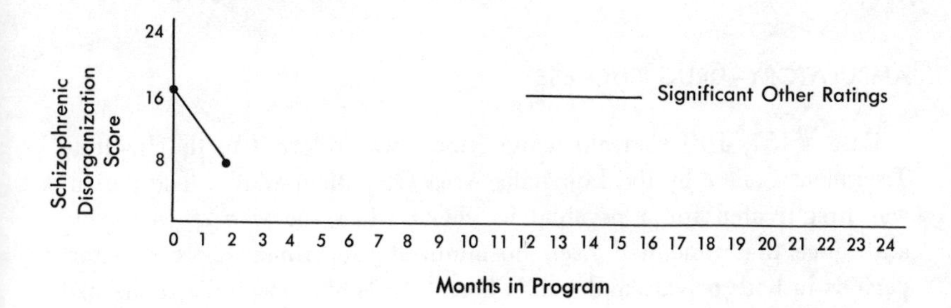

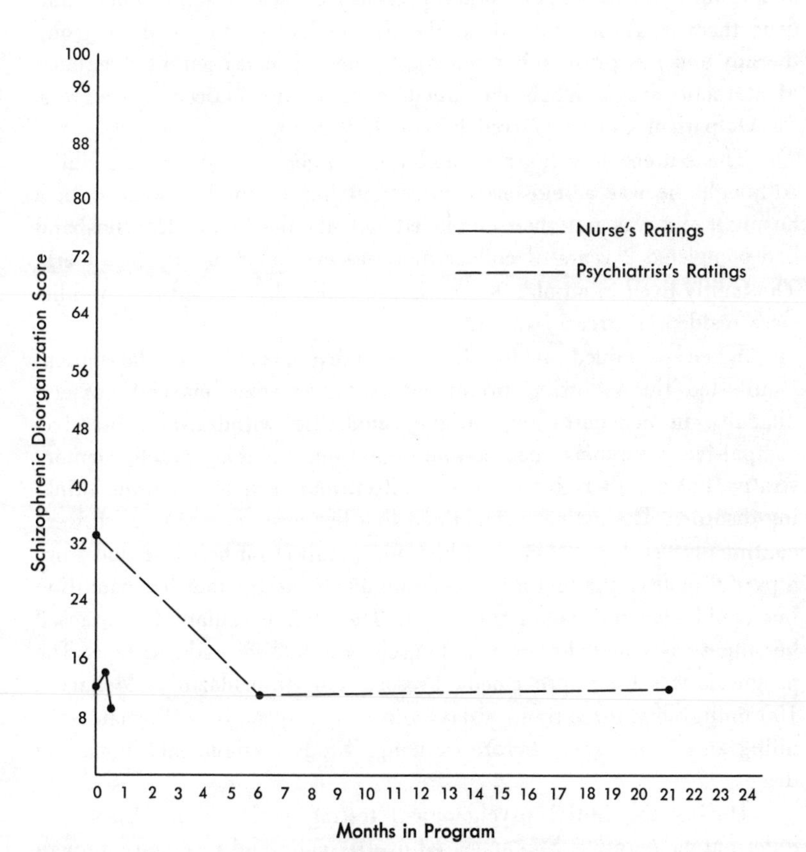

Patient #146. Schizophrenic Disorganization Ratings by Psychiatrist, Nurse, and Significant Other

AMBULATORY—DRUG SUCCESS

Case #157, a 31-year-old white female was referred to the Institute Treatment Center by the Louisville Area Outpatient Clinic. The patient was first treated for a psychiatric illness when she was 26 years old and since that time had been hospitalized four times for very short periods in both private and public hospitals. While hospitalized she had undergone individual psychotherapy, electroshock, insulin shock, and drug therapy. As an outpatient, the patient had participated in group therapy and just prior to her referral to the ITC had been on a regimen of ataractic drugs. When she failed to make any noticeable progress, the Outpatient Clinic referred her to the Center.

The patient was married and the mother of a 4-year-old child. Although she was a registered nurse and had previously worked in a hospital, she was not then employed outside the home. Her husband had completed 2 years of college and was employed as an office clerk. The family lived in an old, 9-room house which they rented in a middle-class residential area of the city.

When examined at the Institute Treatment Center, the patient manifested the following prominent features: some marked anxiety, difficulty in concentrating, fatigue, moderate withdrawal, obsessive-compulsive symptoms, depression, agitation, voluble speech, demonstrative but definitely inappropriate affect, and clear and definite thinking disorder. The patient complained that her nose, face, and teeth were continually "shifting" (she had had an operation on her nose and wore a partial plate). She had a modest amount of insight into her condition but could give no explanation of it. The staff psychiatrist diagnosed her illness as schizophrenic reaction, chronic undifferentiated type. The prognosis was for improvement. Prescription: thioridazine, (Mellaril), 100 milligrams, three times a day, and tranylcypromine, (Parnate), 10 milligrams, one tablet before retiring. Study assignment: home on drugs.

During the initial psychological testing period the subject was quiet but cooperative. She appeared overtly calm and reserved although indications of anxiousness and depression were noted from her test performance. She appeared to be concerned about the test outcome and expressed a general lack of self-assurance.

The public health nurse assigned to the case visited the patient's home the next day.

6/9/62. Patient appeared pleased to see PHN and to be under our treatment. Is worried that she may have to return to hospital. Feels she needs more shock treatments. Appears depressed; feels at times she wants to "end it all." Talked about the operation on her nose and the trouble she is having with her teeth. Says her entire appearance has changed.

Husband states she shows no interest in anything. Wants to be by herself most of the time. Goes to bed at 6 P.M. every night. Eats no dinner; instead, drinks coffee and smokes cigarettes.

6/11/62. Gave patient enough medicine to last three days and made appointment for visit. After seeing psychologist, she asked to see the nurse and wanted to know if it were at all possible for the "nurse who wears false teeth" to visit her, as she felt she would understand and could help her. She phoned after she returned home to ask if the psychiatrist knew she was on thioridazine (Mellaril), 100 mg. before coming here. We assured her he did.

6/14/62. Patient certainly preoccupied with her face. Has actually been concerned about teeth since childhood when parents could not afford to have braces put on teeth. Feels quite guilty about filing her teeth after they were fixed second time. Says she has told no one except psychiatrist and PHN today about this. Does not want husband to know. Explained this was confidential. I told her things would probably change after she received partial plate. It would be hard to get used to, but could be done. Encouraged her to become interested in something. Does like to read. Was quite depressed, but do not feel she was suicidal today. Says husband has great faith in ITC. Says she is lonely.

Home conditions. Patient, husband, and 4-year-old son live in 9-room, 2-story frame house in middle-class neighborhood. Family uses only the downstairs which consists of double living room, dining room, 2 bedrooms, bath, and kitchen. Fairly clean and fairly well-furnished. Couple's family own the house and are allowing them to live here for 5 years because patient took care of father-in-law who had a colostomy and because couple have had medical bills—first with son who had surgery on feet and then with patient. The 5 years will soon be up.

6/21/62. Believe that patient a little improved today. Still is obsessed by face, but could divert patient occasionally to talk of other things. Seemed a little more alert. Would like to feel able to work again. Asked PHN what a drink would do to her. Urged patient to think more about husband's and child's welfare and pleasures. Seems to feel shock treatments necessary for improvement. Do not believe patient functioning as well in home as she could with more effort. Very pleasant to PHN and seems to enjoy the companionship. Very tense, holds head rigid.

6/29/62. Not much change noted in patient's condition. Called ITC last week that she was too sleepy. Suggested dropping 1 dosage. Still sleepy so suggested patient take full dosage and cut out tranylcypromine (Parnate) for several days. Patient refuses to accept any explanation for face. Feels that with her teeth she looked like a beautiful model she once saw in Sears catalogue. Has very little energy; very tense and says she is uncomfortable most of time. Very little pain and PHN has impression patient mostly concerned with appearance.

7/5/62. Patient still preoccupied with the idea that face is changing constantly and very uncomfortable. Does not complain of pain, just discomfort and difficulty in breathing through nose at times. Have noticed that patient has most difficulty on particularly humid days. Very depressed today and says she would as soon be dead. Yet, when nurse probed, said she wanted to live. Still quite tense.

As nurse, wish I could do more toward finding key to help patient overcome obsession; however, patient seems to enjoy talking to nurse. Made long home visit, but patient was reluctant even then for nurse to leave. Said she was lonesome and liked to talk with nurse.

7/12/62. Patient complains of lower teeth bothering her; feels as though they are moving. Also worried that she won't be able to wear upper plate. Worried about her nose and feels she needs another operation. States all the discomfort is "driving her crazy."

7/19/62. Patient said she was more concerned today, but PHN felt she seemed improved. Patient wearing her old partial plate today. Says she can't wear new one and told in detail how even old one bothered her. Explained she could expect some discomfort and would have to bear it. Said she felt she would have to have shock treatment. Told patient it was up to her. Says shock treatments help mouth discomfort. Told her shock treatments would not help discomfort so therefore part of it is mental. Patient says doctor is giving her birth control pills to regulate her menstrual periods which are very irregular. Has not been taking her tranylcypromine (Parnate). Suggested she do so and she said she would comply. Rapport is good.

7/26/62. No improvement noted. Patient seems more preoccupied with face than ever, if that is possible. Says she wants to get well, but doesn't think she ever will. Still feels she may need shock treatments. Is to have face

X-rayed tomorrow for possible nose surgery in future. Not wearing partial plate today. Has already tried to adjust new plate herself. Told her she shouldn't do this, but go to the dentist for adjustment. Patient seems to function at home on a fairly low level.

8/2/62. Patient's whole conversation revolved around her ideas that her nose and teeth were changing positions. Patient doesn't seem to have any interest in anything at all. PHN encouraged patient to start working on some type of hobby that doesn't require concentration. Also suggested that she spend some time telling her youngster about trees, flowers, etc. when she is sitting in the yard with him. PHN explained that this wouldn't alleviate her problems, but that it was better than walking the floor thinking about herself constantly. Patient doesn't appear to want to take suggestions. I explained that it would probably be hard, but that she had to try to help herself.

8/9/62. Patient moans and whines continuously, saying "I just can't stand this. My teeth and nose have been moving out of place all day." The patient first said she was having severe pain. Later she said, "No, I'm not having pain. It is just extremely uncomfortable." Patient got a photograph (a glamorous one) and said, "This is what I used to look like. I can't ever look like this again. This medicine isn't doing me any good. I may have to go back to the hospital."

Patient answered telephone twice while PHN was there. In the second conversation, the patient started out by whining and before long was talking in a normal tone.

On the last two visits the patient hadn't taken her 2 P.M. medicine by the time I arrived. The patient said that she didn't take her medicine on schedule. I personally wonder if the patient is taking all of her medication and taking it as it should be taken. I brought all extra medicine back except for 3 capsules. Will check to see if there are more than 3 caps. left over on the next visit.

9/16/62. Patient seemed more disturbed about face than usual today. Cried and talked with a whine. Despairs of getting any better. "Teeth have shifted worse than ever, teeth will never fit now." This may be triggered by the fact that nothing unusual was found on X-rays, and doctor told patient there was no necessity for nasal surgery. Says she knows she will have to have shock treatment again, but was quite perturbed when told ITC would no longer treat her if she entered hospital. Patient seems to want to retreat by sleeping a great deal of the time. Told her to go back to her 3 times per day dosage. Yawned frequently during interview. Made appointment for her to see psychiatrist at 11:00 A.M., 9/17/62. Patient fast becoming a slovenly housekeeper and son seems unmanageable. She seems to be completely wrapped up in self and fancied ailments.

8/20/62. Made home visit today to take additional medicine to patient. States she feels no better, but appears improved. Said she put her teeth in for a couple of days and went to a picnic Sunday. Couldn't stand the teeth. Told her she couldn't expect to get used to them in so short a time. Keep trying to stress importance of becoming interested in a hobby, housework, etc., to no avail. Patient always seems slightly better after participating in some activity.

8/24/62. Patient seemed quite disturbed. Talked about going back to hospital and suicidal thoughts (reported this to psychiatrist immediately). Suggested she not touch her face for 48 hours except to wash it and brush her teeth once and not look in the mirror. Last week patient complained of right side of face "shifting." This week the left. Always says it won't get any better. Told her she said the same thing about the right side last and it is apparently better. Said that husband thinks she should go to hospital. States she feels better mentally after nurse's visit, so told her I would visit twice a week for a while. Stressed how important she was to son and husband. Seemed restless today.

8/30/62. Patient seemed about the same as earlier this week. Preoccupied with face to exclusion of all else. Still seems to have note of hysteria in voice. Husband to be on vacation and wants to go to Tennessee this weekend. Patient doesn't see how she can go. Rejects or ignores all suggestions for help from nurse.

9/6/62. Patient states her teeth "shifted back" for approximately 36 hours when couple and child went to Chattanooga last weekend. Otherwise, no apparent change in condition. Stated husband became irritated with her this week and this seemed to upset patient. Gave patient appointment to see psychiatrist at 1 P.M., 9/7, for 3 mos. evaluation.

9/13/62. Patient does not seem improved. Husband wants her to go to Central State Hospital this weekend. Still seems rather hysterical. Talked to patient about psychiatrist's suggestion that she go to work (patient is RN). Said she would like to, but didn't feel that she was able to get ready to go to work.

9/20/62. Patient would not admit to feeling better, but patient looked better today. Patient will always bring conversation back to shifting teeth, etc. Will talk in a normal voice to nurse and child at times, then suddenly switch to whine about symptoms. Thinks illness is physical with mental involvement as result. Feels that medicine is the only thing that keeps her going. I have the feeling that patient is drinking some. Know that she has occasional highball, but thought I smelled whiskey during last few home visits.

9/27/62. Patient seemed improved today. Eyes don't hurt, but teeth still shifting. SO (significant other) and nurse have noticed patient improves when family is ill and seems to resent husband's good health and vitality. Patient says husband having some back trouble and she is concerned. Has been rubbing his back and humoring him.

10/4/62. Patient had the usual complaints—shifting teeth, nose and eye discomfort. Note that if nurse talks about any illness or problem she or patient's husband has, patient seems to cheer up temporarily. Child of a patient's friend choked on candy when patient was visiting recently and she seemed to be able to handle the emergency. Continue mentioning patient returning to work each home visit. Believe that patient is giving more thought to working at hospital weekends. Still have the feeling patient drinking some. Was drinking a Coke at time of visit. Denied it was anything but Coke, but thought I smelled whiskey.

10/11/62. Patient had new upper plate today. Stated they fit better than any she has had, but yet excused herself several times during interview to file on teeth. Was a little more cheerful today. Told her a joke and she really laughed and told me one in return. Taking very little thioridazine (Mellaril) because she says it makes her fat. Would like tranylcypromine (Parnate) tid. (three times a day) and no thioridazine (Mellaril).

10/25/62. Patient still complains of shifting in mouth and nose. Feel that patient is improved, however, because she seems to be making an effort to wear new partial plate. This is the first time I have felt as if patient is trying. Still feel she may have some real discomfort due to being double-jointed. She visited mother for 1 week. Also, patient took son to see a movie yesterday afternoon. Patient is definitely drinking some. Did not talk about going to Central State Hospital today. Blood pressure higher today. Stated she is taking her thioridazine (Mellaril). Seemed to have more energy and personal appearance improved.

10/27/62. Home visit made to do SO evaluation. Patient stated she applied at hospital 10/26/62 for general duty as RN for Saturday and Sunday work. SO feels patient is drinking too much.

11/1/62. Patient depressed, nervous, and tense over "teeth shifting" again. Also husband has put his foot down on drinking. Feels she needs this very much, but doesn't want her to become an alcoholic. Tried to reassure patient the teeth would go back as they had before if she would only relax.

Always feels they won't this time. Picking almost constantly and moving body in repetitive gestures or motions.

11/8/62. Patient's actions and looks seem improved today, but no change noted in complaints. Still feels she will have to go back to Central State Hospital. Has appointment with dentist next week and then plans to go to ear, nose, and throat (ENT) specialist. Still planning to try to go to work weekends if called. Does not feel that medicine is doing her any good.

11/21/62. Patient really crying tears today. Very upset. "Teeth have shifted again and will never go back." Usual complaint. Feel that patient probably more upset than usual because she has been better recently. Went to the dentist to have tooth filled and teeth cleaned and he adjusted partial plate. This plate had been fitting better than any before. Suggested she go back to dentist this afternoon.

Patient worked on maternity floor at hospital last weekend. Is to work again this weekend. Apparently got along very well. Hard to get patient to talk about anything but teeth and nose today. Patient seemed to have very little patience with son today.

12/6/62. Patient depressed as usual over teeth. Has filed on her partial plate this week and is quite upset over this. Wonders why she did it. Working at hospital 2-4 days a week on 3-11 shift and seems to like it. Certainly seems to have helped her. Seems to be neater and more energetic about house. Did not talk about teeth shifting today.

12/20/62. Patient says she is quite depressed about teeth and nose and has broken a tooth on partial plate. Still feel that patient seems improved. Is quite interested in her job and is practically working full time. Says it is hard for her to do so. Had woman cleaning house for her today. Is not taking medicine regularly. Urged her to do so. Feel that patient is afraid of feeling too well. Says she will keep appointment with psychiatrist tomorrow.

1/3/63. Patient seems improved. Seemed to have difficulty at times getting back on the subject of the shifting teeth. Admits part of her trouble is mental. Also said she had to go to the dentist Monday to have impression made since she broke tooth on plate and made the statement that she felt sorry for the dentist. Says she feels wonderful from the neck down. Said she had never told the nurse, but had felt her uterus was misplaced since birth of son and even that righted itself the other day. Does not menstruate. Seems to love her job and also seems to have self-confidence in her ability to do the work. Admits, also, that she isn't a good housekeeper. Doesn't like it.

1/31/63. No particular change. Still working. Says she would like for nurse to visit more often than every 4 weeks to reassure her that her teeth would slip back into place. Likes her job, but says it is hard due to mouth feeling the way it does.

2/28/63. Patient seems much improved. Seems to have better insight. ENT specialist examined her face and feels something is wrong and is to X-ray jawbones Monday. Patient working approximately 5 days a week. Feels thioridazine (Mellaril) is causing her to gain weight, so just takes it 2 times/day instead of four. Says she has quit drinking for Lent except for martinis on Sunday. Has less repetitive movements. Seems to be facing reality better. However, she became angry with son last week and slapped him in jaw. Feels that jaw looks different and child complains. Took him to doctor who prescribed muscle relaxant and heat.

3/28/63. Seems to be in a depressive period. Crying, doesn't know what she'll do if face doesn't get more comfortable, feels she will never be well. Uncle and nephew came in during visit and patient changed completely. She is also working 3 and 4 days a week. Feels husband is critical. Patient doesn't belong to any organizations or go anywhere. Urged her to have more social life and stressed importance of taking drugs as prescribed.

5/1/63. Patient seemed about the same to me as she did last home visit. Wishes she could have some kind of therapy that could help her get over her obsession about her shifting teeth and nose. Feels that if she doesn't, she will end up in mental hospital for life. Feel patient is improved but is afraid to admit it.

5/29/63. Patient still working 4 days a week and still complaining about teeth and nose. Feels illness is physical. Got a new partial plate recently. Likes the looks of it, but very despairing about her mouth and nose. Going to oral surgeon next week. Says she felt and heard jaw pop 6 years ago when she filed on her own teeth. Does not take all of thioridazine (Mellaril). Usually takes 100 milligrams a day. Patient seems to be functioning better. Always seems glad to see nurse.

6/27/63. Patient and husband both feel patient's condition is worse. Husband unemployed at present and they have been together more and had quite an argument this morning. Patient feels that husband doesn't love her as he formerly did. Quite depressed—says doesn't want to live. Husband and son would be better off without her. Teeth still shifting. I have always been impressed by husband's attitude, but received a little different impression today. Husband says wife only works a couple of days per week at hospital, but patient usually says she works about 4 and will name the days. Patient says husband frequently threatens to put her in hospital.

7/24/63. No particular change noted. As previously noted by nurse, patient has a tendency to have an alcohol problem. Husband is aware and being very firm. Patient resents this. Still working.

8/21/63. Only talked with patient for a short time. Patient was getting ready to go to work. Usual complaints about teeth. Says nose bleeds occasionally. Has appointment with doctor Friday about nose.

9/25/63. Patient, as usual, says she feels worse. Actions indicate otherwise. I believe that admitting to too much improvement is a threat to patient. Still talking about having surgery on her nose. Working 3 days one week and 4 days the next. Seems to realize she is better off working. Still has alcohol problem. Realizes it would be very easy for her to become an alcoholic. Concerned about her weight. Says she feels medicine causes weight gain, but can't do without medicine.

10/23/63. Patient seemed slightly improved. Rationalizes some better. Talked about self and past life a lot. Trying to decide about having plastic surgery done on nose and this led to a long discussion. Asked patient if she was fearful of becoming well. Said she felt better last Friday, Saturday, Sunday, and Monday. Took son to doctor Friday, worked Saturday and Sunday and shopped Monday. Asked her if she thought about this. Will admit that working helps her, but she always feels she can't make it before she goes to work. Asked her if she didn't feel better when she got to work —evaded this. Patient apparently liked it better when husband babied her more. I feel she would like to be beautiful, the life of party, and center of attraction.

11/20/63. Patient seemed a little gayer than usual. May have had a few drinks; could not detect this, however. States she realizes she will have to learn to live with her condition and that it is not as bad as it used to be. Has only been taking 1 thioridazine (Mellaril) and 1 tranylcypromine (Parnate) a day. Works 3 days one week and 4 the next. Talked with husband via phone. Rather concerned about wife's drinking, particularly in the morning. Patient will be due for 18 mos. check in December. Told husband this and that psychiatrist would talk with her.

12/19/63. Patient seemed about the same. Teeth had just shifted again and as usual feels they won't go back this time. Says she is jealous of happy people. Asked her if she would be happier on medical floor rather than OB where people are usually happy, but she doesn't want this. Says she feels former friends don't like her anymore. Suggested she act happier and not tell them constantly about her shifting teeth. She can talk to doctor and nurse about this. Husband apparently doesn't cater to her as he did formerly.

1/12/64. Patient still preoccupied with shifting teeth. Says she realizes now that she will have to learn to live with this condition. Talks a great deal. Says she loves her work, but doesn't know how long she will be able to work. House has been sold and planning to buy another one.

1/21/64. No particular change noted. Usual complaints. Says dentist has said that patient's oral problems stem particularly from being double jointed. Reported dentist claims nothing can be done about this.

3/23/64. Patient seems about the same. Has same problems. Says she knows she would not transfer phobia to something else if she could keep her teeth from shifting. Plans to go to orthodontist. Dentist had her wearing

Case #157. Psychological Test Results

Test	*Direction of Change*	*1st Testing Initial*	*2nd Testing 6 Mo.*	*3rd Testing 18 Mo.*	*4th Testing 24 Mo.*
Reaction time	=	3212	3228	3212	NSO
Maze QE	–	055	072	063	NSO
Maze IQ	–	122	129	118	NSO
WAIS, verbal IQ	–	099	099	097	NSO
WAIS, performance IQ	+	098	097	107	NSO
WAIS, full IQ	+	099	097	101	NSO
Bender Z	=	126	133	114	NSO

+ Improvement
– No improvement
= No consistent change
NSO No score obtained

Case #157. Medications

6/ 8/62. Thioridazine–100 milligrams, three times a day
Tranylcypromine–10 milligrams, once a day before retiring

8/17/62. Thioridazine–100 milligrams, four times a day
Tranylcypromine–10 milligrams, twice a day, morning and evening

4/25/63. Thioridazine–100 milligrams, three times a day

1/11/64. Tranylcypromine–10 milligrams, twice a day, morning and evening
Thioridazine–100 milligrams, three times a day

1/16/64. Thioridazine–100 milligrams, twice a day

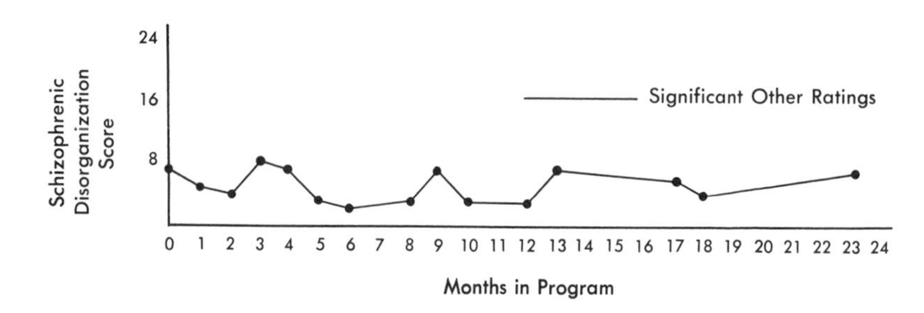

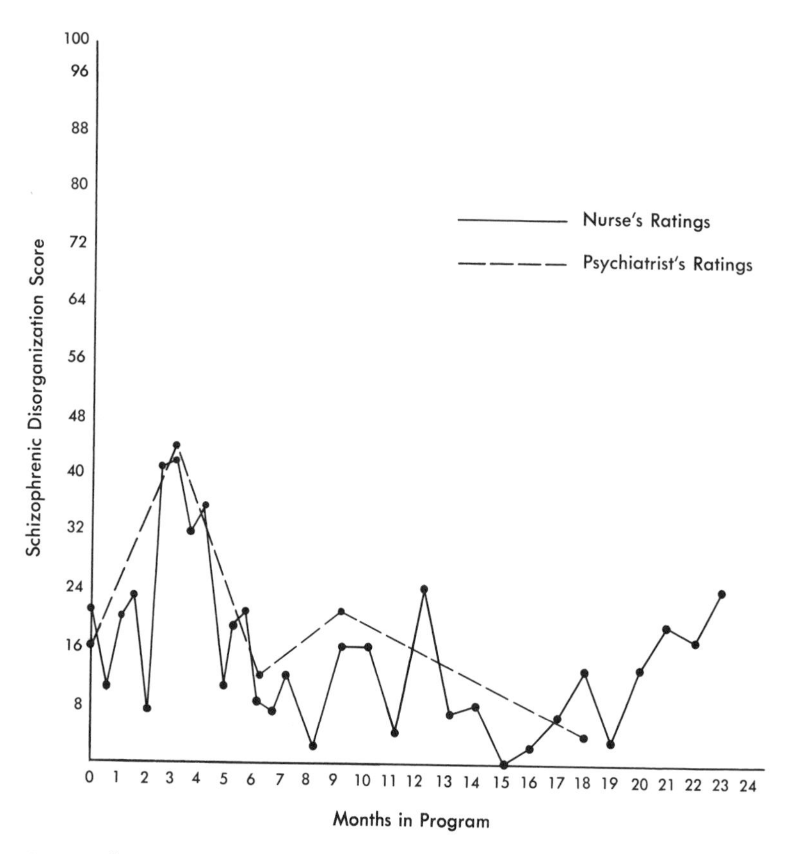

Patient #157. Schizophrenic Disorganization Ratings by Psychiatrist, Nurse, and Significant Other

splints on her jaws recently to hold them in place, but said they hurt. Still despairs of ever being helped.

4/20/64. No particular change. Patient moving to home they have purchased. Did not like it when husband attempted to restrict patient's smoking and drinking. Now patient says he won't object if she drinks. The patient also said he has swung the other way with regard to her smoking. This seems to threaten her more than the restriction. Was quite perturbed about ITC program ending and expressed no desire for referral. Will visit next month.

5/18/64. Patient had usual complaint, but her heart didn't seem to be in it as much today. Family has bought a house and moved and patient seems to be interested in buying things for home. Still works 3 days one week and 4 days the next. Was a little perturbed over no more home visits.

Due to circumstances beyond the control of the study staff, the psychiatrist was not able to examine this patient before she was released from the home care program. However, 5 months earlier he did examine her and at that time found her to be moderately anxious, slightly withdrawn, mildly depressed, and agitated. Her affect was appropriate, but her insight had not improved. The prognosis continued to be for improvement, and on May 18, 1964, the patient was released from treatment.

HOME CARE—DRUG SUCCESS

Case #164, a 30-year-old white male was referred to the Institute Treatment Center on July 11, 1962, by Central State Hospital where he had admitted himself voluntarily. Three months prior to that, he had experienced his first mental hospitalization in a private institution where he was kept only a few weeks. On both occasions, the patient had admitted himself to the hospital on the recommendation of a general practitioner whom he had been seeing. While hospitalized the first time, he had been given 6 to 10 electroshock treatments and was on a regimen of ataractic drugs.

The patient was born and raised in rural Kentucky and was the ninth of 10 children. However, he has lived in Louisville all of his adult years. He reportedly has only a second grade education, no military experience, and for the past 13 years has worked as a car man's helper on a railroad. However, for the past 3 months he has been unable to work regularly. When working, the patient had an income of approximately $4000 per year. He has been married for 12 years and is the father of three children. The patient, his wife, three children, and mother-in-law live in a 3-room apartment.

At the time of his referral to the home care study, this patient displayed to some extent the following symptoms: marked anxiety, difficulty in concentrating, mild withdrawal, obsessive-compulsive symptoms, marked depression, agitation, retarded speech, definite ideas of influence, bland and definitely inappropriate affect, clear and definite thinking disorder, and unsystematized paranoid delusions. The patient felt that the cause of his illness was within himself but was unable to give any explanation. His illness was diagnosed as schizophrenic reaction, paranoid type. The prognosis was for improvement with minor difficulties and complaints continuing. Prescription: thioridazine (Mellaril), 100 milligrams, three times a day and tranylcypromine (Parnate), 10 milligrams before retiring. Study assignment: home on drugs.

At the time of his initial examination at the Institute Treatment Center, the patient's orientation to time and place seemed poor. He walked with a wide gait and had difficulty climbing steps. During the psychological evaluation, he was quiet and passively cooperative, offering only minimal responses. He worked very slowly in a belabored, unsure manner. His visual-motor coordination showed marked signs of impairment.

As usual, the patient was visited by his nurse the next day, and his week-to-week adjustment in the community can best be followed through her reports.

7/12/62. Patient denies problems. Suggests no complaints. Pleased to be home. Appears a little preoccupied. Speech is slowed and appears slurred. Expresses little emotion. Is concerned with time when he is able to return to work. Asked about his clothes at CSH. Advised patient about driving until he is stabilized on medication. Cautioned about drinking alcoholic beverages. Appears to be well oriented. Confused about onset of mental illness. Taking medicine as prescribed.

7/18/62. Patient appears in cheerful mood. Expresses desire to return to work. Feels he is mentally and physically capable of doing his regular job with the RR. Feels medication may be too strong and is causing drowsiness.

Answered questions freely; appeared relaxed and comfortable during interview. Admits feeling people are against him and talk about him because he was in mental hospital. Denies depression. Taking medication as prescribed. Patient's wife is pleased with his progress.

7/25/62. Patient in cheerful mood. Reports no problems, symptoms, or complaints. Only question he asks frequently throughout interview is when he will be able to return to work. Advised patient that at present it was not practical to resume job. He states he is anxious to return to job so that his wife will not have to go to work. This seems to worry patient. Wife says family can manage financially at present on patient's disability compensation. Taking medication as directed.

8/1/62. Patient in cheerful mood. Interested in environment and family activities. States he is comfortable among groups of people now. He denies symptoms and illness. Very anxious to return to work. Asked about when he can go to work several times during interview.

Taking medication as prescribed.

Patient's wife appears satisfied with his treatment and progress. States he is restless and moves around a lot in the early mornings.

8/8/62. Patient appears more alert than on previous visits. Getting more restless now and very impatient to return to work. Wife states he is also getting more irritable. She is not concerned about this, because he was more like this when he was well.

8/15/62. Patient becoming more demanding for doctor's permission to return to work. He repeats question about when he can go back to work at every opportunity throughout interview. Wants an appointment to discuss this with the doctor next week. He denies all symptoms of illness. He answers all questions readily. Interview with wife suggests he is industrious around the house, participates in social situations, is less restless and his behavior is normal. He sometimes has difficulty getting started on now jobs around the home, but does well after he begins. He watches TV for relaxation.

8/22/62. Patient expressed hope that the doctor would permit him to return to his job. He said he felt guilty about taking money from the RR when he felt he should be working. He apparently enjoys the type of work he does. He denies symptoms, and admits his medication is helping him. He will keep appointment with doctor on Friday and has agreed that he will abide by doctor's decision about going to work.

8/29/62. Patient cheerful. Plans to return to work next week. It is satisfactory with employer that patient work part time; however, it is a rigid company policy that he must remain at the shop for the 8-hour period. Patient insists that he be given a letter of release from psychiatrist to take to the company doctor in spite of repeated explanation that the letter would be sent directly.

9/5/62. Patient expressed disappointment that he was denied work on part-time basis by RR. However, he states the local company doctor is to contact the head doctor of RR in Chicago and he will be put on full time with this approval. He anticipates a release for full time employment from psychiatrist. Patient expressed guilt for taking financial compensation from RR when he is able to work. He also said he worries about the family bills. He feels that working and drawing a full salary will relieve him of his worries. He denies symptoms of emotional illness. He agrees to cooperate with ITC if he returns to work.

9/11/62. Patient is required to have evaluation by RR physician in their Chicago hospital before he may return to work. He plans to leave tonight and asked that he be given a week's supply of medicine to take with him. He is apprehensive about his exam and a little tense today.

He is becoming restless at home, and his wife thinks he will be more satisfied if he is permitted to return to work.

9/19/62. Patient very impatient to return to work. Had brief checkup at RR hospital in Chicago last week. He was not informed of physical findings. He is discontented staying at home and beginning to get restless. He is confident he will be satisfied and happy at his job.

9/26/62. Patient perturbed because company doctor will not permit him to return to work. It was necessary for nurse to reassure patient that psychiatrist would re-evaluate him at end of 3 mos. treatment and make decision regarding his being able to return to work.

10/3/62. Admits he worries frequently about himself, his family, his financial problems. He has always worried about things. Patient does not volunteer any information. It is necessary to ask him specific questions. He is very anxious to return to his job. He thinks he will have less to worry about when he is working.

10/10/62. Patient states he's doing well. Is anxious to return to work—bored with staying at home although he tries to keep busy doing odd jobs around house.

10/29/62. Patient appears in cheerful mood. Pleased to be back at work. States he is aware that he is not yet able to do as much as before he became ill; however, this may be a matter of adjusting. He appears relaxed and comfortable during interview. Answers questions easily, denies problems or symptoms. He is extremely reserved and information must be elicited through direct questioning.

11/10/62. Patient was quiet. Answered questions with minimal responses. Appeared in apathetic mood. Admits having occasional depression and anxiety. States he is satisfied and happy back at work.

11/20/62. Apparently progressing all right. He remarked that he "wouldn't need to take his medicine much longer." Denies psychiatric symptoms. Patient does not volunteer much information. He will give minimal answers to all questions. He is usually tense and uncomfortable during the interview. States he is having no difficulty or problems at work.

12/19/62. Patient has a drawn, anxious expression. Not doing as well as previously. Admits occasional depression and irritability. Does not have same feelings toward his wife. Says he would like their relationship to be like it used to be. Says he wants to get away from home sometimes. Does not have same enthusiasm for work.

Respondent (wife) reports change in patient's behavior—more interested in himself, almost selfish attitude, speaks of buying clothing for himself, does not seem to care about the needs of her or the children. He refuses to discipline the children and will criticize her for doing so. His appetite is not as good. When he is tired he is very irritable. She observed that she answered all the questions negative on the SO Rating Scale because she did not detect any abnormal behavior relating to the questions asked; however, she is aware there is something different about him. He seems to have withdrawn from her. Recently he told her he thought he needed more shock treatments. This alarmed her because she said he always expressed fear of EST.

Patient admits being unhappy. This couple might benefit from counselling with Family Service. He takes his medicine; wife sees to this.

1/2/63. Patient appears slightly improved since last interview. Better mood. Admits occasional depression usually in mornings. Feels he and his wife are not very close anymore. They have little conversation between them. Patient will come for psych. testing Friday morning.

1/30/63. Did not see patient due to weather, but talked with wife who seems to feel that husband has improved a great deal. States he sleeps well and she is well pleased with progress and with help from ITC and Public Health Nurse. Wife seems very grateful. Took 4 weeks medicine. Told wife to call ITC if any change.

2/27/63. Patient appears in cheerful mood. Appears better adjusted than last interview. More interested in environment and seeming to take more responsibility in the home. Does not appear anxious or apprehensive. States he feels more sensitive about the lack of opportunity in his early childhood for a better education. Taking medicine as prescribed.

3/27/63. Patient believes he is watched and talked about by other people. States he feels awkward and clumsy. States he feels better than 6 mos. ago, but he's far from being all right. Worries a great deal about himself and his job. Says he "studies" and thinks a great deal. Feels inadequate because of his lack of education. Doesn't enjoy his family or home very much. Really doesn't get any pleasure out of things. Sees nothing to make him happy or laugh. He thinks his nervous breakdown was caused by his jealousy and suspicions of his wife. He thought she was going out with other men.

Patient feels he has some insight into his problems. He asked the question "How do you solve them?" Knowing what bothers him without being able to change it is very disturbing to patient.

4/24/63. At times patient feels inferior and inadequate. He seems to require reassurance and an occasional expression of confidence. He is anxious and apprehensive. He frequently expresses fears of EST and hospitalization. States he feels tense and nervous in the early morning. He appears to be functioning adequately on the job and at home. Patient states he doesn't get enjoyment out of life anymore.

6/19/63. Wife reports patient feels tired all the time. Says he doesn't have much energy. Will often fall asleep when sitting around home. Patient appears in mildly cheerful mood. Smiling, which is unusual for him. States he is feeling somewhat better than last time. He indicated he thinks frequently of his childhood, looking for the cause of his illness and the reason for his guilt feelings. He informed nurse that a psychiatrist who treated him when he became ill told him that he must have done something in his youth that he is ashamed of. He also states he does not seem to enjoy life as much as he used to nor does he feel really cheerful or happy. He indicates the EST may be responsible for his feeling. EST appears to have had a traumatic effect on patient.

7/17/63. Apparently all right. Patient reports he has vomited his evening meal 3 or 4 times the past month. Says he is not as efficient in his work as he formerly was. Says he is forgetful. Lacks confidence in himself. Implies he feels inferior and inadequate because of his lack of education. Says he is preoccupied with thoughts of the past when he was happier. He recognizes these things as undesirable symptoms.

8/14/63. Patient relates an unfortunate experience of 2 nights ago. His wife's uncle was staying all night with the family and he died suddenly of heart attack during the night while sleeping in same bed with patient. He admits this experience and shock upset him rather badly. Patient is working today. In the future patient will be visited at home on his regular day off which has recently been changed to Monday.

9/9/63. Patient reports he had difficulty keeping down food several days last month. He feels he is doing well emotionally at present. Reports no symptoms. Working everyday without difficulty.

10/7/63. Wife reports patient is less cooperative about taking his medicine. He says he no longer needs it. Patient complains he is unable to relate to people. Says he has no enthusiasm or interests for social contacts. Doesn't enjoy life. Lacks zest. Thinks he is not doing as well as he should on his job. Appears discontented.

11/4/63. Patient appears better adjusted. Less preoccupied with matters that previously bothered him. In a more cheerful mood. More optimistic about himself. Suggests no problems or unusual anxieties. He thinks he is functioning better and outlook is improved.

12/2/63. Patient denies symptoms. Says he is getting along well. No problems or complaints. Patient appears more satisfied and confident at present.

1/20/64. Patient appears in cheerful mood. Is a little embarrassed about drinking episode a week ago. Says there was no special reason why he did it.

Respondent SO reports there has been no recurrence or any problems since then. Patient went to work last Monday and on Tuesday he was required to work an 18-hour period because of a RR accident. He has had no difficulty on the job and continues to like it very much.

2/27/64. Patient appears to be doing all right. No complaints or problems. Appears more relaxed and comfortable during interview.

3/16/64. Patient appears to be doing well. Says he thinks he could get along without medicine now. Will come to see psychiatrist next month.

SO reports patient's interest and responsibility around home continue to increase. Attitude very much improved. She continues to remind him occasionally to take his medicine and she says she can observe a change in him if he fails to take it. She would not like to see his medicine discontinued.

4/3/64. Appears to be doing well. Feels like he could do without medicine although his wife wants him to continue taking medicine because she is afraid of the recurrence of his symptoms.

5/11/64. Patient appears to be functioning well in all areas. No complaints. Denies problems. In cheerful mood.

After 22 months of home care, the patient was examined by the staff psychiatrist for the last time. The patient displayed only mild anxiety, no ideas of influence, ordinary and appropriate affect, and no suspiciousness. He appeared to have developed some insight and a partial understanding of the importance of emotional factors. The prognosis was good and the patient was released from treatment.

Case #164. Psychological Test Results

Test	*Direction of Change*	*1st Testing Initial*	*2nd Testing 6 Mo.*	*3rd Testing 18 Mo.*	*4th Testing 24 Mo.*
Reaction time	+	3342	3250	3250	NSO
Maze QE	=	085	073	075	NSO
Maze IQ	+	062	066	070	NSO
WAIS, verbal IQ	–	083	079	077	NSO
WAIS, performance IQ	=	068	065	078	NSO
WAIS, full IQ	=	075	070	076	NSO
Bender Z	=	071	070	114	NSO

+ Improvement
– No improvement
= No consistent change
NSO No score obtained

Case #164. Medications

7/11/62. Thioridazine–100 milligrams, three times a day
Tranylcypromine–10 milligrams, once a day before retiring

12/21/62. Thioridazine–100 milligrams, four times a day
Tranylcypromine–10 milligrams, three times a day

10/ 8/63. Trifluoperazine–5 milligrams, three times a day
Chlorpromazine–50 milligrams, three times a day

1/ 2/64. Tranylcypromine–10 milligrams, twice a day
Chlorpromazine–50 milligrams, three times a day
Trifluoperazine–5 milligrams, twice a day

4/16/64. Chlorpromazine–50 milligrams, twice a day
Trifluoperazine–5 milligrams, twice a day

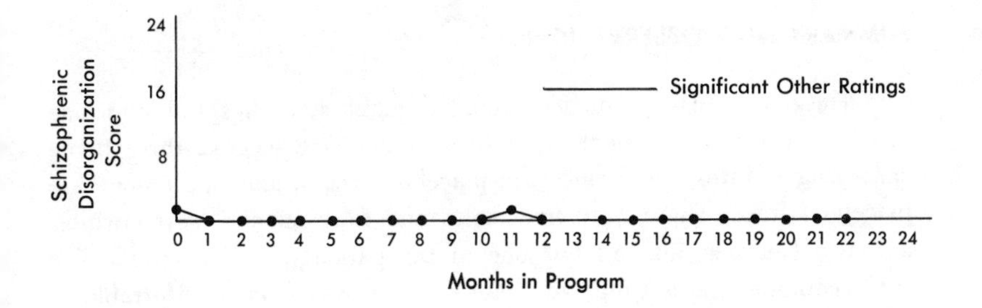

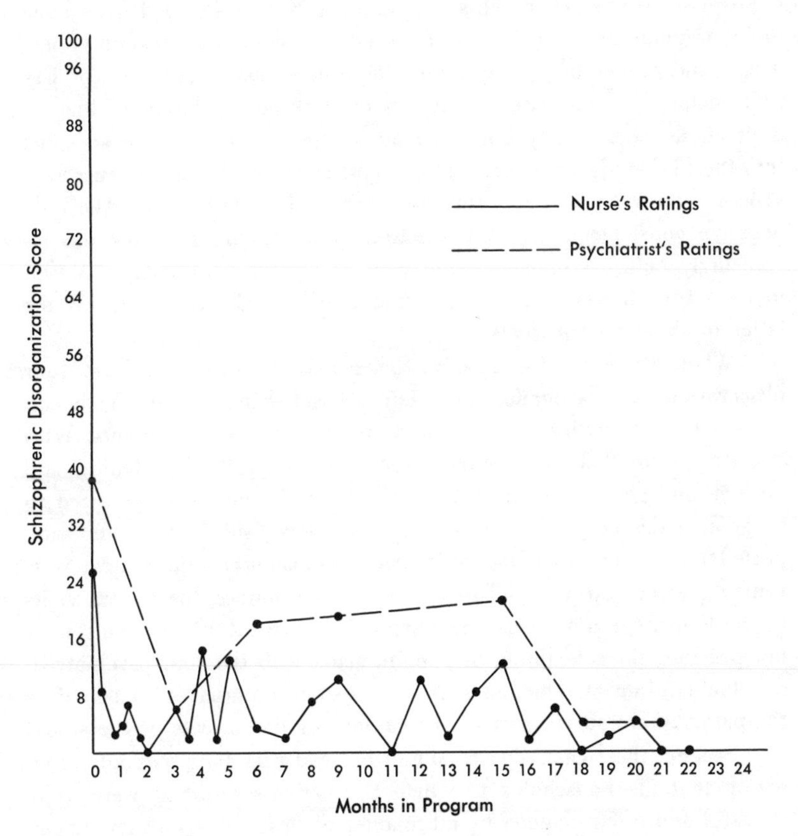

Patient #164. Schizophrenic Disorganization Ratings by Psychiatrist, Nurse, and Significant Other

SUMMARY AND OBSERVATIONS

These nine case histories included eight state hospital and one community referred patient; four drug home care success, three home care drug failures, one home care placebo success, and one home care placebo failure. There were five males and four females, seven whites and two Negroes, and all but one of the patients were married. The socioeconomic status range of these patients was from comfortable to impoverished. Pre-ITC psychiatric treatment histories varied from none to 11 previous hospitalizations and treatment with EST, insulin shock, drugs, and psychotherapy. In short, these nine cases were more or less representative of the case registry in most respects. The chief bias in their choice was largely innocent; all of the nine cases were accepted into the ITC study in its early stages and because of this, the successes at least were with the study through nearly all of its entirety. The only negative consequence of this selection is its failure to show the increasingly bold use of medication with new patients over time. A hint of even this, however, is to be found in the medication data on the latter of these nine patients.

Whatever else these case histories may illustrate, at least four observations can be made from their perusal. First, the public health nurses showed anything but *affective neutrality* to their patients. With one exception, that of a patient who was physically threatening and abusive and clearly required hospitalization, the nurses empathized to so great a degree with their patients that they "sided" with and supported them even when the objective circumstances might have warranted greater objectivity. This concern of the nurses, their extra visits to the home, the numerous telephone calls when additional visits were not possible, the scheduling of appointments with the staff psychiatrist, and the cajoling of reluctant spouses to extend themselves on behalf of the patients, are surely part of the reason for the success of the study.

Second, these case reports cannot be read very long without recognizing that the households to which the patients returned were quite stressful and often plagued by all manner of problems—poverty, unemployment, inadequate housing, filth and squalor, marital difficulties and infidelity, problem children, insensitivity and utter callousness of family members to one another, ignorance, and physical ailments. Perhaps some of these same patients could have made more satisfactory adjustments had they been placed in lodgings, or in almost any less stressful environment in preference to their often inadequate home situations. On the other hand, one wonders whether some of the patients—the nurse obsessed with her shifting teeth, jaws, and nose; the continually pregnant 21-year-old patient; the two cases with religious delusional difficulties—would or could have been tolerated in better organized and more cohesive households. Thus, this matter of to whom and where patients are returned deserves further careful research.

Third, the perusal of these histories, in the absence of the introductory statement as to whether the outcome was success or failure, in themselves provide no special clues as to case outcome. Again, with but one exception, the histories indicate that successes could almost as likely have been failures and the reverse, too. During the months of home care, nearly all of the patients experienced periods of both improvement and deterioration in their mental status and functioning. These fluctuations are testimony to the chronicity of schizophrenia and to the need of continuous care, supervision, and medication as the basis for the prevention of hospitalization. The only alternative seems to be a cycle of frequent hospitalizations, the remission of more acute symptoms, hospital discharge, and eventual readmission.

Fourth, of all the problems exemplified in these nurses' reports, the most persistent concerned medication. Patients either defected entirely, underdosed, overdosed, or experienced undesirable side effects the most common of which were lethargy and drowsiness. Purely as an aside, was the placebo case in which the significant other reported improvement when the patient, after a period of defection, returned to the use of the medication as prescribed. On the other hand, this "placebo effect" failed when one of the cases overdosed and reported no change in his status to the nurse on her next visit. A form of medication which could be administered parenterally, and whose effect would be long lasting could obviate many of these difficulties with regard to drug usage.

9

OVERVIEW

This experimental home care program for the treatment of schizophrenics has yielded solid scientific results. The project demonstrated in a most conclusive way that home care under drug medication with systematic public health nursing care is quite feasible both for newly hospitalized and ambulatory schizophrenic patients. Even the minimal type of home care provided proved in every respect at least as effective, and in most respects, clearly superior, to treatment in a hospital. An enriched, expanded, and more comprehensive program such as now envisioned and planned in many community mental health centers can be expected to be even more successful not only in keeping many patients out of the hospital but in restoring them to at least as adequate a level of functioning as they would have achieved from conventional treatment in a state hospital. Whatever additional practical consequences of this investigation may emerge, this study has provided convincing evidence for the validity of the principles of community psychiatric treatment programs at least as these apply to typical state hospital schizophrenic patients. It is also a reasonable inference that other categories of the mentally ill may be successfully treated in this way.

RECAPITULATION

The rigor of the experimental design and the unequivocal nature of the findings have implications for programs rarely found in this field. Several aspects of the enterprise seem to us to warrant recapitulation at this point.

After 3 years of frustration in getting the investigation started, the Institute Treatment Center was finally established in downtown Louisville, Kentucky, in the latter half of 1961. The staff included a director, a part-time psychiatrist, a psychologist, a social worker and five nurses with public health nursing experience. Only one of the nurses had any prior training or experience in psychiatric nursing. A psychiatrist was employed at the hospital to do the initial screening of patients to determine their eligibility for inclusion in the program. Newly admitted state hospital patients had to meet the following criteria to be admitted to the project: a diagnosis of schizophrenia, nonsuicidal or homicidal, be between 18 and 60 years of age, have residence in Louisville or surrounding counties, and have a family or relative willing to provide supervision of the patient at home. State hospital admissions who met these criteria were sent to the Institute Treatment Center for further evaluation. If the ITC staff psychiatrist confirmed the diagnosis and deemed the patient suitable for the program and the family agreed to cooperate, the patient was accepted. Using a deck of random cards, the study director then assigned the patient to one of three groups as follows: home on drugs (40 percent), home on placebo or on inert medication (30 percent), or hospital care (the control group, 30 percent).

State hospital schizophrenic patients do not, of course, include all schizophrenics. Many schizophrenic patients, because their symptoms are not especially florid and can therefore be tolerated more readily, typically remain in the community and are not hospitalized. To have this population represented as well, particularly for the purpose of determining the effectiveness of drug medication, referrals from community sources other than the state hospital and from private physicians were welcomed. In order to qualify for inclusion in the study, these referrals had to meet the same diagnosis, age, residence, family, and other requirements. The only difference from the aforementioned study group resulted from their "ambulatory" status. Their random assignment permitted just two categories: home on drug or home on placebo.

Shortly after each patient returned home, the public health nurse assigned to the case visited the patient and family. The same nurse made weekly calls the first 3 months, bi-monthly visits during the second 3 months, and monthly visits thereafter. On every visit she left the medication prescribed by the staff psychiatrist. She also completed a written report on the status of the patient which was reviewed by the ITC psychiatrist. Patients and families experiencing difficulties were free to call the treatment center and speak to or make appointments to see the social worker and psychiatrist. Usually, however, it was the nurse who arranged for such consultation.

In order to reach a judgment as to the feasibility of home care and the efficacy of drug therapy, the following instruments, tests, and measures were used:

Psychiatric evaluation. Two instruments (a psychiatric inventory and the Lorr IMPS) were used by the staff psychiatrist to evaluate the mental status of all patients on a regular basis. Home care patients were examined at intake and at 6-month intervals thereafter. Hospital control patients were evaluated at intake and again after 6 and 18 months whether or not they still were hospitalized.

Psychological tests. All groups were studied by the staff psychologist who administered the Wechsler Adult Intelligence Scale, a sequential reaction time test series, and the Bender Gestalt and Porteus Mazes tests. Testing periods were the same as for the psychiatric evaluations.

Social history. A complete social history was taken by the social worker at the time of admission of the patient to the project.

Nurses reports and ratings. The public health nurse completed a mental status rating form (the Lorr IMPS) on each visit to the home care patient. She also completed a behavior chart checklist, a physical status rating sheet, a nursing report, and a monthly report from the responsible relative concerning the patient's functioning.

Hospital control patients were visited by the nurse 1 month after hospital release, and these same instruments were administered at that time.

In all, 152 state hospital patients were involved in the project, 57 drug home care patients, 41 placebo home care cases, and 54 hospital controls. All were followed up for a period ranging from well over 6 months at the least to 30 months. In addition, 29 community drug home care cases and 23 community referred placebo home care patients were in the project for from 6 to 27 months.

The principal substantive findings were these:

1. Over 77 percent of the drug home care patients but only some 34 percent of the placebo cases remained in the community throughout their participation in the project. All controls, of course, were hospitalized. Not only did the program, by averting hospitalization, save a considerable amount of bed-patient time, but this saving permitted in

theory at least the possibility of more intensive care for the fewer hospitalized patients.

2. Drug and placebo home care patients in the project for a longer time period were no less successful than those in the program for shorter periods. Thus, it is fair to speak of *prevention* of hospitalization as such rather than merely of *delay* in institutionalization.

3. Patients who failed (13 drug and 27 placebo) and had to be hospitalized usually failed soon after acceptance into the program. Nearly all failures occurred within 6 months.

4. Even after initial hospitalization averaging 83 days and the presumable remission of the grosser symptoms, the *hospital controls failed more often at the termination of treatment than did the home care patients.*

5. When home care patients failed it was frequently of the "last straw" variety. Either patient behavior was bizarre or dangerous, or the responsible relatives could no longer cope with the patient and his needs. Changes in the family situation sometimes resulted in a lack of supervision of the patient and so precipitated failure.

6. On the more subjective evaluation level—that is, according to the nurses, psychiatrist, and relatives—patients improved in mental status, psychological test performance, domestic functioning, and social participation. These gains were considerable and frequently statistically significant. *In all of the many specific measures, home care patients were functioning as well or better than the hospital control cases.*

7. *Most of the improvement in performance occurred during the first 6 months of the study.* Thereafter functioning improved very little, if at all. In other words, once the acute signs and symptoms abated and functioning returned to a pre-episode level, there was little more gain made.

8. At their best, some of these patients still showed considerable difficulty in performing at what might be termed an adequate level. Both on the instrumental role performance level and on the psychological symptom level, some of the home care patients as well as some of the controls were still exhibiting low quality performance. Perhaps this is really all one might realistically expect, however, from a chronically impaired population.

9. Regarding the community referred drug and placebo patients, nearly 76 percent of the drug and 61 percent of the placebo cases suc-

ceeded on home care. Length of time on the project was not a major correlate of failure. In instances of hospitalization, failure occurred early and the precipitants were generally of the same nature. In the case of the state hospital patients, functioning improved, and most of the gains in the psychiatric, psychological, and social functioning measures were registered between intake and the 6 month's testing.

IMPLICATIONS

There were other more specific findings which have been dealt with earlier and need no additional consideration here. From a practical standpoint this research has important implications for several areas of concern: schizophrenia, the community mental health center, patient care cost, and manpower problems.

Schizophrenia

It would have been far less complicated to select either a cross-section of the mentally ill or a nonpsychotic population to test the feasibility of a home care program. Instead, schizophrenics were deliberately chosen for a variety of compelling reasons. First, there is clear professional agreement that the schizophrenias are chronic and disabling disorders, not merely the consequence of difficulties experienced in the everyday process of living and adjusting. If ever a case can be made for mental illness as a disease, schizophrenia would be one of the prime illustrations. Unlike the characterological disorders, the neuroses, the psychosomatic problems, and other clinical entities, there is almost no dispute that schizophrenia fits, by almost any conventional definition, the disease model. This point is important. If so severe an illness as schizophrenia, accounting for about half of all mental hospital resident patients, and nearly a fourth of the new admissions, can be controlled and treated effectively in a community setting, other difficult behavioral problems presumably can also be managed without recourse to institutionalization, except in extreme cases.

Second, it is well to note, too, that all of the "loading" or biasing in this study was in the direction of selecting sicker rather than less impaired schizophrenic patients for study. Two psychiatrists evaluated each patient—one in the state hospital at admission of the patient and the other in the treatment center. Only when both agreed on the diagnosis as schizophrenia was the patient accepted into the program. For this reason, it is likely that very few, if any, nonschizophrenics were included in this investigation.[1]

Third, regardless of the high reliability in the diagnosis of schizophrenia, and the great amount of conflict over the etiology of this disorder, there is no argument at all that schizophrenic patients require protracted care and treatment. The layman's concept of "cure" in the sense of complete remission of symptoms and the absence of later pathology is wholly inadequate. Instead, a more accurate assumption is that schizophrenics are sick continually and that this illness is, at times, exacerbated. On such occasions, hospitalization usually results. When the acute phase passes, the patient continues to be ill but at a level which often permits him to return to the community and remain there until the next major episode.

Our home care data on the state hospital patients offers reasonably good evidence of this. Once the florid symptoms had passed, the patients settled into a routine which showed almost no superior functioning on any level and mostly minimal functioning on all levels. The community referred schizophrenics, while better than the state hospital patients, and despite their lack of episodic flareups, were not functioning at a very high level either. These are not the great innovators, or activists ahead of their time; they are, along with the state hospital patients, the leftovers in society who are and will undoubtedly continue to be burdens to their families and to society until specific preventive or therapeutic measures are developed. In short, they are sick persons who require continuous attention, not only when their symptoms are at a peak but also when the peaks have flattened. Up to now, attention

[1] It is true, of course, that schizophrenia is sometimes confused with the psychoneuroses in middle- and upper-class patients. It is also a fact that there are variations across cultures and countries in the clinical manifestations and signs in which a diagnosis of schizophrenia seems warranted. Thus in England, the presence of hallucinations is not considered nearly as critical as in the United States. Again, while the overall interrater reliability in the diagnosis of schizophrenia is high, the reliability falls precipitously when the specific categories of schizophrenia such as paranoid and hebephrenic and simple are considered. Finally, the longer and more frequently a patient is hospitalized, the more likely that he will ultimately be classified as a schizophrenic. All of these qualifications, while significant, do not alter the fact that of all major functional psychiatric disorders, schizophrenia commands the greatest reliability in diagnosis.

in or out of the hospital has been largely reserved for those patients whose symptoms were exaggerated and who were acutely ill. With limited resources and personnel, the more floridly ill were the most likely to receive what attention was available. Home care offers to all patients continuous management not otherwise possible.

Present evidence from drug and other studies indicates that care given to schizophrenic patients only in times of acute episodes is far from adequate treatment.[2] Indeed, continued drug and other treatment is exceedingly important not only in the control of acute flareups but also in reducing the frequency or eliminating entirely the periodic episodes normally resulting in hospitalization. *This type of continuous care, then, in the absence of knowledge of the etiology or specific treatment of schizophrenia may be, and probably is, the only type of prevention available to us now.* Such secondary prevention is clearly preferable to releasing patients back home without follow-up care and treatment and with the certain knowledge that many will return again for another round of hospitalization. *Thus, in hard terms, nearly half of the hospital control patients, 25 of 54, after an average initial period of 83 days in the state hospital had to be rehospitalized.* This is not only uneconomic but unnecessary since, as this study indicates so definitively, much of both the initial institutionalization and the rehospitalization could have been prevented by even a modest home care program.[3]

It is instructive to compare the community home care approach with the historic hospital treatment accorded the schizophrenic. In the hospital, between acute episodes, patients are mostly left alone to stare vacantly into space, to walk down the corridors and back again, to sit, rock, and hallucinate, or to partake of inmate culture. In time, this lack of normal stimulation—intellectual, interpersonal, even physical—has

[2] Martin Katz and Jonathan Cole, "Research on Drugs and Community Care," *A.M.A. Arch. gen. Psychiat.*, **7** (November, 1962), 345–359.

[3] On this point, recent data from Maryland indicate that of 1,984 state hospital psychotic patient admissions, 55 percent were released in 3 months, 74 percent in 6 months, and 85 percent within a year. Of those released within the year, 17 percent required rehospitalization within 3 months, 37 percent in 12 months, and 45 percent in 18 months. (It is these rehospitalizations which were prevented in the home care study.) See "Patterns of Retention, Release and Rehospitalization," Statistics Newsletters, Department of Mental Hygiene, State of Maryland, December 10, 1965.

usually resulted in deterioration and impairment of functioning which was wholly unnecessary.[4] Between episodes, many of these patients could have been released had there been any provision for supervision and aftercare. As a result, because such patients were lost in the institutional process and were not frequently returned to the world outside the hospital walls, schizophrenia became identified in the public (and often in the professional) mind with hopelessness and despair. In the past, instead of questioning the necessity for continued and prolonged hospitalization, the focal point of concern was the humanizing of the institution itself. Hardly anyone, before the advent of the psychoactive drugs plus the other changes described at the outset of this volume, was foolhardy enough to propose seriously that hospitalized schizophrenics could survive the pressures of living in a normal family setting without harm to themselves or to others. Whatever else may eventuate from this investigation and related studies, one conclusion seems warranted: in the absence of considerable deterioration, an acute episode, or grossly exaggerated symptoms, no special reason exists for keeping schizophrenic patients hospitalized.[5] Community facilities now being established and those already in existence are reasonable, preferable, and necessary alternatives.

It is hoped that this study and its findings will serve as a model for demonstration projects and programs for care and treatment of the aged, the retarded, and even the alcoholic and addicted, all of whom have been woefully neglected and shunted aside. The aged and the retarded, in particular, share many of the characteristics of the schizophrenic—chronicity, disabling character of the problem, poor functioning, limited productive or economic potential, and of course, the absence of specific treatment. Like the schizophrenic, too, the senile and retarded numerically constitute an inordinately large number of all those newly admitted and resident in state institutions. Home care and drug and other therapy would seem to be most applicable as a substitute for institutionalization and in reducing the hopelessness and stigma presently associated with these problems.

[4] See again. *Mental Disorders: A Guide to Control Methods*, American Public Health Association, 1962, Chapter 1.

[5] Even, and perhaps especially, family-less schizophrenics deliberately excluded from this study who might be placed in hostels.

The Community Mental Health Center

The Institute Treatment Center home care study has significant implications not only for the management and treatment of schizophrenia as a psychiatric disorder but for the community mental health center movement as well.

In the past one of the major drawbacks to community programs was the presumed risk involved in keeping disturbed persons outside a custodial setting. Families were afraid to take such risks, physicians were not enthusiastic either, and the police and courts were certainly not willing to propose any such reorientation. The ITC study, and other posthospital outcome investigations, have shown that the risks to patient, family, and community are well within the range of tolerance and acceptance. Actually, once the very high risk patients are screened out, the remaining patients are not very dangerous. It may even be possible to return potentially aggressive and violent patients to home care once they have been given very short term and intensive therapy as inpatients and treated continuously thereafter as outpatients. Of the patients seen by the ITC staff and found otherwise eligible for study inclusion by diagnosis, age, and place of residence, only 5 percent were deemed suicidal or too disturbed to warrant risking their admission to the program. Also, during the 30 months of the program, two patients (both placebo) attempted suicide through an overdose of medication and the behavior of several of the failure cases necessitated calling the police. Surely these negative experiences are no worse than those encountered in a posthospital population or conceivably for that matter even in a general population.[6]

The important thing in establishing community mental health center programs is to make sure that community leadership and the mass media as well as the various professions are alerted and educated

[6] Mark Lefton, Simon Dinitz, Shirley Angrist, and Benjamin Pasamanick, "Former Mental Patients and their Neighbors: A Comparison of Performance Levels," *J.Hlth & human Behav.*, in press. See also, Kathleen Smith, Muriel W. Pumphrey, and Julian C. Hall, "The 'Last Straw': The Decisive Incident Resulting in the Request for Hospitalization in 100 Schizophrenic Patients," *Amer. J. Psychiat.*, **120** (September, 1963), 228–233. Some of this discussion is taken from and/or parallels the content of Dinitz, Scarpitti, Albini, Lefton, and Pasamanick, "An Experimental Study in the Prevention of Hospitalization and Schizophrenics: Thirty Months Experience," *Amer. J. Orthopsychiat.*, **35** (January, 1965), 8–9.

to the objectives, meaning, and nature of community mental health care and mostly to the *scientific basis* for the program. This is a task for the various county and state mental health associations and for the "helping professions" in general. The job of gaining acceptance for community mental health center care will be far easier in the larger urban areas which already have outpatient centers, open door institutions, and clinics of various kinds, than in the less urbanized areas where psychiatry may still be viewed with some suspicion.

At the present time patients and their families are very likely to defer seeking care because such treatment means being "put away," voluntarily or by commitment, in a custodial mental hospital. In removing the fears and images long associated with almost automatic institutionalization of schizophrenics and possibly also of other psychotics, the community mental health center and its diverse facilities should encourage earlier identification and earlier treatment of disturbed persons in a community. The anxieties of the patient and the guilt of the families in having played an active role in the removal of the patient would also largely be eliminated. This, in turn, would create a spiral effect. Once the fears, anxieties, and guilt are gone, the mental patient may come to be viewed as not very much different from other chronically ill, ineffective, and inadequate people. The archaic system which made the mentally ill into social pariahs—feared, shunned, and isolated—will then be changed. In analogical terms, then, what psychoanalysis did to alter attitudes and to facilitate the acceptance of the nonpsychotic disorders, the newer drugs and community mental health center care will almost certainly do for the psychotic and other more serious disorders.

A related issue which merits extended discussion concerns the nature and inclusiveness of the community mental health approach. Why are so many different kinds of services—inpatient, outpatient, emergency, day care, night care, and others—needed for an adequate program? Why isn't it enough to send patients to a general hospital where they can be treated intensively for a week or two and then returned home to convalesce as they would if they had almost any other type of disorder? General hospital care would just about eliminate all the negative aspects associated with the concept of mental illness, would be reasonably inexpensive, and the costs could be wholly or partly defrayed by hospital insurance plans. With drugs, psychotherapy, group therapy, and other treatment techniques which could be continued after general hospital discharge, the treatment of the mental disorders could finally be integrated into the mainstream of medical practice in the United States.

Unfortunately for the patient, his family, and for society, too, a complete reliance on general hospital care for the mentally ill, as some have persistently urged, is a short-sighted prescription. Except for acute, self-limited, brief, general medical problems, and for the more affluent patients who can then help themselves, the general hospital does not offer the range of care that the chronically ill (as well as) lower- and even middle-class patients require. For one thing, the general hospital assumes responsibility for patients for only a very short time period —a week or two, or rarely, a month. It is not geared for patients who need 60, 90, or more days of intermediate management—and at $30–$40 per day. To all intents and purposes the patient has no history other than that which is germane and specific to the medical problem leading to his hospital admission. Nothing much is known of his background and functioning as a person. He enters the hospital as a stranger and leaves a stranger. In between the coming and leaving, the patient is treated only in terms of the specific medical problems he presents. Sometimes there is not even treatment of medical complaints other than those specific to his hospitalization. Certainly there is very little attention devoted to the patient's family, economic, psychological, and social problems. After hospital discharge, there is no follow-up. Little is done to prevent the recurrence of the problem, to alleviate related conditions, to guide or counsel the patient, or to provide him with the wide variety of services that may be needed. The hospital washes its hands of the patient and his problems once discharge occurs.

These limitations of the general hospital have been described, discussed, and argued at length and in detail in connection with the larger question of providing adequate medical care. To replace the state hospital with the general hospital as the chief medical treatment center for the mentally disturbed is only to substitute fragmented and partial services for poorer ones.

On the practical level, too, experience in the ITC home care project confirmed the need for a much more inclusive, integrated, and broadly based program than the general hospital could conceivably offer. The treatment of the ITC patients wtih drugs and public health nursing care, although very successful in keeping them at home, left much to be desired. In the daily operation of the Center, and as exemplified in the case history materials, too, a very sizable number of patients needed specialized services which were either not readily available or too costly for them. These included both general and specialized medical and dental care, vocational counseling and guidance, family counseling, and homemaking services.

Male patients, although generally better in their functioning than before admission to the study, were still all too often inadequate as employees. Not only did they need vocational evaluation, guidance, and placement services, but many could have benefited from a more or less pressure-free job environment such as that in a sheltered workshop situation. Since productive work is the central role of the male, it is difficult to see how patients can be returned to normal functioning unless some provision is made for them to be gainfully employed and stimulated within the limits of their abilities and tolerance levels for stress. Thus, community program planners need seriously consider establishing or utilizing existing sheltered workshops not only to serve patients who may some day be employable but for those whose employability will be problematic in the foreseeable future.

On the other side of the coin, many female patients, if they are to remain in the community for protracted periods, will require help with child care, cooking, shopping, cleaning, and in the performance of routine household tasks. Since most families cannot afford to employ domestic help even when confronted with prolonged or even temporary inability of the wife and mother to assume her responsibilities, any comprehensive program must somehow incorporate such services—if only for the sake of the other family members and the functioning of the household.

Similarly, family members need, want, and deserve professional advice as well as reassurance in their relationships with the patient. Unfortunately, there is and can be no manual on how to deal with a disturbed person in the household. Still, questions do arise and decisions must be made. The ITC nurses were continually besieged with questions about patient management, prognosis, and treatment. The nurses were frequently as baffled as the family members in answering these questions. The staff psychiatrist and, more immediately, the staff social worker provided many of the answers to the nurses, who then relayed them to the families. Family counseling personnel and services would have great value in reassuring and helping the famliies cope with troublesome and worrisome patient behavior. Even beyond this immediate gain, state hospital schizophrenic patients and many community referred cases, too, come from multiproblem families and settings that are hardly conducive to patient welfare. While family counseling cannot resolve these difficulties or generate improvement in the low socioeconomic status of the families, it can be of great utility when combined with more specific services such as job placement, homemaking help, and remedying or at least alleviating some of the economic problems.

Thought should also be given to relieving part of the load of patient supervision which now falls exclusively to family members. Even the most tolerant, accepting, and loving husband, wife, or parent will almost inevitably become disenchanted with home and community treatment unless the burdens and worries and stress can at times be relaxed. Again, the case histories as well as the reports of the public health nurses amply document the need to work out arrangements which would give the responsible family members occasional respite from the unceasing concern with patient care. There are a number of ways this can be achieved. For example, a community mental health facility might well include a day care center featuring recreational activities, social participation in organized groups, and occupational therapy. Equally or even more valuable would be a night hospital facility or even a less pretentious hostel where patients can be sent for overnight care and housing on those occasions when they become too difficult and disruptive. Such a facility would have made a very important contribution to the ITC program and possibly conserved several of the failures whose families were still willing but no longer able to tolerate the stress of having the sick member constantly at home.

One of the errors in design in the ITC investigation is instructive for planning community mental health center facilities. In attempting to show that hospitalization could be prevented by sound home care procedures and drug therapy, patients newly admitted to the state hospital were returned to their families within a day or two after their admission and prior to receiving any therapy at all. Inevitably their behavior was little better than at the time of hospitalization. Since several failed within 7 days and even more within a fortnight, it is likely that at least some of these patients might have succeeded had their acute manifestations of illness been reduced or alleviated prior to their return home. Many other families in which the patients managed to remain at home would have been much happier, less skeptical, and more cooperative had the patients been treated in a hospital setting for a few days or even a week before being returned to them.

To eliminate this problem, a community mental health center facility should include an emergency care service either attached to a general hospital or to a local short term inpatient mental health institute where patients can be treated intensively for a short time or until sufficiently stable to be sent home. If properly managed and administered, these emergency and short-run treatment settings will neither stigmatize and isolate the patient nor place him back with the family before he and they are prepared for his return.

Thus, in the course of the 30 months of home care of schizophrenic patients it became abundantly clear why planning for community mental health centers had to be predicated on the criteria of continuous, coordinated, and comprehensive services. According to these guidelines, essential elements in such a facility should include: inpatient and outpatient services, partial hospitalization facilities such as day care or night care or both, emergency 24-hour services, and consultation and education services to professional personnel and community agencies. Beyond these essential services an adequate or more complete center would also provide diagnostic and evaluative services, rehabilitative activities such as vocational programs, pre- and after care services, training, and research.

Had the ITC program continued to operate beyond its experimental expiration date, the nature, intensity, and quality of the problems of the schizophrenic patients would have compelled a broader and more inclusive array of services, more closely interwoven with other welfare and health agencies in the community, and providing more continuous (longitudinal) services.

The Cost of Adequate Care[7]

The ITC program being limited to a research rather than a treatment focus does not in itself permit of generalizations regarding the costs of adequate community mental health care.

[7] On the topic of costs, see Rashi Fein, *Economics of Mental Health:* (Report to the Joint Commission on Mental Illness and Health), No. 2, New York: Basic Books, 1958.

The ITC project, as such, was quite costly principally because of its research aspects. No doubt without the research expenditures, the patient costs might have been acceptable and comparable to those for intensive outpatient care. Without going into elaborate fiscal details, a similar home care program with a case load of 400 patients, but without research and evaluation procedures, would not be substantially less expensive than the present United States per capita mental hospital operating outlays of approximately $6 per patient-day. It is estimated that a clinic serving 400 schizophrenic home care patients would require the services of a full-time psychiatrist, a clinical psychologist, two psychiatric social workers, and eight public health nurses as well as psychiatric aides and secretarial personnel.

The addition of any care facilities such as a sheltered workshop, family counseling services, or an occupational therapy program would add substantially to the costs involved in home care treatment. An even modestly enriched program realistically would cost more per capita than present patient expenditures, but probably still less than services in state hospital admission and treatment units which average about $15 to $20 a day.

Thus, home care programs will not materially reduce the financial problems besetting mental institutions. However these home care programs will (1) prevent the hospitalization of a very significant number of schizophrenics, (2) provide continuous care for patients including regular visits from a public health nurse, contact with a psychiatrist and psychologist, and community services through a social worker, (3) prevent most patients from experiencing the problems associated with hospitalization, (4) educate families to develop a more accepting attitude toward the patient, and (5) reduce to some extent the need for providing more beds at an approximate average cost of $10,000 each for the care of the mentally ill.

If even modestly expanded home care programs, as noted, are not likely to be very much less expensive than intensive hospitalization, community mental health centers featuring comprehensive, coordinated, and continuous services will surely be very much more expensive. State expenditures for mental health care will have to be increased, perhaps doubled or even quadrupled, if these new center programs are to operate according to the specifications outlined for them. Whatever the additional sources of funds to be tapped—federal, private insurance, medicare—states must be prepared to increase their support of mental health care and treatment or else these emerging centers will have no more chance for success than did the state hospital system.

In view of these cost factors, if for no other reason, it is mandatory that the efficacy of each component service and facility be studied and evaluated, through careful research, for its contribution to the total mental health center program before it becomes permanent. Unless this is done services may proliferate that, while generally desirable, add little to the overall substance and efficacy of the community program. At present, basic services are costly and in short supply. Thus, community mental health centers cannot afford to be saddled with activities whose impact for prevention and treatment are negligible or which can be better provided in another context or by other agencies.

Despite these cautions regarding the inclusion of only necessary and efficacious services, it is equally necessary to avoid rejecting or including services solely on a cost basis. One of the ironies of the "cost accounting mentality," which has even become fashionable with professionals who should be immune by now, is to accept per patient expenditures for state hospital care as the cost baseline for judging the budgets for other kinds of service. This mentality can preclude improvement. Services and facilities should instead be evaluated in terms of their *efficacy for patient welfare.* Relating them to the minimal per patient operating expenses of the state hospital is to use a faulty and misleading yardstick. One of the reasons for the present rebellion against the state hospital as a treatment center derives precisely from the fact that the state hospital system was starved so long that it could not innovate very much, attract many capable professionals, or provide much in the way of therapy. Chronic shortages of funds fostered a custodial orientation. It was and still is cheaper to do nothing than something. In offering something, community treatment will of necessity be more costly, at least in its initial stages. In view of the staggering direct and indirect costs of mental disorder to society, the monetary difference between more adequate and less adequate treatment should not be subjected to unimaginative accounting techniques.

Manpower Implications

One of the most critical, even desperate, needs in the whole mental health area is for trained staff to serve the sizable number of patients who seek care and treatment for their diverse neuropsychiatric disorders.[8] Indeed, as the population of the United States increases, doubling every 37 years, the gap between the small numbers of professionals who can provide treatment and those ever larger numbers who need it, will steadily widen. Unfortunately, there are not enough private and institutional mental health specialists to staff the various facilities even now in operation. Thus, the small manpower gains so laboriously achieved since World War II will soon be entirely depleted. The devastating complaint of the state hospital professionals that the community mental health centers will denude them of staff is not without foundation. Gains in the community area will come at the expense of the institutional setting. The state hospital will not only be treating the least hopeful patients, such as those who failed or were ineligible for community care, but will be doing so with fewer and less capable staff members.

The logic of the problem is as simple as it is distressing. As Albee has indicated, some 7200 physicians accept internships each year. Nearly every one of these physicians is needed as a replacement for those who die or retire. Meanwhile, some 3 million people are added to the United States population each year. To maintain the present physician-population ratio requires 4000 new physicians *above* the 7200 replacements! Thus, there is an enormous net loss of medical practitioners every year.[9] Given present facilities for training, and the seemingly unchanging and frequently dysfunctional traditions of both training and practice itself, this lag is not likely to be much reduced in the near future.

The situation in psychiatry is just as gloomy. Although there are presently some 16,000 trained psychiatrists in the United States, a fourfold increase in the last two decades, and although the percentage of medical school graduates interested in the specialty of psychiatry has risen, the demand still dwarfs the supply. Further, since the vast majority of psychiatrists are in private practice and can see only a very small number of patients, the great mass of predominantly psychotic lower-class patients have almost no access to these practitioners. Also, outside of the highly urban areas psychiatrists are nearly as scarce as

[8] With regard to manpower, see George W. Albee, *Mental Health Manpower Trends*, (Report to the Joint Commission on Mental Illness and Health), No. 3, New York: Basic Books, 1959.

[9] George W. Albee, unpublished speech.

phrenologists. In 28 southeastern Ohio counties with a population of about a million persons, for example, there were four psychiatrists in 1965. In less wealthy and populous states, even this very inadequate ratio would seem excellent by comparison. Finally, even when a patient is institutionalized in a public mental hospital his access to a psychiatrist is still extremely limited. He may even have trouble seeing an ordinary hospital physician, psychologist, graduate nurse, or social worker. Many clinical psychologists and psychiatric social workers, following the example of medical people, are entering private practice, often in conjunction with psychiatrists.

Despite these problems, there has been a steady improvement in the patient-personnel ratios since World War II in state hospitals.[10] Yet, patient-personnel ratios were probably as good or better before World War II when professional staff left to serve in the war effort. This steady improvement, then, is from a very low point indeed, and may still be under pre-war levels of staffing. One estimate indicates that it will be at least another decade before state hospitals are staffed for therapy rather than custody. With the steady drain into private and other nonhospital practice and with the community mental health centers almost a reality, it will take far longer than a decade to staff for treatment despite the decrease in the number of resident patients. The state hospital system may yet lose additional ground in the face of these changes.

The ITC project was obviously too narrow in scope to yield generalizations about the problems of staff recruitment, training, responsibilities, and division of labor either in community centers or in state hospitals. Combined with other data, observations, and discussions in the literature, the ITC experience, however, does permit some tentative suggestions about the directions the quest for personnel might take. These suggestions are on three levels: (1) the recruitment of wholly new and presently inexperienced and nonprofessional persons into mental health work, (2) recruitment of professional persons not now connected directly with the treatment of the mentally disturbed, and (3) the reorientation of the psychiatric profession and the refocusing of psychiatric training and practice.

[10] *Fact Sheet,* Joint Information Service, American Psychiatric Association and National Association for Mental Health, No. 1, March, 1957.

Recruitment of nonprofessionals. It is the hallmark of highly technological societies like ours that proportionately more and more people are involved in service occupations than in materially productive jobs. In truth, proportionately fewer and fewer persons are required to man the assembly lines and to expend their physical energies in the production of goods. Automation and increasing affluence are causing or will shortly result in monumental changes in the type of work people do, in their preparation for it, and in their attitudes towards it. The upshot of this technological revolution is that, among other changes like increasing leisure, there will be a substantial segment of the population whose labor can now be channeled into the public sector and into health, welfare, and educational activities. This trend is already partly visible in the volunteer and community activity fields. Health causes of one kind or another enlist large numbers of volunteers and well-meaning amateurs who do some excellent work, especially in soliciting funds. The point is that this fund of manpower, with a bit of training or at least realistic exposure to the mental health field, could contribute on a part-time or even full-time salaried basis as mental health visitors, as sympathetic listeners, in child care activities, as patient "sitters" to relieve family members, as group discussion leaders, and in a myriad of other useful ways.

Such people, once the roles and responsibilities were clearly defined, could relieve professional personnel of many of the time-consuming chores which now prevent the most efficient utilization of their skills. Just as an aide or ward attendant probably knows the patients most intimately and can communicate with patients most freely and observe, record, and report, if not evaluate, changes in functioning, so nonprofessional people would be able to provide the support and empathy which patients and families need. Mental health centers will be compelled to rely on untrained staff members to carry on many of the routine activities. Under supervision, such staff can not only relieve the shortage, but can turn into useful and important functionaries, even if still technically remaining nonprofessional people.

Recruitment of Professionals from Other Fields. A reorientation in the nature of psychiatric care through greater reliance on methods other than institutionalization in a state hospital makes it possible to use trained and qualified people in the treatment process who were previously excluded from involvement in such care. If there is one implication of this study for manpower recruitment and training which should be acted on quickly, it is that there are many professional people in the community who, with a modest degree of familiarity with mental illness and its problems and treatment, could be utilized to provide care. The mental health specialist, and particularly the psychiatrist, the clinical psychologist, and the psychiatric social worker instead of providing only direct service could function also as consultants to these other persons. This would compel them to grapple with practical alternatives in treatment, to interest themselves in case outcome, and to expand what for all too many is a dogmatic, parochial conception of etiology and dynamics, which presently precludes experimenting and embracing new treatment techniques.

More to the point of reducing the manpower shortage is the concrete evidence that public health nurses, with intensive training, can be utilized in community mental health center programs, especially home care. Thousands of highly respected public health nurses with access to a great many homes can be effectively enlisted in such programs. It is likely that after considerable experimentation and operational research, the public health nurse will be able to integrate some mental health functions into her daily nursing practice.

Not only can public health nurses play a major role in community oriented projects but so could practical nurses, particularly in relieving the family of the ceaseless responsibility of care and supervision. Home economists, too, could create a useful role in the training and supervising of homemakers, and in helping female patients plan and carry out routine household chores. Classes offered at or in conjunction with community mental health centers could prepare and school some of the female patients in the performance of these instrumental roles. Vocational training and education specialists could also participate in these endeavors once it is recognized that schizophrenia and other forms of mental illness affect not only the psychological but the economic, social, and familial functioning of the patient, and that psychiatric care alone, however adequate, will sometimes do very little to improve functioning and reduce incompetence in these other areas.

Similarly, teachers, social workers, occupational and recreational therapists, and other specialists not now involved in mental health care to any appreciable extent could also be recruited and utilized. Finally, and above all, the general medical practitioner is the largest and most important source of potential manpower. His participation in mental health care is surely a necessity if community programs are to operate at maximum efficiency. Yet this participation, crucial as it is, may present the largest problem.

The general medical practitioner had traditionally avoided, in so far as possible, the extended treatment of mentally ill patients. For one thing, he had no specific cures in his bag. For another, his medical training was largely devoid of any serious preparation for treating or even understanding the problems involved in mental illness. For a third, he tended to become inured to the complaints of his more mildly disturbed patients by classifying them as "nervous" and avoiding them as too demanding of his time and effort. The seriously psychotic he arranged to have confined to hospitals and consequently learned little about them. Finally, it was a seeming waste of time to be involved with disturbed patients—time could more usefully be given to the treatment of other patients with more well defined ailments. Thus, the medical profession generally shunned the mental health area, and in so doing, not only relegated psychiatry to a low status as a medical specialty, but encouraged psychiatry in America to dissociate itself from the mainstream of scientific and pragmatic medical practice.

The community mental health center movement and the drug revolution permits the medical practitioner to make a new start in the treatment of disturbed patients. By providing a nearby facility for patients who need intensive care, and the opportunity to work and interact with mental health specialists, the community program enables the medical generalist to become better informed and educated in this field, and to become involved by carrying some of the patients himself. Apart from the mechanics, which are always difficult to define and implement at the outset, the entry of local physicians as well as other community based professionals into this area will help make of neuropsychiatric impairment a legitimate disease problem not unlike others now being handled routinely, if not always wholly effectively, in a rehabilitation context.

The New Psychiatrist. The community mental health center era, now just around the corner, will not only usher in a new era of treatment by persons never before directly participating in such care and in facilities that are new in concept and use, but it also will profoundly affect psychiatric training and practice.[11]

In the past, two distinct strains of psychiatric practice were evident. There was, on the one hand, a small number of psychiatrists who went into the practice of institutional psychiatry. Too few in number to be very effective in the state hospital as far as providing individual patients with treatment, many of these psychiatrists were elevated into administrative posts both in the hospitals and in the central offices of the state departments of mental health. Composed of a great many altruists, even more foreign physicians who were preparing for examinations so that they could obtain a medical license to practice, and many depression era graduates in psychiatry, these men and women were preoccupied with the problems of mass care in institutions geared to custody. The second group consisted of the vast majority of psychiatrists who preferred private rather than institutional practice. In the main, the private practice of psychiatry involved, and still does, the treatment of predominately nonpsychotic patients, of middle-class status, in the professional occupations, and with college education. These "Significant Americans"[12] were seen in pleasant surroundings and treated with respect and dignity. The treatment given them was psychotherapy that is severely limited by the patient's ability to communicate, conceptualize, understand, and reconstruct life's experiences.[13]

Psychiatric training programs tended to follow the latter strain. Little emphasis was devoted to diagnosis and classification, to work in the basic biological sciences, to the social sciences, to treatment other than psychotherapy and its variants, and to research. The narrow parochialism of schools and of dogma characterized much of the training and tended to create "true believers" rather than scientifically oriented practitioners. At any rate, this type of preparation was reasonably well suited to the art, if not the science, of psychiatry. Of course, not every training center featured this orientation. It was the exceptions

[11] This section based on paper presented by Benjamin Pasamanick, "Education for the Future Instead of the Past" at the American Psychiatric Association Meeting in New York City, May, 1965.

[12] A felicitous term serving as the title of a recent book: John Cuber and Peggy Harroff, *The Significant Americans*, New York: Appleton-Century, 1965.

[13] August B. Hollingshead and Frederick C. Redlich, *Social Class and Mental Illness*, New York: Wiley, 1958.

plus the European training centers that perpetuated what there is of a more or less scientific stream in modern psychiatry.

The issue here is far from academic. The very modest, even minimal, ITC program if adopted nationally, for example, would require the services of about one-third of all psychiatrists in the United States. Comprehensive community mental health centers would exhaust the supply entirely. Since community care seems to be the trend for the future, training programs must begin to prepare psychiatrists for the future, not the past; for dealing with the majority of the mentally ill, not only the minority; for treating the medically indigent as well as the affluent; for providing care for the psychotic and not only the neurotic.

To achieve this goal of preparing psychiatrists for participation in such programs and for dealing with large numbers of patients, let us consider a number of suggestions for training. First, psychiatric training must be made comparable to genuine graduate level education rather than continuing along the apprenticeship-preceptor model presently in vogue. With the rapid acceleration in the accumulation of knowledge, the preceptorship system makes little sense now and probably less sense for the future. Second, graduate education in psychiatry must be concerned with producing thoroughly educated practitioners who are knowledgeable in the life and social sciences in addition to having clinical competence. Of special importance should be those biological disciplines specifically concerned with nervous system structure and functioning such as neuroanatomy, neuroendocrinology, and neurochemistry, and those concerned with abnormal functioning such as neuropathology and neurology. In the social sciences, more than a superficial knowledge of psychology and sociology is nearly mandatory. Third, as things stand now in residency programs in psychiatry, the resident (trainee) provides much of the care of patients and in turn is paid a small salary, given minimal formal clinical and other instruction and some supervision of his practice and activities. Without residents, patient care would be minimal at the very best, and the system would probably collapse entirely. In this situation residents are overworked, and not enough time is ever available for even proper clinical instruction to say nothing of basic scientific education. This obviously must be remedied. Fourth, residents in psychiatry are in a seller's market. This means that they are in a position to determine, by where they go and whether they remain in training, what will be taught them and in what proportions. As a result, basic biological and social science education, being less palatable and glamorous, becomes secondary to psychodynamics, psychotherapy, and individual analyses. Less adequate preparation for participation in community mental health center care could hardly be imagined. Nor could a more frustrating task be placed before such a practitioner when he is expected to utilize in everyday practice techniques and concepts that he cannot understand.

The enormity and circularity of the problem is thus evident. Treatment is moving in one direction, training remains rooted in the other. Psychiatrists are being prepared to practice a form of medicine which is already archaic, utilizing knowledge and skills which daily approach obsolescence. Training more psychiatrists in this framework cannot resolve the dilemma, since as Walter E. Barton put it, "The numbers of persons requiring help are such as to make prolonged psychotherapy impractical in the majority of cases."[14] It is conceivable, however, that given proper training so that they could be better integrated and play a more appropriate role in mental health care, we might not require the enormous increase in the number of psychiatrists presently projected. The obvious need then is for practitioners to be so well trained, so eclectic, and so adaptable that they can deal successfully with large numbers of patients in a community setting by utilizing a variety of treatment methods as need, experiment, and ingenuity justify.

These recommendations obviously go far beyond the ITC study itself. Most will agree with some, but fewer with all of the assumptions, implications, and suggestions made here. Yet, whether to accept or reject none, some, or all of these implications is less important than is the recognition that the findings of this carefully controlled experimental home care investigation offer concrete and indisputable support for the validity of the community mental health center approach in the treatment of mental illness. Such a recognition presses for implementation, and implementation requires some sharp changes in current thinking and associated professional practices.

[14] Walter E. Barton, Introduction to *The Community Mental Health Center: An Analysis of Existing Models* by Raymond Glasscote, David Sanders, H. M. Forstenzer, and A. R. Foley, American Psychiatric Association, 1964, p. xvi.

Appendix A

TESTS AND INSTRUMENTS

SOCIAL HISTORY INVENTORY

Patient's Name ____
(Last) (First) (MI)

Patient's Address ____
(No.) (Street) (City) (County)

____
Phone Number

Respondent's Name ____
(Last) (First) (MI)

Respondent's Address ____
(No.) (Street) (City) (County)

____
Phone Number

Interviewer ____

Date of 1st Interview ______________________ (End interview only at the end of a section)
(Month) (Day) (Year)

Date of 2nd Interview ______________________ (N/A if schedule completed first time)
(Month) (Day) (Year)

SECTION I

Column
1, 2, 3 ___ ITC case no.

4 _ Study group

5, 6 __ Month patient (pt) admitted to treatment program

Card: Column

__ 01 January __ 07 July
__ 02 February __ 08 August
__ 03 March __ 09 September
__ 04 April __ 10 October
__ 05 May __ 11 November
__ 06 June __ 12 December

7 __ Year pt admitted to treatment program (1, 2, 3)

8 __ For how long were pt and respondent living together prior to pt's hospitalization?

__ 1 Were not living together
__ 2 One or two weeks
__ 3 Three or four weeks
__ 4 One to three months
__ 5 More than three months

9 __ Respondent's relationship to pt

__ 1 Husband __ 6 Sister
__ 2 Wife __ 7 Grandparent
__ 3 Father __ 8 Other relative (specify) ________
__ 4 Mother
__ 5 Brother __ 9 Friend
0 Other (specify) ________

10 __ Sex of pt

__ 1 Male __ 2 Female

11, 12 __ __ Card number (this card is 01)

1: 13, 14 __ __ Birthdate – month

__ 01 January __ 07 July
__ 02 February __ 08 August
__ 03 March __ 09 September
__ 04 April __ 10 October
__ 05 May __ 11 November
__ 06 June __ 12 December
__ XX DK (No information)

Card: Column

1: 15 __ Birthdate – year ____________

1:16, 17 __ __ Exact age ___ (within 6 months of birthday)

1:18 __ Marital status

__ 1 Married
__ 2 Single (never married)
__ 3 Widowed
__ 4 Divorced
__ 5 Separated
__ 6 Common-law
__ 7 Casual alliance or other
__ X DK

1:19 __ Religion (pt's preference)

__ 1 Protestant (Methodist, Congregationalist, Presbyterian, Baptist, Lutheran, Unitarian, Episcopalian, Quaker, etc.)
__ 2 "Fundamentalist" (Seventh Day Adventist, Nazarene, Pillar of Fire, etc.)
__ 3 Roman Catholic
__ 4 Eastern Orthodox (Greek, Syrian)
__ 5 Christian Scientist
__ 6 Mormon
__ 7 Jewish
__ 8 Atheist or Agnostic
__ 9 None
__ 0 Mohammedan, Buddhist, Hindu
__ X DK

1:20 __ Race

__ 1 White
__ 2 Negro
__ 3 Other
__ X DK

Pt's occupation

Record actual occupation ____________________
(note if student or house-wife)

Card: Column

Check all appropriate categories which follow:

Interviewer

___1 Self-employed
___2 Retired
___3 Regular job with regular income (full time)
___4 Regular job with regular income (part time)
___5 Sporadic employment (odd jobs)
___6 If farmer: tenant yes___no___

Approx. size of farm ___________________
___X DK

1:21 ___ Coder only (see manual)

1:22 ___ Pt's education

___1 Graduate professional training
___2 Standard college or university graduation
___3 Partial college training
___4 High school graduation
___5 Partial high school (10th–11th grades)
___6 Junior high school (7th–9th grades)
___7 Less than 7 years of school (6th grade or less)
___X DK

Husband's occupation

Record actual occupation ___________________________
(if husband is pt write pt above)

Check all appropriate categories which follow:

Interviewer

___1 Self-employed
___2 Retired or deceased (underline which)
___3 Regular job with regular income (full time)
___4 Regular job with regular income (part time)
___5 Sporadic employment (odd jobs)
___6 If farmer: tenant yes___no___

Approx. size of farm ___________________
___X DK

1:23 ___ Coder only (see manual)

Card: Column

1: 24__ Husband's education

__1 Graduate professional training
__2 Standard college or university graduation
__3 Partial college training
__4 High school graduation
__5 Partial high (10th-11th grade)
__6 Junior high school (7th-9th grades)
__7 Less than 7 years of school (6th grade or less)
__X DK

Father's occupation (note : record for real father, if for step-father, underline)

Record actual occupation ______________________

Check all appropriate cagetories which follow:

Interviewer

__1 Self-employed
__2 Retired or deceased (underline which)
__3 Regular job with regular income (part time)
__4 Regular job with regular income (part time)
__5 Sporadic employment (odd jobs)
__6 If farmer: tenant yes__ no__

Approx. size of farm ______________________
__X DK

1: 25__ Coder only (see manual)

1: 26__ Father's education (note : record for real father if possible; if for step-father, underline)

__1 Graduate professional training
__2 Standard college or university graduation
__3 Partial college training
__4 High school graduation
__5 Partial high school (10th - 11 grades)
__6 Junior high school (7th - 9th grades)
__7 Less than 7 years of school (6th grade or less)
__X DK

1: 27-29 ______ HI Index (coder only: see manual)

Card: Column

1: 30__ Birthplace of pt

__1 U.S.A.
__2 Foreign born (specify)
__X DK

1: 31__
__1 Kentucky
__2 Other (specify)
__X DK

1: 32__
__1 Jefferson County
__2 Hardin
__3 Bullitt
__4 Nelson
__5 Spencer
__6 Shelby
__7 Oldham
__8 Trimble
__9 Henry
__0 Carroll
__X DK
__X N/A

1: 33__
__1 Farm
__2 Village, under 2500 population
__3 Small town, 2500-10,000
__4 Small city, 10,000-50,000
__5 Medium sized city, 50,000-10,000
__6 Suburban community where many residents commute to a large city
__7 Large city, over 10,000 population
__X DK

1:34 __ Pt's living arrangement immediately prior to present hospitalization (check the most important)

__1 Alone
__2 With husband or wife (or person of opposite sex, not a blood relative)
__3 With parent(s)
__4 With child or children
__5 With sibling(s)
__6 With other relative(s) (specify)
__7 With roommate(s) or friend(s)

Card: Column

___8 In a group: e.g., dormitory, women's residence, etc.
___9 Other: ______________________________
___X No information or DK

1: 35___ Is this the home situation to which pt will be discharged for home care?

___1 Yes (in either case be certain of address and
___2 No telephone)
___3 X DK

____

____

____

1: 36___ Living arrangement to which pt will go

___1 Alone (N/A)
___2 With spouse
___3 With parents
___4 With child(ren)
___5 With sibling(s)
___6 With other relative(s) (specify) ______________
___7 With roommate(s) or friend(s)
___8 In a group; e.g., dormitory, etc.
___9 Other: ______________________________
___X DK

1: 37___ Pt's home immediately prior to hospitalization (this time)

___1 Farm
___2 Village, under 2500 population
___3 Small town, 2500-10,000
___4 Small city, 10,000-50,000
___5 Medium sized city, 50,000-100,000
___6 Suburban community where many residents commute to a large city
___7 Large city, over 100,000 population
___X DK

1: 38___ Length of residence at present address

Card: Column

__1 Under 1 month
__2 1-6 months
__3 7-12 months
__4 1-3 years
__5 4-7 years
__6 8-10 years
__7 11-15 years
__8 16-20 years
__9 Over 20 years
__X DK

1: 39__ Home locations – number of homes pt has had during past 5 years: Count as a new home any residence of family household for more than 2 weeks which was not a vacation. The minimum possible is "1." Record "X" if no information.

__0 Did not move
__1 - 8 Actual number of times (1,2,3, etc.)
__9 Nine or more moves
__X DK

Family History

1: 40__ Father's birthplace

__1 U.S.A.
__2 Foreign born (specify) ______________
__X DK

1: 41__
__1 Kentucky
__2 Other (specify) ______________
__X DK
__Y N/A

1: 42__
__1 Farm
__2 Village, under 2500 population
__3 Small town, 2500-10,000
__4 Small city, 10,000-50,000
__5 Medium sized city, 50,000-100,000
__6 Suburban community
__7 Large city, over 100,000
__X DK

Card: Column

1: 43 ___ Is father alive?

___ 1 Yes
___ 2 No
___ X DK

Mother's birthplace

1: 44 ___
___ 1 U.S.A.
___ 2 Foreign born (specify)
___ X DK

1: 45 ___
___ 1 Kentucky
___ 2 Other state (specify) ____________________
___ X DK
___ Y N/A

1: 46 ___
___ 1 Farm
___ 2 Village, under 2500 population
___ 3 Small town, 2500-10,000
___ 4 Small city, 10,000-50,000
___ 5 Medium sized city, 50,000
___ 6 Suburban community
___ 7 Large city, over 100,000
___ X DK

1: 47 ___ Is mother alive?

___ 1 Yes
___ 2 No
___ X DK

1: 48 ___ Economic activities of mother

___ 1 No economic activities outside the home
___ 2 Worked part time at steady job outside the home
___ 3 Earned about half the family income
___ 4 Earned all the family income
___ X DK

1: 49 ___ Mother's education (note: if stepmother, underline)

___ 1 Graduate professional training
___ 2 Standard college or university graduation
___ 3 Partial college training

Card: Column

__4 High school graduation
__5 Partial high school (10th-11th grades)
__6 Junior high school (7th-9th grades)
__7 Less than 7 years of school (6th grade or less)
__X DK

1: 50__, 51__ Pt's current or recent relationship with parents: physical

(50) Father	(51) Mother
__1	__1 In same home
__2	__2 Frequent visiting – twice a week or more
__3	__3 Occasional visiting – 1-2 a month
__4	__4 No contact although parent living
__X	__X DK
__Y	__Y N/A (parent dead)

1: 52__, 53__ Pt's current or recent dependency feelings on parents

(52) Father	(53) Mother
__1	__1 Very independent: seldom if ever feels dependent or parent
__2	__2 Fairly independent: sometimes dependent
__3	__3 Neither particularly dependent nor particularly independent
__4	__4 Usually dependent
__5	__5 Completely dependent
__X	__X DK
__Y	__Y N/A (parent dead)

1: 54__ Religious upbringing (not pt's current preference)

__1 Protestant (Methodist, Congregationalist, Presbyterian, Baptist, Lutheran, Unitarian,. Espicopalian, Quaker, etc.)
__2 "Fundamentalist" (Seventh Day Adventist, Nazarene, Pillar of Fire, Fundamentalist Protestant, etc.)

Card: Column

__ 3 Roman Catholic
__ 4 Eastern Orthodox (Greek, Syrian, etc.)
__ 5 Christian Scientist
__ 6 Mormon
__ 7 Jewish
__ 8 Atheist or Agnostic
__ 9 None
__ 0 Mohammedan, Buddhist, Hindu
__ X DK

Pt's Siblings

Include here as siblings all children born alive to the pt's true mother. Be accurate.

1: 55 __ Birth order of pt among his siblings

__ 1 Pt was the first born (an only child will be scored here)
__ 2 Pt was the second born
__ 3 Pt was the third born
__ 4 Pt was the fourth born
__ 5 Pt was the fifth born
__ 6 Pt was the sixth born
__ 7 Pt was the seventh born
__ 8 Pt was the eight born
__ 9 Pt was the ninth born, or more; if more, write actual number here: ________________
__ X No information

1: 56 __ Total number of children born alive to pt's mother:

__ 1 One (an only child will be scored here)
__ 2 Two
__ 3 Three
__ 4 Four
__ 5 Five
__ 6 Six
__ 7 Seven
__ 8 Eight
__ 9 Nine or more; if more, write actual number here: ____
__ X No information

Card: Column

1: 57 __ Multiple births:

__ 1 Pt not a twin nor triplet
__ 2 Pt a twin or triplet
__ X No information

1: 58 __ Do you live in an apartment or house?

__ 1 Apartment
__ 2 House
__ 3 Trailer
__ X DK

1: 59 __ Do you own or rent?

__ 1 Own
__ 2 Rent
__ X DK

1: 60 __ How much does your rent (if owned: taxes, mortgage and interest) come to each month?

Rent Per Month
__ 1 Under $30
__ 2 $31-$40
__ 3 $41-$50
__ 4 $51-$60
__ 5 $61-$70
__ 6 $71-$80
__ 7 $81-$100
__ 8 $101-$120
__ 9 $121-$150 or over
__ X DK
__ Y N/A

1: 61 __ How many rooms do you have?

__ 1-8 (actual number)
__ 9 Nine or more
__ X DK

1: 62 __ How many bedrooms do you have?

__ 1-8 (actual number)

Card: Column

__ 9 Nine or more
__ X DK

1: 63 __ To which of these groups do <u>you</u> feel closest?

__ 1 Working class
__ 2 Middle class
__ 3 Upper class
__ X No information or DK

1: 64 __ What about ***? To which of these groups does he/she feel closest?

__ 1 Working class
__ 2 Middle class
__ 3 Upper class
__ X No information or DK

1: 65 __ How about most of the people who live around you? Where do they belong?

__ 1 Working class
__ 2 Middle class
__ 3 Upper class
__ X No information or DK

1: 66 __ Chief breadwinner in pt's household

__ 1 Pt
__ 2 Pt's husband
__ 3 Pt's father
__ 4 Pt's wife
__ 5 Pt's mother
__ 6 Pt's sibling
__ 7 Pt's uncle
__ 8 Pt's grandparent
__ 9 Other
specify ________________
__ X DX

If breadwinner is not pt, pt's husband or father, record breadwinner's occupation.

____

Check all appropriate categories which follow:

__ 1 Self-employed
__ 2 Retired

Card: Column

Interviewer

__ 3 Regular job with regular income (full time)
__ 4 Regular job with regular income (part time)
__ 5 Sporadic employment (odd jobs)
__ 6 If farmer: tenant yes__ no__

Approx. size of farm: ____________________

__ X DK

1: 67__ Coder only (see manual) occupational code

1: 68__ (If breadwinner is not pt, pt's husband or father, breadwinner's education

__ 1 Graduate professional training
__ 2 Standard college or university graduation
__ 3 Partial college training
__ 4 High school graduation
__ 5 Partial high school (10th-11th grades)
__ 6 Junior high school (7th-9th grades)
__ 7 Less than 7 years of school (6th grade or less)
__ X DK

1: 69 - 71__,__,__ HI Index (coder only: see manual)

1: 72__ Total annual income of breadwinner

__ 1 No income
__ 2 Under $1500
__ 3 $1500-3500
__ 4 $3500-5500
__ 5 $5500-7500
__ 6 $7500-9500
__ 7 $9500-11,500
__ 8 $11,500-13,500
__ 9 Over $13,500
__ X Cannot estimate or DK

Weekly ____________________
Monthly ____________________

1: 73__ Total annual income of pt's household: (approximate dollar amount only, during most recent period of regular work. Include value of room and board where applicable.)

__ 1 No income
__ 2 Under $1500
__ 3 $1500-3500
__ 4 $3500-5500

Card: Column

__ 5 $5500-7500
__ 6 $7500-9500
__ 7 $9500-11,500
__ 8 $11,500-$13,500
__ 9 Over $13,500
__ X Cannot estimate or DK

Weekly ____________

Monthly ____________

1: 74 __ Financial support other than from salaries and wages

__ 1 None
__ 2 Welfare (relief)
__ 3 Pension
__ 4 Insurance (e.g., unemployed benefits)
__ 5 Relatives and/or friends
__ 6 Other (specify) ______________________________
__ 7 Two or more of the above types
__ X DK

SECTION II

Hospital Record

2: 13 __ Hospital or agency making referral to ITC

__ 1 Central State
__ 2 General
__ 3 Bridgehaven
__ 4 Bridgehaven Clinic
__ 5 VA
__ 6 Norton
__ 7 Louisville Outpatient Clinic
__ 8 Private psychiatrist:

name: ______________________________
address: ______________________________
phone: ______________________________

Card: Column

__ 9 Other (specify) ______________________
__ X DK

2: 14 __ How many times before has the pt been hospitalized?

__ 0 Never before hospitalized
__ 1-8 Actual Number of times (1,2,3, etc.)
__ 9 Nine or more times
__ X DK

2: 15, 16__,__ Age at time of first mental hospitalization

__ (Score XY if pt never before hospitalized or XX if DK)

HOSPITAL OR AGENCY CASE NO. ______________

DATE ADMITTED TO HOSPITAL OR AGENCY ______

DIAGNOSIS (including alternatives and sub-classifications)

____

____

____

2: 17 __ Nature of hospital or agency referral

__ 1 Voluntary: pt realizes some kind of visit to a psychiatrist is necessary
__ 2 Ostensibly voluntary: pt comes to a psychiatrist only because of family or social pressure or because he really wants a physical exam
__ 3 Definitely involuntary: pt comes only under direct legal or physical pressure
__ X No information

2: 18 __ Person or agency recommending pt to hospital or clinic

__ 1 self

Card: Column

__2 Spouse
__3 Parent, sibling or child
__4 Medical certificate
__5 Social agency (includes Health Officer Warrant)
__6 Physician or other hospital (except State Hospital transfer and Medical Certificate)
__7 State Hospital Transfer
__8 Court or police
__9 Other ______________________
__X No information

2: 19__ Person who accompanied pt to the hospital (could be either General or Central) or agency

__1 Wife
__2 Husband
__3 Mother
__4 Father
__5 Son
__6 Daughter
__7 In-law
__8 Friend
__9 Alone
__0 Other (specify) __________
__X No information

2: 20__ Total psychiatric inpatient hospitalization

__1 None
__2 1 day to 1 week
__3 1 week to 1 month
__4 1-3 months
__5 3 months to 1 year
__6 1-2 years
__7 2-4 years
__8 4-6 years
__9 Over 6 years
__X No information

HOSPITAL HISTORY: (If applicable)

	Hospital	Type (State) (Federal) (Private)	Approx. Dates	Approx. Length of Stay (use above categories)
1.	______	______	______	______
2.	______	______	______	______
3.	______	______	______	______

Card: Column

2: 21 __ Number of times pt received outpatient psychiatric treatment (not individual treatments but episodes)

__ 0 None
__ 1 - 8 Actual number of times (1,2,3, etc.)
__ 9 Nine or more
__ X DK

2: 22,23 __ __ Age at time of first outpatient contact

__ (Score XY if no contact or XX if DK)

2: 24 __ Previous total psychiatric outpatient treatment

__ 1 None
__ 2 1 day to 1 week
__ 3 1-3 weeks
__ 4 1-3 months
__ 5 3 months to 1 year
__ 6 1-2 years
__ 7 2-4 years
__ 8 4-6 years
__ 9 Over 6 years
__ X No information

OUTPATIENT HISTORY: (If applicable)

	Agency	Type (State) (Federal) (Private)	Dates	Length of Treatment (use above categories)
1.	________	________	________	________
2.	________	________	________	________
3.	________	________	________	________
4.	________	________	________	________

2: 25 __ 26 __ Individual psychotherapy

(25) Inpatient

__ 1 No treatment

(26) Outpatient

__ 1 No treatment

Card: Column

___ 2 1 interview	___ 2 1 interview
___ 3 1-4 weeks	___ 3 1-4 weeks
___ 4 1-4 months	___ 4 1-4 months
___ 5 4-8 months	___ 5 4-8 months
___ 6 8-12 months	___ 6 8-12 months
___ 7 1-2 years	___ 7 1-2 years
___ 8 2-4 years	___ 8 2-4 years
___ 9 Over 4 years	___ 9 Over 4 years
___ X No information or DK	___ X No information or DK
___ Y N/A (never hospitalized)	Y N/A (no outpatient contact)

2: 27___ 28___ Group pyschotherapy including A.A., Recovery Inc., etc.

(27) Inpatient	(28) Outpatient
___ 1 No treatment	___ 1 No treatment
___ 2 1 visit	___ 2 1 visit
___ 3 1-4 weeks	___ 3 1-4 weeks
___ 4 1-4 months	___ 4 1-4 months
___ 5 4-8 months	___ 5 4-8 months
___ 6 8-12 months	___ 6 8-12 months
___ 7 1-2 years	___ 7 1-2 years
___ 8 2-4 years	___ 8 2-4 years
___ 9 Over 4 years	___ 9 Over 4 years
___ X No information or DK	___ X No information or DK
___ Y N/A (never hospitalized)	___ Y N/A (no outpatient contact)

2: 29___, 30___ Electrotherapy – of any kind

(29) Inpatient	(30) Outpatient
___ 1 No treatment	___ 1 No treatment
___ 2 1-5 treatments	___ 2 1-5 treatments
___ 3 6-10 treatments	___ 3 6-10 treatments
___ 4 11-20 treatments	___ 4 11-20 treatments
___ 5 21-30 treatments	___ 5 21-30 treatments
___ 6 31-40 treatments	___ 6 31-40 treatments
___ 7 41-50 treatments	___ 7 41-50 treatments
___ 8 51-60 treatments	___ 8 51-60 treatments
___ 9 Over 60 treatments	___ 9 Over 60 treatments
___ X No information or DK	___ X No information or DK
___ Y N/A (never hospitalized)	___ Y N/A (no outpatient contact)

Card: Column

2: 31__ , 32__ Insulin shock treatment

(31) Inpatient

__ 1 No treatment
__ 2 1-5 treatments
__ 3 6-10 treatments
__ 4 11-20 treatments
__ 5 21-30 treatments
__ 6 31-40 treatments
__ 7 41-50 treatments
__ 8 51-60 treatments
__ 9 Over 60 treatments
__ X No information or DK
__ Y N/A (never hospitalized)

(32) Outpatient

__ 1 No treatment
__ 2 1-5 treatments
__ 3 6-10 treatments
__ 4 11-20 treatments
__ 5 21-30 treatments
__ 6 31-40 treatments
__ 7 41-50 treatments
__ 8 51-60 treatments
__ 9 Over 60 treatments
__ X No information or DK
__ Y N/A (no outpatient contact)

2: 33__, 34__ Special ataractic drugs (any of the new "tranquilizers" or "energizers")

(33) Inpatient

__ 1 No treatment
__ 2 Less than 1 week
__ 3 1-4 weeks
__ 4 1-4 months
__ 5 4-8 months
__ 6 8-12 months
__ 7 1-2 years
__ 8 2-4 years
__ 9 Over 4 years
__ X No information or DK
__ Y N/A (never hospitalized)

(34) Outpatient

__ 1 No treatment
__ 2 Less than 1 week
__ 3 1-4 weeks
__ 4 1-4 months
__ 5 4-8 months
__ 6 8-12 months
__ 7 1-2 years
__ 8 2-4 years
__ 9 Over 4 years
__ X No information or DK
__ Y N/A (no outpatient contact)

2: 35__ Family physician ___1 Yes___2 No___X DK

2: 36__ Medical treatment within past two years (other than strictly psychiatric)

__ 1 No treatment
__ 2 1-5 visits
__ 3 6-10 visits
__ 4 11-20 visits

NAME AND ADDRESS OF FAMILY PHYSICIAN ____________
____
____

Card: Column

___5 21-30 visits
___6 31-40 visits
___7 41-50 visits
___8 51-60 visits
___9 Over 60 visits
___X No information or DK

2: 37___ Military service experience

___1 No military service (if scored here, omit next item)
___2 World War I service
___3 Service between 1920 and 1939
___4 World War II service
___5 Service since World War II (Korea)
___6 Other military service ________________
___X No information

2: 38___ Type of discharge from military

___1 Honorable
___2 Dishonorable
___3 Bad conduct
___4 Medical (nonpsychiatric)
___5 Psychiatric
___X No information or DK
___Y N/A (no military service)

2: 39___ Onset of present illness: How long has the pt been sick this time (duration of precursory symptoms up to present hospitalization)?

___1 Acute: present illness developed over a very short period with no indication of definite precursory symptoms before that time: less than 2 months.
___2 Intermediate (2-6 months)
___3 Insidious: present illness developed over a period of from 6 months or longer
___X DK

Marriage

2: 40___ Number of marriages: Include as "marriages" all sustained and lasting heterosexual relationships, whether legally recognized or not.

Card: Column

___0 Pt never married
___1-8 Actual number (1,2,3, etc.)
___9 Nine or more
___X DK

Most recent marriage: Score for the most recent sustained and lasting heterosexual relationship

2: 41___ Type:

___0 Pt never married
___1 Legal
___2 Common-law
___3 Casual alliance – 1 yr or less
___4 Casual alliance – 1-6 yrs
___X DK

2: 42___, 43___ Age of pt first marriage: ____(XX-DK; YY-N/A)

2: 44___, 45___ Age of pt this marriage: (XX-DK; YY-N/A)

2: 46___, 47___ Age of current spouse when married: ____(XX-DK; YY-N/A)

2: 48___ Duration (most recent)

___0 Never married
___1 Under 1 year
___2 1-2 years
___3 3-5 years
___4 6-10 years
___5 11-15 years
___6 16-20 years
___7 21-30 years
___8 Over 30 years
___X DK

2: 49___ Spouse (most recent)
___0 Pt never married
___1 Spouse living with pt prior to present hospitalization
___2 Spouse dead
___3 Divorced or formally separated
___4 Informally separated
___X DK

Card: Column

2: 50 __ Children: number of children born to pt (including children of all marriages and illegitimate children)

__ 0 No children
__ 1-8 Record actual number
__ 9 Nine or more
__ X DK
__ Y N/A (pt never married)

2: 51 __ Children of most recent marriage only

__ 0 No children
__ 1-8 Record actual number
__ 9 Nine or more
__ X DK
__ Y N/A (pt not married)

2: 52 __ Number of boys (pt's) under 12 living with pt (all marriages)

__ 0 None
__ 1-8 Record actual number
__ 9 Nine or more
__ X DK
__ Y N/A (pt never married)

2: 53 __ Number of girls (pt's) under 12 living with pt (all marriages)

__ 0 None
__ 1-8 Record actual number
__ 9 Nine or more
__ X DK
__ Y N/A (pt never married)

2: 54 __ Number of boys (pt's) 13-15 living with pt (all marriages)

__ 0 None
__ 1-8 Record actual number
__ 9 Nine or more
__ X DK
__ Y N/A (pt never married)

2: 55 __ Number of girls (pt's) 13-15 living with pt (all marriages)

Card: Column

__0 None
__1-8 Record actual number
__9 Nine or more
__X DK
__Y N/A (pt never married)

2: 56 __ Number of boys (pt's) 16-18 living with pt (all marriages)

__0 None
__1-8 Record actual number
__9 Nine or more
__X DK
__Y N/A (pt never married)

2: 57 __ Number of girls (pt's) 16-18 living with pt (all mariages)

__0 None
__1-8 Record actual number
__9 Nine or more
__X DK
__Y N/A (pt never married)

Others living in pt's household (note: other than pt's children recorded above) (ask also for sex of others, and enter age under appropriate sex)

Boys	Girls	Relation to pt	Men	Women	Relation to pt

Card: Column

2: 58___ Number of males through 16 (exclusive of pt's children)

___ 0
___ 1-8 Record actual number
___ 9 Nine or more
___ X DK

2: 59___ Number of females through 16 (exclusive of pt's children)

___ 0
___ 1-8 Record actual number
___ 9 Nine or more
___ X DK

2: 60___ Number of males over 16 (exclusive of patient)

___ 0
___ 1-8 Record actual number
___ 9 Nine or more
___ X DK

2: 61___ Number of females over 16 (exclusive of patient)

___ 0
___ 1-8 Record actual number
___ 9 Nine or more
___ X DK

This section is applicable only if respondent and patient are closely related (i.e., married, parent-child, sibling) and reside in the same household.

Family Relations

2: 62___ How would you describe *** illness?

___ 0 Denies that pt is ill
___ 1 Mental illness (with high degree of knowledge and "sophistication")
___ 2 Mental illness (low or minimal degree of knowledge and "sophistication")
___ 3 Nervous breakdown
___ 4 "Nerves"
___ 5 A physical disorder
___ 6 Other (specify) ______________________

Card: Column

__ X DK
__ Y N/A (R not in same household)

2: 63 __

Do you feel that *** has to be watched (observed) more closely and more often than other people?

__ 1 Yes __ 2 No __ X DK __ Y N/A

2: 64 __

Do you feel that *** should be getting (psychiatric) help (treatment)?

__ 1 Yes __ 2 No __ X DK __ Y N/A

2: 65 __

Do you think that *** ought to be in a mental hospital?

__ 1 Yes __ 2 No __ X DK __ Y N/A

2: 66 __

Do you know what is done in a mental hospital to help pts get well? (check the <u>most important</u> and circle others they mention)

__ 1 Nothing
__ 2 Rest
__ 3 Restraint (Seclusion)
__ 4 Shock treatment
__ 5 Psychotherapy
__ 6 Medication (Drugs)
__ 7 "Depends on the patient"
__ 8 Other (specify) ______________________
__ X DK
__ Y N/A

2: 67 __

If it is decided that *** should be treated at home instead of in the hospital, how would you feel about it?

__ 1 Positive feelings about keeping pt at home
__ 2 Negative feelings about keeping pt at home

(in either case, specify reasons, if any)

Card: Column

__X DK
__Y N/A

2: 68__ If you were called out of town for some reason, who would look after your family?

__0 No one else available
__1 Relative
__2 Neighbor Specify: Name: ______________
__3 Friend Address: ______________
__X DK
__Y N/A Phone: ______________

Has *** actually lived somewhere else at any time in the last 2 years? (Note: Apart from family, exclusive of hospitalization.)

2: 69__ Number of times

__0 None
__1-8 Record actual number
__9 Nine or more
__X DK
__Y N/A

Have you actually lived somewhere else in the past 2 years? (Note: Concern here is not with family movement but with whether respondent removed himself or herself from the patient.)

2: 70__ Number of times:

__0 None
__1-8 Record actual number
__9 Nine or more
__X DK
__Y N/A

2: 71__ Pt's desire to end most recent marriage

__1 Wishes to continue
__2 Pt not sure
__3 Pt wishes to end marriage
__X DK
__Y N/A

Card: Column

2: 72 __ Spouse's desire to end marriage

__ 1 Wishes to continue
__ 2 Spouse not sure
__ 3 Spouse wishes to end marriage
__ X DK
__ Y N/A

Involvement in extramarital "affairs"
By an "affair" is meant a man chosing the company of another woman in preference to his wife (or a woman vice versa). This is not meant to include relationships necessitated by work.

2: 73 __ , 74 __

(73) Patient	(74) Spouse
__ 0 No involvement	__ 0 No involvement
__ 1 One affair	__ 1 One affair
__ 2 A few	__ 2 A few
__ 3 Several	__ 3 Several
__ 4 Many	__ 4 Many
__ X DK	__ X DK
__ Y N/A	__ Y N/A

2: 75 __ Expression of hostility within most recent marriage on the part of the patient – refers to worst period of most recent marriage.

__ 1 No hostility ever expressed
__ 2 Very rare expression of hostility
__ 3 Some expression of hostility
__ 4 Frequent expression of hostility without physical violence
__ 5 Frequent expression of hostility with physical violence
__ X No information
__ Y N/A

2: 76 __, 77 __ Satisfaction in sexual relationship (most recent 2 years of marriage)

(76) Patient	(77) Spouse
__ 1 Never gets satisfaction	__ 1 Never gets satisfaction

Card: Column

___2 Only occasional satisfaction	___2 Only occasional satisfaction
___3 Satisfaction about half the time	___3 Satisfaction about half the time
___4 Usually gets satisfaction	___4 Usually gets satisfaction
___5 Almost always gets satisfaction	___5 Almost always gets satisfaction
___6 Always gets satisfaction	___6 Always gets satisfaction
___X No information	___X No information
___Y N/A	___Y N/A

2: 78___ Separations or divorces in most recent marriage at any time. Do not include separations because of military service, illness, employment, etc.

___1 Not considered
___2 Talked about
___3 1 Separation or divorce
___4 2-6 Separations or divorces
___5 Many separations, which may or may not include divorce
___X No information
___Y N/A

SECTION III

This section is applicable only if respondent and patient are closely related (i.e., married, parent-child, sibling) and reside in the same household.

Patient's Behavior

Now, I would like to ask you some specific questions about ***'s behavior these last few weeks (prior to hospitalization).

3: 13___ How much trouble has *** been at night (noisy, wandering, etc.)?

___1 No trouble at all
___2 Some trouble

Card: Column

___3 Very difficult
___4 DK
___Y N/A (respondent not in patient's household)

3: 14___ Has *** been a nursing problem (bed-ridden, incontinent, feeding, washing)?

___1 No problem
___2 Sometimes
___3 Often
___X DK
___Y N/A

3: 15___ Has ***'s safety been a soruce of worry (wandering off, car, gas)?

___1 No problem
___2 Sometimes
___3 Often
___X DK
___Y N/A

3: 16___ Has *** caused anxiety (worry) about the safety of others?

___1 No problem
___2 Sometimes (specify)________________

___3 Often (specify)________________
___X DK
___Y N/A

3: 17___ Has *** caused difficulty by being uncooperative?

___1 No problem
___2 Sometimes (specify)________________

___3 Often (specify)________________
___X DK
___Y N/A

3: 18___ Is *** a strain in relying and depending on people too much?

___1 No problem

Card: Column

___ 2 Sometimes (specify) ____________________

___ 3 Often (specify) ____________________
___ X DK
___ Y N/A

3: 19___ Has ***'s constant restlessness, noisiness, or talking been upsetting?

___ 1 No problem
___ 2 Sometimes
___ 3 Often
___ 4 DK
___ Y N/A

3: 20___ Have frequent complaints about bodily (physical) symptoms worried you?

___ 1 No
___ 2 Sometimes
___ 3 Often
___ X DK
___ Y N/A

3: 21___ Has *** been a problem because of sexual, rude, or objectionable behavior?

___ 1 No
___ 2 Sometimes
___ 3 Often
___ X DK
___ Y N/A

3: 22___ Has *** caused anxiety (worry) by speaking or behaving oddly, or by having unusual or unreasonable ideas?

___ 1 No
___ 2 Sometimes
___ 3 Often
___ X DK
___ Y N/A

3: 23___ Has *** caused any trouble with the neighbors?

___ 1 No

Card: Column

__ 2 Sometimes (specify)
__ 3 Often (specify)
__ X DK
__ Y N/A

3: 24 __ Is household work or routine upset by ***?

__ 1 No Specify:
__ 2 Occasionally
__ 3 A great deal
__ X DK
__ Y N/A

3: 25 __ Are social or leisure activities interfered with because of ***?

__ 1 No Specify:
__ 2 Occasionally
__ 3 A great deal
__ X DK
__ Y N/A

3: 26 __ Has anyone in household had to stay away from work because of ***?

__ 1 No
__ 2 Yes, occasionally
__ 3 Yes, a great deal (more than 14 days since discharge)
__ X DK
__ Y N/A

Specify:

3: 27 __ Has anyone in the household had to stay away from school because of ***?

__ 1 No
__ 2 Yes, occasionally
__ 3 Yes, a great deal
__ X DK
__ Y N/A

Card: Column

3: 28 __ Has ***'s behavior caused you (respondent) much worry?

__ 1 No
__ 2 Sometimes
__ 3 Yes, a great deal
__ X DK
__ Y N/A

3: 29 __ Has *** been a physical strain on you?

__ 1 Not at all
__ 2 Some strain
__ 3 Marked strain
__ X DK
__ Y N/A

3: 30 __ Does *** require an excessive amount of attention or companionship?

__ 1 No
__ 2 Sometimes
__ 3 Very demanding
__ X DK
__ Y N/A

3: 31 __ Are the children ashamed because of ***?

__ 1 No
__ 2 Sometimes
__ 3 A great deal
__ X DK
__ Y N/A

3: 32 __ Are the children afraid of ***?

__ 1 No
__ 2 Sometimes
__ 3 To a great extent
__ X DK
__ Y N/A

3: 33 __ Do you feel ashamed because of ***?

__ 1 No

Card: Column

__ 2 Sometimes
__ 3 A great deal
__ X DK
__ Y N/A

3: 34__ Are you afraid of ***?

__ 1 No
__ 2 Sometimes
__ 3 Often
__ X DK
__ Y N/A

3: 35, 36__ __ Total Problems Score (coder only: see manual)

3: 37__ Use of alcohol by patient: score in terms of the most serious disturbance evident during the last 3 years. Use the most accurate information available. A "drink" includes any alcoholic beverage.

__ 1 Abstinent: consumed no alcohol
__ 2 Less than one drink per week on the average
__ 3 Up to 2–3 drinks per day on the average, or occasionally intoxicated
__ 4 4–6 drinks per day or regularly intoxicated: Has been in no trouble outside the home socially or legally
__ 5 Averages a higher consumption than above, but has been in no trouble medically or outside the home socially or legally: can keep his job
__ 6 Occasionally in trouble socially outside the home, or legally with police because of drinking
__ 7 Frequently in trouble outside the home socially or legally (Inculde here those who have lost their jobs because of drinking)
__ 8 Has had delirium tremens within past 3 years (Include here all cases irrespective of drinking pattern)
__ 9 Alcoholic psychosis currently (Inculde D.T.'s, Korsakoff's, hallucinosis, and deterioration)
__ X No information or DK
__ Y N/A

Card: Column

This section applicable if respondent is spouse, close relative, and/or person who resides in patient's household.

Social Participation

3: 38 __ About how many times during the month does *** go to church services, including weekdays as well as Sundays?

__1 More than four times a month (more than once a week)
__2 Four times a month (once a week)
__3 Two or three times a month
__4 Once a month
__5 Less than once a month (sporadic)
__6 Never
__X DK
__Y N/A

3: 39 __ About how many times during the month do you go to church services, including weekdays as well as Sundays?

__1 More than four times a month (more than once a week)
__2 Four times a month (once a week)
__3 Two or three times a month
__4 Once a month
__5 Less than once a month (sporadic)
__6 Never
__X No information or DK
__Y N/A

Do you belong to or take part in any clubs or groups like –

			About How Often Do You Attend Meeting?		Are You an Officer or Committee Member?		Does the Group Meet In or Out of the Neighborhood?	
	2 No	1 Yes	Usually (or Always)	Only Occasionally	1 Yes	2 No	Inside-1	Outside-2
Professional organization								
Union								
Fraternal								
Religious								
Veterans								
Athletic								
PTA								
Political								
Social								
Charitable								
YM – YWCA								
Other (specify)								

Does *** belong to or take part in any of these clubs or groups?

			About How Often Does *** Attend Meetings?		Is *** an Officer or Committee Member?		Does the Group Meet In or Out of the Neighborhood?	
	2 No	1 Yes	Usually (or Always)	Only Occasionally	1 Yes	2 No	Inside-1	Outside-2
Professional organization								
Union								
Fraternal								
Religious								
Veterans								
Athletic								
PTA								
Political								
Social								
Charitable								
YM – YWCA								
Other (specify)								

Card: Column

3: 40 __

__0 Respondent does not belong to any organization
__1 Belongs to 1 organization
__2 Belongs to 2 organizations
__3 Belongs to 3 organizations
__4 Belongs to 4-7 organizations
__5 Belongs to 8 or more organizations
__X DK

3: 41 __

__0 Patient does not belong to any organization
__1 Belongs to 1 organization
__2 Belongs to 2 organizations
__3 Belongs to 3 organizations
__4 Belongs to 4-7 organizations
__5 Belongs to 8 or more organizations
__X DK

3: 42 __

Patient's friendship pattern: does *** have any friends?

__1 Has almost not friends and usually prefers to be by himself
__2 Has no close friends, but does spend a little time in social activities
__3 Has a few friends, but has trouble getting along with them or spends little time with them
__4 Has friends and spends time with them, but does not always enjoy doing so
__5 Has good friends and enjoys spending time with them
__X DK

3: 43 __

Did *** vote in the last election?

__1 Yes
__2 No
__X DK
__Y N/A (ineligible)

3: 44 __

Did you vote in the last election?

__1 Yes
__2 No
__X DK
__Y N/A

Card: Column

3: 45 ___ Does your family own or have ready access to a car?

___ 1 Own
___ 2 Have access
___ 3 Does not own or have access
___ X No information or DK
___ Y N/A

3: 46 ___ Does *** have a driver's license?

___ 1 Has one now
___ 2 Did but has expired
___ 3 No
___ X No information or DK
___ Y N/A (ineligible)

3: 47 ___ Who in the family does most of the driving?

___ 1 ***
___ 2 Respondent
___ 3 Other (specify) ______________________
___ X No information or DK
___ Y N/A

3: 48 ___ If *** drives: needs or functions of driving

___ 1 Work
___ 2 Household (e.g., shopping)
___ 3 Pleasure (e.g., visiting, etc.)
___ 4 All three above
___ 5 2 and 3 above
___ X No information or DK
___ Y N/A

We are also interested in knowing some of the other things *** has done, say, in the past month (period before hospitalization)

Did ***, for example –

3: 49 ___ Go to the movies?

___ 1 No
___ 2 Yes
___ X DK
___ Y N/A

Card: Column

3: 50 __ Would you say that this is normal for *** or unusual behavior (i.e., compared to movie going behavior in the past)?

__ 1 Unusual
__ 2 Usual
__ X DK
__ Y N/A

3: 51, 52__,__ Read any books for pleasure?

__ 1 No
__ 2 Yes
__ X DK
__ Y N/A

Was this: __ 1 Unusual
__ 2 Usual
__ X DK
__ Y N/A

3: 53, 54__,__ Read any magazines for pleasure?

__ 1 No
__ 2 Yes
__ X DK
__ Y N/A

Was this: __ 1 Unusual
__ 2 Usual
__ X DK
__ Y N/A

3: 55, 56__,__ Work on a hobby of any sort?

__ 1 No
__ 2 Yes
__ X DK
__ Y N/A

Was this: __ 1 Unusual
__ 2 Usual
__ X DK
__ Y N/A

3: 57, 58__,__ Write any letters?

__ 1 No
__ 2 Yes
__ X DK
__ Y N/A

Was this: __ 1 Unusual
__ 2 Usual
__ X DK
__ Y N/A

3: 59, 60__,__ Read the daily newspaper?

__ 1 No
__ 2 Yes
__ X DK
__ Y N/A

Was this: __ 1 Unusual
__ 2 Usual
__ X DK
__ Y N/A

3: 61, 62__,__ Go to church?

__ 1 No

Was this: __ 1 Unusual

Card: Column

	__ 2 Yes		__ 2 Usual
	__ X DK		__ X DK
	__ Y N/A		__ Y N/A
3: 63, 64__,__	Watch television or listen to the radio?		
	__ 1 No	Was this:	__ 1 Unusual
	__ 2 Yes		__ 2 Usual
	__ X DK		__ X DK
	__ Y N/A		__ Y N/A
3: 65, 66__,__	Visit friends or relatives?		
	__ 1 No	Was this:	__ 1 Unusual
	__ 2 Yes		__ 2 Usual
	__ X DK		__ X DK
	__ Y N/A		__ Y N/A
3: 67, 68__,__	Entertain friends or relatives?		
	__ 1 No	Was this:	__ 1 Unusual
	__ 2 Yes		__ 2 Usual
	__ X DK		__ X DK
	__ Y N/A		__ Y N/A
3: 69, 70__,__	Attend club, lodge, or organization meetings?		
	__ 1 No	Was this:	__ 1 Unusual
	__ 2 Yes		__ 2 Usual
	__ X DK		__ X DK
	__ Y N/A		__ Y N/A
3: 71, 72__,__	Shop "downtown"?		
	__ 1 No	Was this:	__ 1 Unusual
	__ 2 Yes		__ 2 Usual
	__ X DK		__ X DK
	__ Y N/A		__ Y N/A
3: 73, 74__,__	Play cards or table games involving others?		
	__ 1 No	Was this:	__ 1 Unusual
	__ 2 Yes		__ 2 Usual
	__ X DK		__ X DK
	__ Y N/A		__ Y N/A

Card: Column

3: 75, 76__,__ Bowl or other athletic activity?

__1 No	Was this:	__1 Unusual
__2 Yes		__2 Usual
__X DK		__X DK
__Y N/A		__Y N/A

3: 77, 78__,__ Watch a spectator sport (other than on TV)?

__1 No	Was this:	__1 Unusual
__2 Yes		__2 Unual
__X DK		__X DK
__Y N/A		__Y N/A

3: 79, 80__,__ Total SP score: (coder only: see manual)

SECTION IV

Prehospital Work Performance and Adjustment (males only)

4: 13__ How many jobs has *** had in the last 5 years?

__0 No jobs
__1-8 Record actual number
__9 Nine or more
__X DK
__Y N/A

4: 14__ Was *** working just before coming to the hospital (this time)?

__1 No
__2 Yes
__X DK
__Y N/A

4: 15__ How long did *** have this job?

__0 Was not working
__1 Under 3 months
__2 3-6 months
__3 7 months to 1 year
__4 1-3 years
__5 4-6 years

Card: Column

__6 7–10 years
__7 Over 10 years
__X DK

4: 16__ How long has it been since *** has worked regularly?

__1 Under 3 months
__2 3–6 months
__3 7 months to 1 year
__4 1–3 years
__5 Over 3 years
__X DK
__Y N/A (has been working regularly)

4: 17__ How old was *** when he started to work full time?

__1 Has never worked full time
__2 Under 16 years of age
__3 16–20 years
__4 21 or over
__X DK

4: 18__ Has *** had any kind of special job training (exclusive of military)?

	Number of years
__1 None	
__2 Technical (specify)________	______
__3 Professional (specify)________	______
__4 Other (specify)________	______
__X DK	

4: 19__, 20__ How old was *** when he had his highest paying job?

__Record actual age
__XX DK
__YY N/A

Of the jobs *** has had, which did he like the most?

Specify: ______________________________

4: 21__ How long ago did *** have this job?

__1 Current job
__2 Up to 6 months ago

Card: Column

__3 7 months to 1 yr ago
__4 2-5 yrs ago
__5 6-10 yrs ago
__6 Over 10 years ago
__X DK
__Y N/A (e.g. never worked)

If *** had his choice, what kind of work do you think he would want to do?

____

4: 22__ How did *** go about getting his last job?

__1 Want ads
__2 Employment agency (private)
__3 Employment agency (state or federal)
__4 Union
__5 Social worker (community agency)
__6 Social worker (hospital)
__7 Relative
__8 Friend
__9 Other (specify) ______________________
__X No information or DK
__Y N/A (e.g. never worked)

4: 23__ How much time does (did) *** devote to his (last) job?

__1 Full time, 30 hours plus per week
__2 More than half time but considered to be a part-time position by respondent
__3 Half time
__4 Less than half time, less than 16 hours per week
__5 A few hours a week
__X No information or DK
__Y N/A

4: 24__ Is (was) *** expected to work every week, or does (did) the job call for some other kind of arrangement?

__1 Job is on a regular week-to-week basis
__2 Job is on week-to-week basis but for less than 9 months but more than 6 months during the year
__3 Job requires 3-6 months per year

Card: Column

___4 Job requires less than 3 months of regular work
___X No information or DK
___Y N/A

4: 25___ When working, is (was) *** expected to work every day?

___1 yes ___2 No ___X DK ___Y N/A

4: 26___ When *** is (was) working, how good is (was) his attendance on the job?

___1 No absences or out only rarely
___2 Out from time to time but infrequently, and absences are justified – realistic (e.g., illness, important business, etc.)

___3 Out from time to time (infrequently) but not adequately justified
___4 Absences are relatively frequent, but adequately justified
___5 Absences are relatively frequent, but not adequately justified
___6 Out most of the time
___X No information or DK
___Y N/A

4: 27___ In general, how difficult has it been for *** to work?

___1 not difficult at all
___2 Some difficulty
___3 Very difficult
___X DK
___Y N/A

4: 28___ In general, would you say that the way ***'s handling of his job (work) is pretty much what it has usually been or very different from the way he did in the past (before he got sick)?

___1 Same
___2 Some difference
___3 Very different
___X DK
___Y N/A (e.g., has never worked or had a job)

Card: Column

Before coming to the hospital (this time) did *** do any of these things?

4: 29 __ Help with household chores

__ 1 Could not
__ 2 Occasionally
__ 3 Often
__ 4 Would not
__ X DK
__ Y N/A

4: 30 __ Help you entertain at home

__ 1 Could not
__ 2 Occasionally
__ 3 Often
__ 9 Would not
__ X DK
__ Y N/A

4: 31 __ Visit his friends

__ 1 Could not
__ 2 Occasionally
__ 3 Often
__ 9 Would not
__ X DK
__ Y N/A

4: 32 __ Visit his relatives

__ 1 Could not
__ 2 Occasionally
__ 3 Often
__ 9 Would not
__ X DK
__ Y N/A

4: 33 __ Help manage the family finances

__ 1 Could not
__ 2 Occasionally
__ 3 Often
__ 9 Would not
__ X DK
__ Y N/A

Card: Column

4: 34 __ Help with family's shopping

__ 1 Could not
__ 2 Occasionally
__ 3 Often
__ 9 Would not
__ X DK
__ Y N/A

4: 35 __ Go to parties and other social activities

__ 1 Could not
__ 2 Occasionally
__ 3 Often
__ 9 Would not
__ X DK
__ Y N/A

4: 36, 37__,__ Score: total 1,2,3's only ______(coder only)

4: 38 __ Would you say that ***'s mental illness has affected his ability to do the kinds of things you expect him to do?

__ 1 Yes, some
__ 2 Yes, a great deal
__ 3 No
__ 4 Respondent denies that pt is mentally ill
__ X DK
__ Y N/A

Specifically now, suppose *** were to receive psychiatric treatment at home instead of in the hospital, would you expect him to do any of these things?

4: 39 __ Be working full time

__ 1 No __ 2 Yes __X DK __Y N/A (e.g., never has)

4: 40 __ Be working part time

__ 1 No __ 2 Yes __X DK __Y N/A (e.g., never has)

4: 41 __ Help with household chores

__ 1 No __ 2 Yes __X DK __Y N/A (e.g., never has)

Card: Column

4: 42 __ Help you entertain at home

__1 No __2 Yes __X DK __Y N/A (e.g., never has)

4: 43 __ Go visit his friends

__1 No __2 Yes __X DK __Y N/A (e.g., never has)

4: 44 __ Go visit his relatives

__1 No __2 Yes __X DK __Y N/A (e.g., never has)

4: 45 __ Help manage the family finances

__1 No __2 Yes __X DK __Y N/A (e.g., never has)

4: 46 __ Help with the family's shopping

__1 No __2 Yes __X DK __Y N/A (e.g., never has)

4: 47 __ Go to parties and other social activities

__1 No __2 Yes __X DK __Y N/A (e.g., never has)

4: 48, 49 __, __ Total Expectation Score (coder only) ____ (see manual)

SECTION V

Pre-hospital Homemaking Experiences (females only)

5: 13 __ Before coming to the hospital (this time) how much of ***'s time was spent in homemaking activities?

__1 Full time (no outside employment of any kind)
__2 Virtually full time (minimal or sporadic employment outside the home)
__3 Half time (gainfully and/or nongainfully* employed outside the home)
__4 Minimal (works full time but has homemaking obligations)

Card: Column

___5 Not at all
___X DK
___Y N/A (specify) ______________________

* (Note: An example of nongainful employment would be aiding husband in his business or store.)

5: 14 ___ What kind of job does *** have? Or: What kind of work did *** do the last time she did have a job?

___1 Does not and did not have any job
___2 Clerk-typist
___3 Secretarial (with some administrative responsibility)
___4 Sales
___5 Professional (e.g., school teacher, nurse)
___6 Domestic (e.g., cook, maid, cleaning)
___7 Unskilled or semi-skilled factory work
___8 Other (specify) ______________________
___X DK

WHERE DID *** WORK AND FOR HOW LONG?

WHERE? ______________________ ___X DK
HOW LONG? ______________________ ___X DK

___Y N/A (did not work)

5: 15 ___ Was this job full or part time?

___1 Did not work
___2 Full time
___3 Half time (20–25 hrs./week)
___4 Less than half time (less than 20 hrs./week)
___5 Minimal (less than 10 hrs./week)
___X DK

5: 16 ___ How important is ***'s income to the family?

___1 Did not work

Card: Column

__ 2 *** is chief dreadwinner (contribution is more than 50% of total income)
__ 3 Supplementary but substantial (20–50% of total family income)
__ 4 Supplementary but minimal (10–20% of total family income)
__ 5 Supplementary but only token contribution (less than 10%)
__ X DK

5: 17 __ Do you consider *** earnings to be a necessary contribution to the family's income?

__ 1 Yes __ 2 No __ X DK __ Y N/A

5: 18 __ Did *** have sole responsibility as a homemaker or did she share her responsibility with another person(s)?

__ 1 Sole responsibility
__ 2 Major responsibility
__ 3 Shared responsibility on 50/50 basis
__ 4 Only minor responsibility
__ 5 No responsibility
__ X DK
__ Y N/A

(IF ANYTHING BUT "SOLE RESPONSIBILITY"): WITH WHOM WAS RESPONSIBILITY SHARED OR PERSON WHO ASSUMED HOMEMAKING ROLE FOR PATIENT'S FAMILY?

NAME: ______________________________

RELATIONSHIP TO PATIENT: ____________________

__ X DK
__ Y N/A

Card: Column

5: 19 __ Would you say that *** is satisfied in being a homemaker?

__ 1 Yes __2 No __X DK __Y N/A

5: 20 __ If *** had her choice between being a homemaker and working outside the home, which would she choose?

__ 1 Homemaking __2 Work __3 Combination

__ X DK __Y N/A

5: 21 __ In general, how difficult has it been for *** to do the kinds of things that most other women of her age do?

__ 1 Not difficult at all
__ 2 Some difficulty
__ 3 Very difficult
__ X DK
__ Y N/A

5: 22 __ In general, would you say that the way *** handles her chores (domestic duties and responsibilities, etc.) is pretty much what it has usually been or very different from the way she did in the past (before she got sick)?

__ 1 Same
__ 2 Some difference
__ 3 Very different
__ X DK
__ Y N/A

Specifically now, before coming to the hospital (this time) did *** do these things by herself or did she need help (or was unable to)?

Card: Column

		(1) Could not do	(2) Needed Some Help	(3) Did by Self	(9) Would not Do	(X) DK	(Y) Did not Have to do
5: 23__	Attended to house cleaning chores						
5: 24__	Prepared meals						
5: 25__	Attended to laundry and cleaning						
5: 26__	Shopped for groceries						
5: 27__	Did other shopping (e.g. clothing, household items)						
5: 28__	Budgeted for the household (including writing checks or handling money)						
5: 29__	Planned own daily activities						
5: 30__	Solved daily problems						

5: 31, 32__,__ Coder only Total: ______ (include only 1,2, & 3)

5: 33__ Would you say that ***'s mental illness has affected her ability to do the kinds of things you expect her to do?

__1 Yes, some
__2 Yes, a great deal
__3 No
__4 Respondent denies that pt is mentally ill
__X DK
__Y N/A

Card: Column

Specifically now, suppose *** were to receive psychiatric treatment at home instead of in the hospital, would you expect her to do any of these things?

5: 34 __ Dust, sweep, and do other usual cleaning

__1 No __2 Yes __X DK __Y N/A

5: 35 __ Cook for the family

__1 No __2 Yes __X DK __Y N/A

5: 36 __ Take care of the lanudry, etc.

__1 No __2 Yes __X DK __Y N/A

5: 37 __ Grocery shopping

__1 No __2 Yes __X DK __Y N/A

5: 38 __ Other shopping (household, clothing, etc.)

__1 No __2 Yes __X DK __Y N/A

5: 39 __ Handle and budget grocery money

__1 No __2 Yes __X DK __Y N/A

5: 40, 41__,__ Subtotal: (coder only) ______

5: 42 __ Go visit her friends or relatives

__1 No __2 Yes __X DK __Y N/A

5: 43 __ Entertain friends or relatives at home

__1 No __2 Yes __X DK __Y N/A

5: 44 __ Hold a job

__1 No __2 Yes __X DK __Y N/A

5: 45 __ Mix socially with the neighbors

__1 No __2 Yes __X DK __Y N/A

Card: Column

5: 46 __ Go to parties and other social activities

__1 No __2 Yes __X DK __Y N/A

5: 47, 48__ __ Subtotal: (coder only)

5: 49, 50__ __ Total Expectation Score (coder only)

SECTION VI

This section applies if patient and respondent are a married couple and have at least one child 16 years of age or younger.

Children

6: 13 __ Through what grade in school do you hope to be able to send (your child) (your children)

__1 Through grade school or less (any grade 1-6)
__2 To junior high school (grade 7,8, or 9)
__3 Part way through high school (grade 10 or 11)
__4 Through high school graduation (grade 12)
__5 Part way through college
__6 Through college graduation or more
__7 No information or DK
__Y N/A

6: 14 __ How good do you think the chances are of sending (your child) (your children) as far through school as you hope to? Would you say your chances are:

__1 Very good
__2 Fairly good
__3 Not very good
__4 Not at all good
__X No information or DK
__Y N/A

6: 15 __ You mentioned that your (___-year-old) child is a: (Mention oldest child 16 years of age or younger. Check "boy" or "girl.")

Card: Column

___ 1 Girl ___ 2 boy

If boy:

6: 16___ How good do you think the chances are for him someday to have a professional job like a doctor, lawyer, or teacher? Would you say the chances are:

___ 1 Very good
___ 2 Fairly good
___ 3 Not very good
___ 4 Not at all good
___ 5 Isn't what he wants
___ X Don't know how good the chances are
___ Y N/A

6: 17___ What are the chances of his being in business for himself? Would you say:

___ 1 Very good
___ 2 Fairly good
___ 3 Not very good
___ 4 Not at all good
___ 5 Isn't what he wants
___ X Don't know how good the chances are
___ Y N/A

6: 18___ What are the chances of his being a civil service employee? Would you say:

___ 1 Very good
___ 2 Fairly good
___ 3 Not very good
___ 4 Not at all good
___ 5 Isn't what he wants
___ X Don't know how good the chances are
___ Y N/A

If girl:

6: 19___ How good do you think the chances are for her someday to have a professional job like a nurse, social-worker, or teacher? Would you say the chances are:

___ 1 Very good

Card: Column

__ 2 Fairly good
__ 3 Not very good
__ 4 Not at all good
__ 5 Isn't what she wants
__ X Don't know how good the chances are
__ Y N/A

6: 20 __ What are the chances of her being a secretary? Would you say:

__ 1 Very good
__ 2 Fairly good
__ 3 Not very good
__ 4 Not at all good
__ 5 Isn't what she wants
__ X Don't know how good the chances are
__ Y N/A

6: 21 __ What are the chances of her being a civil service employee? Would you say:

__ 1 Very good
__ 2 Fairly good
__ 3 Not very good
__ 4 Not good at all
__ 5 Isn't what she wants
__ X Don't know how good the chances are
__ Y N/A

If at least one child between 3 and 16 years of age, ask following questions.

6: 22 __ Where (does this child) (do these children) play most often? (Check most important)

__ 1 Indoors
__ 2 In the yard
__ 3 On the street
__ 4 On a playground
__ 5 Somewhere else (specify) ____________________
__ X DK or No information
__ Y N/A

6: 23 __ From your point of view, how satisfactory are the places where (this child) (these children) play:

Card: Column

__1 Very satisfactory
__2 Fairly satisfactory
__3 Not very satisfactory
__4 Not at all satisfactory
__X No information or DK
__Y N/A

6: 24__ Can (this child) (these children) have friends come into the apartment without their getting in anyone else's way?

__1 Yes __2 No __X DK __Y N/A

(If "No") can you explain that? ______________

(Probe!)

If at least one child between 6 and 16 years of age, ask the following questions.

6: 25__ How much (does this child) (do these children) help you out around the house? Would you say:

__1 A lot
__2 Quite a bit
__3 Only a little
__4 Not at all
__X No information or DK
__Y N/A

6: 26__ (Does this child) (Do these children) have a place to do homework in the apartment without being bothered by anyone else?

__1 Yes __2 No __X DK __Y N/A

(If "No") can you explain that? ______________

(Probe!)

Card: Column

6: 27 ___ (Does this child) (Do any of these children) go to Sunday or religious school?

___ 1 Yes ___ 2 No ___ X DK ___ Y N/A

(If "Yes") About how many times during the month (does this child) (do these children) go to Sunday or religious school?

___ 0 Do not attend
___ 1 Four times a month (once a week)
___ 2 Two to three times a month
___ 3 Once a month
___ 4 Less than once a month
___ X DK

(Does this child) (Do any of these children) belong to or take part in any clubs or groups like:

Card: Column		1 Yes	2 No	X DK	Y N/A
6: 29 ___	The Boy or Girl Scouts				
6: 30 ___	A social club either at school or somewhere else				
6: 31 ___	A church group other than Sunday school				
6: 32 ___	An athletic group or club				
6: 33 ___	Any other clubs or groups you can think of				

(If "Yes") What? (Enter one item per line.)

___

___

___

___

Card: Column

6: 34 ___ (Does this child) (Do any of these children) suffer from any disabling physical difficulty (rheumatic heart disease, cerebral palsey, polio residual)

___1 Yes ___2 No ___X DK ___Y N/A

(If "Yes") Age and sex of child Problem

____

____

____

____

6: 35 ___ (Does this child) (Do any of these children) have any special behavior problems (e.g., truancy, deliquency)?

___1 Yes ___2 No ___X DK ___Y N/A

(If "Yes") Age and sex of child Problem

____

____

____

____

6: 36 ___ (Is this child) (Are any of these children) intellectually or mentally retarded in any way (e.g., school retardation of more than 2 grades)?

___1 Yes ___2 No ___X DK ___Y N/A

(If "Yes") Age and sex of child Problem

____

____

____

____

Card: Column

6: 37 __ (Does this child) (Do any of these children) have any particular neurotic or psychotic disturbances (e.g., enuresis, nightmares, etc.)?

__1 Yes __2 No __X DK __Y N/A

(If "Yes") Age and sex of child Problem

____

____

____

____

If at least two adults, or if one adult and at least one child ten years old or older, ask the following questions.

We are interested in what things family members do together. How often do any of the members of your family do anything like:

		1 Often	2 Sometimes	3 Never	X DK	Y N/A
6: 38 __	Go shopping together					
6: 39 __	Just sit and talk to each other					
6: 40 __	Go for walks together					
6: 41 __	Play cards, checkers or things like that					
6: 42 __	Go to the movies together					
6: 43 __	Watch TV or listen to the radio together					
6: 44 __	Go to church together					
6: 45 __	Visit friends together					
6: 46 __	Visit relatives together					
6: 47 __	Go on picnics or trips to beaches or parks together					

Card: Column

6: 48 __ In general, how often does *** take part in these things? Would you say:

__ 1 Often
__ 2 Sometimes
__ 3 Rarely
__ 4 Never
__ X No information or DK
__ Y N/A

6: 49 __ In general, how often do the members of the family who live in this apartment try to do things to help one another out? Would you say:

__ 1 Very often
__ 2 Fairly often
__ 3 Occasionally
__ 4 Never
__ X No information or DK
__ Y N/A

6: 50 __ How often does everyone in your family (who lives at the same residence) sit down to the evening meal together? Would you say:

__ 1 Always
__ 2 Most of the time
__ 3 Only some of the time
__ 4 Never
__ X No information
__ Y N/A

6: 51 __ In general, what would you say about ***'s acceptance of his/her responsibility as a parent? In other words, is ***:

__ 1 An excellent parent: assumes full emotional and physical responsibility for child(ren)'s rearing
__ 2 Good: occasional lapses – responsibility usually assumed well, but occasionally abdicated
__ 3 Fair: some failure to accept responsibility for child(ren)'s rearing
__ 4 Poor: definite failure to accept responsibility for child(ren)'s rearing

Card: Column

__5 No significant emotional or physical contact between patient and child(ren) at this time. (Respondent attributes ***'s current parental behavior and lack of responsibility to his/her illness)
__X No information or DK
__Y N/A

6: 52__ (If "Fair" or "Poor") was *** always this way?

__1 Yes __2 No __X DK __Y N/A

(If "No") how do you account for ***'s attitude at this time?

(Probe!)

6: 53__ (If *** and respondent are of childbearing age) Do you expect to have more children?

__1 Yes __2 No __X DK __Y N/A

(If "No") Reasons?

(Probe!)

PROGRESS REPORT (Significant Other)

Date: ____________

Interviewer: ______

Place: ___________

Patient's Name: ____

Patient's Address: ____

Respondent's Name: ____

Respondent's Address: ____

SECTION I

Column

1,2,3__,__,__ ITC case no.

4__ Study group

5__ Sex of pt

__1 male __2 female

6__ Respondent's relationship to pt

Card: Column

__ 1 Husband
__ 2 Wife
__ 3 Father
__ 4 Mother
__ 5 Brother
__ 6 Sister
__ 7 Grandparent
__ 8 Other relative (specify) ________
__ 9 Friend
__ 0 Other (specify) ________

7 __ Place of interview

__ 1 Home of patient
__ 2 ITC
__ 3 Other (specify) ________________.

8 __ Interviewer

__ 1 RN
__ 2 SW
__ Other (specify)

9 __ Interview at: (For HC and failure, count from time of admission to program) (For hospital group, count time of discharge)

__ 1 Second week
__ 2 Fourth week
__ 3 Sixth week
__ 4 Two months
__ 5 Three months
__ 6 Six months
__ 7 Twelve months
__ 8 Eighteen months
__ 9 Twenty-four months
__ 0 Other (specify) ________

10 __ Nature of report

__ 1 Progress report (home care)
__ 2 Progress report (hospital)
__ 3 Failure
__ 4 Other (specify) ________________

11,12 __, __ Card number (this is card 31)

31: 13 __ Residence

__ 1 Same as time of pt's admission to treatment program
__ 2 Different from time of pt's admission to treatment program

Card: Column

31: 14 __ Number of residence changes since pt's admission to treatment program

__ 0 No change
__ 1-8 Actual number of times (1,2,3, etc.)
__ 9 Nine or more
__ X DK

31: 15 __ Marital status of pt

__ 1 Married
__ 2 Single (never married)
__ 3 Widowed
__ 4 Divorced
__ 5 Separated
__ 6 Common-law
__ 7 Casual alliance or other
__ X DK

31: 16 __ Change of pt's marital status since admission to treatment program

__ 0 No change
__ 1 Legally married
__ 2 Common-law marriage
__ 3 Casual alliance
__ Widowed
__ 5 Divorced
__ 6 Separated
__ 7 Other

(If pt is female and has married or remarried since admission to treatment program, record:)

31: 17 __ Husband's occupation

Record actual occupation ______________________
(if husband is pt write pt above)

Check all appropriate categories which follow

__ 1 Self-employed
__ 2 Retired or deceased (under which)
__ 3 Regular job with regular income (full time)
__ 4 Regular job with regular income (part time)
__ 5 Sporadic employment (odd jobs)
__ 6 If farmer: tenant __yes __ no
Approx. size of farm ______________________
__ X DK
__ Y (score Y if pt is male)
__ 0 (score 0 if pt is female and no change in marital status)

Card: Column

31: 18 __ Husband's education

__ 1 Graduate professional training
__ 2 Standard college or university graduation
__ 3 Partial college training
__ 4 High school graduation
__ 5 Partial high (10th-11th grade)
__ 6 Junior high school (7th-9th grades)
__ 7 Less than 7 years of school (6th grade or less)
__ X DK
__ Y (if pt is male)
__ 0 (if pt is female and no change in marital status)

31: 19,20 __,__ HI Index (coder only: see manual) Score YY if pt is male or 00 if pt is female and no change in marital status.

31: 21 __ Pt's current living arrangements (check the most important)

__ 1 Alone (N/A)
__ 2 With spouse
__ 3 With parents
__ 4 With child(ren)
__ 5 With sibling(s)
__ 6 With other relative(s) (specify)
__ 7 With roommate(s) or friend(s)
__ 8 In a group; e.g., dormitory, etc.
__ 9 Other: ______________________________
__ X D/K

31: 22 __ (Coder only) Check previous living arrangement and score score for changes as follows:

__ 0 No change
__ 1-8 Actual number of changes
__ 9 Nine or more changes
__ X DK

Pt's household (Record all individuals exclusive of pt who currently reside at present address – sex, age and relationship to pt.)

Card: Column

Males	Relationship	Females	Relationship

31: 23

(Coder only) Check previous data on household in order to determine changes.

0 No change
1 Fewer household members than before
2 Additional household members
X DK

(Coder only) List below absent members and new members as indicated:

Absent	New

31: 24

How do you feel about ***'s condition now as compared to the time of the last interview? (Note: "last interview" could refer to initial interview, a progress report, or "before hospitalization.")

9 Denies that pt is or has been ill
1 Was ill but now "normal" or recovered
2 Still ill but much better than before

Card: Column

3 About the same as before
4 Worse than before
X DK

31: 25 How would you describe the illness *** has (or had)?

0 Denies that pt is or has been ill
1 As mental (with high degree of insight)
2 As mental (with low or minimal degree of insight)
3 As a "nervous breadkown"
4 "Nerves"
5 As a physical disorder
6 Other (specify)
X DK

31: 26 Do you feel that *** has (or had) to be watched (observed) more closely and more often than other people?

1 Yes 2 No X DK

31: 27 For how long have you felt this way?

1 Feels pt never needed watching
2 Since admission to treatment program (HC)
3 Long time (over 2 years)
4 Since last interview
5 Other (specify)
X DK

31: 28 In your opinion, does *** still need treatment?

1 Yes 2 No X DK

31: 29 (HC) Do you think that *** would be (or is) better off in the mental hospital than at home?

1 Yes 2 No X DK Y N/A

(Hosp.) Do you think that *** should have stayed in the hospital for a longer period of time?

1 Yes 2 No X DK Y N/A

31: 30 Has *** been physically sick recently (since last interview)?

Card: Column

__ 1 Yes (specify)
__ 2 No
__ X DK

31: 31 __ Has *** needed a doctor recently (since last interview)?

__ 1 Yes (specify) ____________________

____

__ 2 No
__ X DK

31: 32 __ Has *** seen a doctor recently (since last interview?

__ 1 Yes (If "Yes") name and address

____

____

__ 2 No
__ X DK

Patient's Behavior

Now, I would like to ask some specific questions about ***'s behavior { these last few weeks / since the last interview / since return from the hospital }

In case of a <u>failure</u>, last week

31: 33 __ How much trouble has *** been at night (noisy, wandering, etc.)?

__ 1 No trouble at all
__ 2 Some trouble
__ 3 Very difficult
__ X DK
__ Y N/A (respondent not in patient's household)

31: 34 __ Has *** been a nursing problem (bed-ridden, incontinent, feeding, washing)?

__ 1 No problem
__ 2 Sometimes

Card: Column

3 Often
X DK
Y N/A

31: 35 Has ***'s safety been a source of worry (wandering off, car, gas)?

1 No problem
2 Sometimes
3 Often
X DK
Y N/A

31: 36 Has *** caused anxiety (worry) about the safety of others?

1 No problem
2 Sometimes (specify)

3 Often (specify)
X DK
Y N/A

31: 37 Has *** caused difficulty be being uncooperative?

1 No problem
2 Sometimes (specify)

3 Often (specify)
X DK
Y N/A

31: 38 Is *** a strain in relying and depending on people too much?

1 No problem
2 Sometimes (specify)

3 Often (specify)
X DK
Y N/A

31: 39 Has ***'s constant restlessness, noisiness, or talking been upsetting?

Card: Column

1 No problem
2 Sometimes
3 Often
X DK
Y N/A

31: 40 Have frequent complaints about bodily (physical) symptoms worried you?

1 No
2 Sometimes
3 Often
X DK
Y N/A

31: 41 Has *** been a problem because of sexual, rude, or objectionable behavior?

1 No
2 Sometimes
3 Often
X DK
Y N/A

31: 42 Has *** caused anxiety (worry) by speaking or behaving oddly or by having unusual or unreasonable ideas?

1 No
2 Sometimes
3 Often
X DK
Y N/A

31: 43 Has *** caused any trouble with the neighbors?

1 No
2 Sometimes (specify)
3 Often (specify)
X DK
Y N/A

31: 44 Is household work or routine upset by ***?

1 No Specify:
2 Occasionally

Card: Column

3 A great deal
X DK
Y N/A

31: 45 Are social or leisure activities interfered with because of ***?

1 No Specify:
2 Occasionally
3 A great deal
X DK
Y N/A

31: 46 Has anyone in household had to stay away from work because of ***?

1 No
2 Yes, occasionally
3 Yes, a great deal (more than 14 days since discharge)
X DK
Y N/A

Specify:

31: 47 Has anyone in the household had to stay away from school because of ***?

1 No
2 Yes, occasionally
3 Yes, a great deal (more than 14 days)
X DK
Y N/A

31: 48 Has ***'s behavior caused you (respondent) much worry?

1 No
2 Sometimes
3 Yes, a great deal
X DK
Y N/A

31: 49 Has *** been a physical strain on you?

1 Not at all

Card: Column

___ 2 Some strain
___ 3 Marked strain
___ X DK
___ Y N/A

31: 50___ Does *** require an excessive amount of attention or companionship?

___ 1 No
___ 2 Sometimes
___ 3 Very demanding
___ X DK
___ Y N/A

31: 51___ Are the children ashamed because of ***?

___ 1 No
___ 2 Sometimes
___ 3 A great deal
___ X DK
___ Y N/A

31: 52___ Are the children afraid of ***?

___ 1 No
___ 2 Sometimes
___ 3 To a great extent
___ X DK
___ Y N/A

31: 53___ Do you feel ashamed because of ***?

___ 1 No
___ 2 Sometimes
___ 3 A great deal
___ X DK
___ Y N/A

31: 54___ Are you afraid of ***?

___ 1 No
___ 2 Sometimes
___ 3 Often
___ X DK
___ Y N/A

31: 55,56___,___ Total Problems Score (coder only: see manual)

SECTION II

This section applies to males only

Card: Column

32: 13 ___ Is *** working now? Or was he working last week (before failure)?

___ 1 Yes ___ 2 No ___ X DK

What kind of job does (did) he have? ________________

32: 14 ___ Is (was) this his "regular" job or kind of work?

___ 0 Not working
___ 1 Yes
___ 2 No
___ X DK
___ Y N/A

32: 15 ___ Did *** have this job at the time of the last interview (or before hospitalization)?

___ 0 Not working
___ 1 Yes
___ 2 No
___ X DK
___ Y N/A

32: 16 ___ How long has *** had the job he now has (had)?

___ 0 Not working
___ 1 Less than 6 months
___ 2 Less than 1 year
___ 3 More than 1 year
___ 4 Long time on and off
___ X DK
___ Y N/A

32: 17 ___ How did *** go about getting this job?

___ 0 Not working
___ 1 Want ads
___ 2 Employment agency (private)

Card: Column

___ 3 Employment agency (state or federal)
___ 4 Union
___ 5 Social worker (community agency)
___ 6 Social worker (hospital)
___ 7 Relative
___ 8 Friend
___ 9 Other (specify) ________________________
___ X No information or DK
___ Y N/A (e.g. never worked)

32: 18 ___ How much time does (did) *** devote to his job?

___ 0 Not working
___ 1 Full time, 30 hours plus per week
___ 2 More than half time but considered to be a part-time position by respondent
___ 3 Half time
___ 4 Less than half time, less than 16 hours per week
___ 5 A few hours a week
___ X No information or DK
___ Y N/A

32: 19 ___ Is (was) *** expected to work every week, or does (did) the job call for some other kind of arrangement?

___ 0 Not working
___ 1 Job is on a regular week-to-week basis
___ 2 Job is on week-to-week basis but for less than 9 months but more than 6 months during the year
___ 3 Job requires 3-6 months per year
___ 4 Job requires less than 3 months of regular work
___ X No information or DK
___ Y N/A

32: 20 ___ When working, is (was) *** expected to work every day?

___ 0 Not working ___ 1 Yes ___ 2 No ___ X DK
___ Y N/A

32: 21 ___ When *** is (was) working, how good is (was) his attendance on the job?

___ 0 Not working
___ 1 No absences or out only rarely

Card: Column

__ 2 Out from time to time but infrequently, and absences are justified-realistic (e.g., illness, important business, etc.)
__ 3 Out from time to time (infrequently) but not adequately justified
__ 4 Absences are relatively frequent, but adequately justified
__ 5 Absences are relatively frequent, but not adequately justified
__ 6 Out most of the time
__ X No information or DK
__ Y N/A

32: 22 __ In general, how difficult has it been for *** to work?

__ 0 Not working
__ 1 Not difficult at all
__ 2 Some difficulty
__ 3 Very difficult
__ X DK
__ Y N/A

32: 23 __ In general, would you say that ***'s handling of his job (work) is pretty much what it has usually been or very different from the way he did in the past (before he got sick)?

__ 0 Not working
__ 1 Same
__ 2 Some difference
__ 3 Very different
__ X DK
__ Y N/A (e.g., has never worked or had a job)

32: 24 __ If *** is (or was) not working, why is (was) *** not working?

__ 1 Too sick to work (mental)
__ 2 Too sick to work (physical)
__ 3 There is no work (seasonal lay-off or other)
__ 4 Doesn't want to work
__ 5 Can't find a job
__ 6 Other

Card: Column

___ X DK
___ Y N/A (e.g., is working)

32: 25 ___ If *** is (or was) not working, is (was) *** looking for work?

___ 1 Yes ___ 2 No ___ X DK ___ Y N/A

32: 26 ___ If ** is (or was) not working, how good are (were) his chances for finding work?

___ 1 Very good
___ 2 Fair
___ 3 Not good
___ X DK
___ Y N/A

32: 27 ___ How important is (was) ***'s employment to the household?

___ 1 *** sole breadwinner
___ 2 *** one among 2 breadwinners
___ 3 *** one among 3 or more contributors
___ 4 *** contribution unimportant
___ 5 Other (specify) ______________________
___ X DK
___ Y N/A

Since the last interview
Since coming home from the hospital } does (did)

*** do any of these things?

32: 28 ___ Help with household chores

___ 1 Could not
___ 2 Occasionally
___ 3 Often
___ 9 Would not
___ X DK
___ Y N/A

Card: Column

32: 29 __ Help you entertain at home

__ 1 Could not
__ 2 Occasionally
__ 3 Often
__ 9 Would not
__ X DK
__ Y N/A

32: 30 __ Visit his friends

__ 1 Could not
__ 2 Occasionally
__ 3 Often
__ 9 Would not
__ X DK
__ Y N/A

32: 31 __ Visit his relatives

__ 1 Could not
__ 2 Occasionally
__ 3 Often
__ 9 Would not
__ X DK
__ Y N/A

32: 32 __ Help manage the family finances

__ 1 Could not
__ 2 Occasionally
__ 3 Often
__ 9 Would not
__ X DK
__ Y N/A

32: 33 __ Help with family's shopping

__ 1 Could not
__ 2 Occasionally
__ 3 Often
__ 9 Would not
__ X DK
__ Y N/A

Card: Column

32: 34 ___ Go to parties and other social activities

___ 1 Could not
___ 2 Occasionally
___ 3 Often
___ 9 Would not
___ X DK
___ Y N/A

32: 35,36___,___ Score: Total 1, 2, 3's only ______________ (coder only)

32: 37 ___ Would you say that ***'s mental illness has affected his ability to do the kinds of things you expect him to do?

___ 1 Yes, some
___ 2 Yes, a great deal
___ 3 No
___ 4 Respondent denies that pt is mentally ill
___ X DK
___ Y N/A

Specifically now, what are some of the things you expect (expected) *** to do? For example, do (did) you expect him to:

32: 38 ___ Be working full time?

___ 1 No ___ 2 Yes ___ X DK ___ Y N/A (e.g., never has)

32:39 ___ Be working part time?

___ 1 No ___ 2 Yes ___ X DK ___ Y N/A (e.g., never has)

32: 40 ___ Help with household chores?

___ 1 No ___ 2 Yes ___ X DK ___ Y N/A (e.g., never has)

32: 41 ___ Help you entertain at home?

___ 1 No ___ 2 Yes ___ X DK ___ Y N/A (e.g., never has)

32: 42 ___ Go visit his friends?

___ 1 No ___ 2 Yes ___ X DK ___ Y N/A (e.g., never has)

Card: Column

32: 43 __ Go visit his relatives?

__ 1 No __ 2 Yes __ X DK __ Y N/A (e.g., never has)

32: 44 __ Help manage the family finances?

__ 1 No __ 2 Yes __ X DK __ Y N/A (e.g., never has)

32: 45 __ Help with the family's shopping?

__ 1 No __ 2 Yes __ X DK __ Y N/A (e.g., never has)

32: 46 __ Go to parties and other social activities?

__ 1 No __ 2 Yes __ X DK __ Y N/A (e.g., never has)

32: 47, 48 __ __ Total Expectation Score (coder only) ______ (see manual)

SECTION III

This section applies only if patient is female

Card: Column

33: 13 __ In general, how much of ***'s time is (was) spent in homemaking activities?

__ 1 Full time (no outside employment of any kind)
__ 2 Virtually full time (minimal or sporadic employment outside the home)
__ 3 Half time (gainfully and/or nongainfully* employed outside the home)
__ 4 Minimal (works full time but has homemaking obligations)
__ 5 Not at all
__ X DK
__ Y N/A (specify) ______________________

* (Note: an example of nongainful employment would be aiding husband in his business or store.)

33: 14 __ (If *** works or was working): What kind of job does *** have? or What kind of job did she have?

Card: Column

__ 1 Does not and did not have any job
__ 2 Clerk-typist
__ 3 Secretarial (with some administrative responsibility)
__ 4 Sales
__ 5 Professional (e.g., school teacher, nurse)
__ 6 Domestic (e.g., cook, maid, cleaning)
__ 7 Unskilled or semiskilled factory work
__ 8 Other (specify) ________________
__ X DK

33: 15 __ Is or was this job full or part time?

__ 1 Did not work
__ 2 Full time
__ 3 Half time (20-25 hrs./week)
__ 4 Less than half time (less than 20 hrs./week)
__ 5 Minimal (less than 10 hr./week)
__ X DK

33: 16 __ How important is (or was) ***'s income to the family?

__ 1 Did not work
__ 2 *** is chief breadwinner (contribution is more than 50% of total income)
__ 3 Supplementary but substantial (20-50% of total family income)
__ 4 Supplementary but minimal (10-20% of total family income)
__ 5 Supplementary but only token contribution (less than 10%)
__ X DK

33:17 __ Do you consider ***'s earnings to be a necessary contribution to the family's income?

__ 1 Yes __ 2 No __ X DK __ Y N/A

33: 18 __ Does or did *** have sole responsibility as a homemaker or did she share her responsibility with another person(s)?

__ 1 Sole responsibility
__ 2 Major responsibility
__ 3 Shared responsibility on 50/50 basis
__ 4 Only minor responsibility

Card: Column

__ 5 No responsibility
__ X DK
__ Y N/A

(IF ANYTHING BUT "SOLE RESPONSIBILITY"): WITH WHOM IS OR WAS RESPONSIBILITY SHARED OR PERSON WHO ASSUMED HOMEMAKING ROLE FOR PATIENT'S FAMILY?

NAME: ____________________

RELATIONSHIP TO PATIENT: ____________________

____ X DK

____ Y N/A

33: 19 __ Would you say that *** is satisfied in being a homemaker?

__ 1 Yes __2 No __X DK __Y N/A

33: 20 __ If *** had her choice between being a homemaker and working outside the home, which would she choose?

__ 1 Homemaking __2 Work __3 Combination

__ X DK __Y N/A

33: 21 __ In general, how difficult is (or has it been) for *** to do the kinds of things that most other women of her age do?

__ 1 Not difficult at all
__ 2 Some difficulty
__ 3 Very difficult
__ X DK
__ Y N/A

33: 22 __ In general, would you say that the way *** handles her chores (domestic duties and responsibilities, etc.) is

Card: Column

pretty much what it has usually been or very different from the way she did in the past (before she got sick)?

___ 1 Same
___ 2 Some difference
___ 3 Very different
___ X DK
___ Y N/A

Specifically now, can you tell me about some of the things *** does (or did) around the house. We are interested in knowing whether she does (or did) these things by herself, whether she needs (or needed) help, or whether she is (or was) unable to do them.

Card: Column		(1) Can or Could not do	(2) Needs or Needed Some Help	(3) Does or Did by Self	(9) Will or Would not Do	(X) DK	(Y) Does or Did not Have to Do
33: 23 ___	Attended to house cleaning chores						
33: 24 ___	Prepared meals						
33: 25 ___	Attended to laundry and cleaning						
33: 26 ___	Shopped for groceries						
33: 27 ___	Did other shopping (e.g., clothing, household items)						
33: 28 ___	Budgeted for the household (including writing checks or handling money)						
33: 29 ___	Planned own daily activities						
33: 30 ___	Solved daily problems						

Card: Column

33: 31,32__,__ (coder only) Total: __________ (include only 1, 2 & 3)

33: 33 __ Would you say that ***'s mental illness has affected her ability to do the kinds of things you expect (or expected) her to do?

__ 1 Yes, some
__ 2 Yes, a great deal
__ 3 No
__ 4 Respondent denies that pt is mentally ill
__ X DK
__ Y N/A

Specifically, do you now expect (or did you expect) *** to do any of these things?

33:34 __ Dust, sweep, and do other usual cleaning

__ 1 No __ 2 Yes __ X DK __ Y N/A

33:35 __ Cook for the family

__ 1 No __ 2 Yes __ X DK __ Y N/A

33: 36 __ Take care of the laundry, etc.

__ 1 No __ 2 Yes __ X DK __ Y N/A

33: 37 __ Grocery shopping

__ 1 No __ 2 Yes __ X DK __ Y N/A

33: 38 __ Other shopping (household, clothing, etc.)

__ 1 No __ 2 Yes __ X DK __ Y N/A

33: 39 __ Handle and budget grocery money

__ 1 No __ 2 Yes __ X DK __ Y N/A

33: 40,41__,__ Subtotal: (coder only)

Card: Column

33: 42 ___ Go visit her friends or relatives

___1 No ___2 Yes ___X DK ___Y N/A

33: 43 ___ Entertain friends or relatives at home

___1 No ___2 Yes ___X DK ___Y N/A

33: 44 ___ Hold a job

___1 No ___2 Yes ___X DK ___Y N/A

33: 45 ___ Mix socially with the neighbors

___1 No ___2 Yes ___X DK ___Y N/A

33: 46 ___ Go to parties and other social activities

___1 No ___2 Yes ___X DK ___Y N/A

33: 47,48___, ___ Subtotal: (coder only) ____ ____

33: 49,50___, ___ Total Expectation Score (coder only)____ ____

PROGRESS REPORT (Male Patient)

Date: ______________________

Interviewer: ______________________

Place: ______________________

Patient's Name: ______________________

Address: ______________________

Column

1, 2, 3 __, __, __ ITC case no. ______

4 __ Study group

5 __ Sex of pt ______ 1 Male ______ 2 Female

6 __ Marital status

- __ 1 Married
- __ 2 Single (never married)
- __ 3 Widowed
- __ 4 Divorced
- __ 5 Separated
- __ 6 Common-law
- __ 7 Casual alliance or other
- __ X DK

7 __ Place of interview

- __ 1 Home of pt
- __ 2 ITC
- __ 3 Other (specify) ______________________

Card: Column

8 ___ Interviewer

___ 1 RN
___ 2 SW
___ 3 Other (specify) ______________________

9 ___ Interview at: (For HC, count from time of admission to program) (For hospital group, count from time of discharge)

___ 1 Second week
___ 2 Fourth week
___ 3 Sixth week
___ 4 Two months
___ 5 Three months
___ 6 Six months
___ 7 Twelve months
___ 8 Eighteen months
___ 9 Twenty-four months
___ 0 Other (specify) __________

10 ___ Nature of report

___ 1 Progress (home care)
___ 2 Progress (hospital)
___ 3 Other (specify) ______________________

11, 12 ___ ___ Card number (this is card 42)

42: 13 ___ How would you say your health is now (lately)?

___ 1 Excellent
___ 2 Good
___ 3 Fair
___ 4 Poor
___ X DK
___ Y N/A

42: 14 ___ Do you feel you are better now than when you first started treatment (or when you went to the hospital)?

___ 1 Better
___ 2 Same
___ 3 Worse
___ 4 Denies being sick

42: 15 ___ Generally, would you say that you are happy living here?

___ 1 Yes

Card: Column

__ 2 No
__ X DK

42: 16 __ If you had a choice, where and with whom would you rather live?

__ 1 Here
__ 2 Alone
__ 3 With others, relatives
__ 4 With others, friends
__ 5 Other (specify) ____________
__ X DK

42: 17 __ Do you have any special problems or difficulties here?

__ 1 Yes
__ 2 No
__ X DK

42: 18 __ What kinds of difficulties are they?

(note: record most important or one mentioned most frequently)

__ 0 No difficulties
__ 1 Financial
__ 2 Relationships
__ 3 Attitudes of others
__ 4 Situational (neighborhood)
__ 5 Other (specify) ____________

42: 19 __ In general, what would you say the attitudes of the others in the house are towards you?

(note: record most important or one mentioned most frequently)

__ 1 Accepting and understanding
__ 2 Wary or suspicious
__ 3 Critical
__ 4 Indifferent
__ 5 Hostile
__ 6 Rejecting
__ 7 Protective
__ 8 Other (specify) ____________
__ X DK

42: 20 __ In general, how would you say you get along with the others in the family (in the house or home)?

__ 1 Very well
__ 2 Pretty well
__ 3 We tolerate each other

Card: Column

___ 4 Not too well
___ 5 Not at all
___ X DK

42: 21 ___ In general, how would you say others in the family get along with you?

___ 1 Very well
___ 2 Pretty well
___ 3 We tolerate each other
___ 4 Not too well
___ 5 Not at all
___ X DK

42: 22 ___ Are you working now?

___ 1 Yes ___ 2 No ___ X DK ___ Y N/A

What kind of a job do you have? ___________________

42: 23 ___ Is this your "regular" job or kind of work?

___ 0 Not working
___ 1 Yes
___ 2 No
___ X DK
___ Y N/A

42: 24 ___ Did you have this job at the time of the last interview (or before hospitalization)?

___ 0 Not working
___ 1 Yes
___ 2 No
___ X DK
___ Y N/A

42: 25 ___ How long have you had the job you now have?

___ 0 Not working
___ 1 Less than 6 months
___ 2 Less than 1 year
___ 3 More than 1 year
___ 4 Long time, on and off

Card: Column

__ X DK
__ Y N/A

42: 26__ How did you go about getting this last job?

__ 0 Not working
__ 1 Want ads
__ 2 Employment agency (private)
__ 3 Employment agency (state or federal)
__ 4 Union
__ 5 Social worker (community agency)
__ 6 Social worker (hospital)
__ 7 Relative
__ 8 Friend
__ 9 Other (specify) ______________________________
__ X No information or DK
__ Y N/A (e.g., never worked)

42: 27 __ How much time do you devote to this job?

__ 0 Not working
__ 1 Full time, 30 hours plus per week
__ 2 More than half time but considered to be a part-time position by respondent
__ 3 Half time
__ 4 Less than half time, less than 16 hours per week
__ 5 A few hours a week
__ X No information or DK
__ Y N/A

42: 28 __ Are you expected to work every week, or does the job call for some other kind of arrangement?

__ 0 Not working
__ 1 Job is on a regular week-to-week basis
__ 2 Job is on a week-to-week basis but for less than 9 months but more than 6 months during the year
__ 3 Job requires 3-6 months per year
__ 4 Job requires less than 3 months of regular work
__ X No information or DK
__ Y N/A

Card: Column

42: 29 __ When working, are you expected to work every day?

__ 0 Not working __ 1 Yes __ 2 No __ Y N/A

42: 30 __ In general, how difficult has it been for you to work?

__ 0 Not working
__ 1 Not difficult at all
__ 2 Some difficulty
__ 3 Very difficult
__ X DK
__ Y N/A

42: 31 __ Do you see this job as a temporary or as a permanent one?

__ 1 Temporary __ X DK
__ 2 Permanent __ Y N/A

42: 32 __ (If pt is not working) Why aren't you working?

__ 1 Too sick to work (mental)
__ 2 Too sick to work (physical)
__ 3 There is no work (legitimate, e.g., seasonal lay-off)
__ 4 There is no work (nonlegitimate excuse)
__ 5 Doesn't want to work
__ 6 Can't find a job
__ 7 Doesn't have to work
__ 8 Other (specify) ____________________
__ X DK
__ Y N/A

42: 33 __ (If pt is not working) Are you looking for work now?

__ 1 Yes
__ 2 No
__ X DK
__ Y N/A

42: 34 __ (If pt is not working) How good do you think your chances are for finding work?

__ 1 Very good
__ 2 Fair

Card: Column

__ 3 Not good
__ X DK
__ Y N/A

42: 35 __ How important is your contribution to the finances of your family?

__ 1 Pt is sole breadwinner
__ 2 Pt is 1 of 2 breadwinners
__ 3 Pt is 1 of 3 or more breadwinners
__ 4 Pt's contribution considered unimportant
__ X DK
__ Y N/A

Next, we would like to know about some of your other activities – the kinds of things you do when you are not working (or when not looking for a job or other work related activities)

For instance: In the last few weeks (or since the last interview) have you done any of these things?

42: 36 __ Have you done work around the house (e.g., painting, fixing, etc.)?

__ 1 No __ 2 Yes __ X DK __ Y N/A

42: 37 __ Have you done any grocery shopping?

__ 1 No __ 2 Yes __ X DK __ Y N/A

42: 38 __ Have you shopped "downtown" (e.g., clothing, household items, etc.)?

__ 1 No __ 2 Yes __ X DK __ Y N/A

42: 39 __ Have you handled or helped handle the family finances (budget, write checks, handle money)?

__ 1 No __ 2 Yes __ X DK __ Y N/A

42: 40 __ Worked on a hobby?

__ 1 No __ 2 Yes __ X DK __ Y N/A

Card: Column

42: 41___ Gone to any parties or social activities?

___1 No ___2 Yes ___X DK ___Y N/A

42: 42___ Visited friends or relatives?

___1 No ___2 Yes ___X DK ___Y N/A

42: 43___ Gone to the movies?

___1 No ___2 Yes ___X DK ___Y N/A

42: 44___ Driven a car?

___1 No ___2 Yes ___X DK ___Y N/A

42: 45___ Have you gone to any club or orgainzation meeting?

___1 No ___2 Yes ___X DK ___Y N/A

Do you belong to or take part in any of these clubs or groups?

(If "Yes")

			About How Often Do You Attend Meetings?		Are You An Officer or Committee Member?		Does the Group Meet In or Out of the Neighborhood?	
	2 No	1 Yes	Usually or (always)	Only Occasionally	1 Yes	2 No	1 Inside	2 Outside
Professional organization								
Union								
Fraternal								
Religious								
Veterans								
Athletic								
PTA								
Political								
Social								
Charitable								
YM – YWCA								
Other (specify)								

Card: Column

42: 46 __

__0 Patient does not belong to any organization
__1 Belongs to 1 organization
__2 Belongs to 2 organizations
__3 Belongs to 3 organizations
__4 Belongs to 4-7 organizations
__5 Belongs to 8 or more organizations
__X DK

Next, we would like to know what you think you should be doing now—that is, what do you expect of yourself?

For instance, do you think that you should be

42: 47 __ Working full time?

__1 No __2 Yes __X DK __Y N/A

42: 48 __ Working part time?

__1 No __2 Yes __X DK __Y N/A

42: 49 __ Helping with household chores?

__1 No __2 Yes __X DK __Y N/A

42: 50 __ Helping entertain at home?

__1 No __2 Yes __X DK __Y N/A

42: 51 __ Visiting friends?

__1 No __2 Yes __X DK __Y N/A

42: 52 __ Visiting relatives?

__1 No __2 Yes __X DK __Y N/A

42: 53 __ Managing (or helping to manage) household finances?

__1 No __2 Yes __X DK __Y N/A

42: 54 __ Helping with family shopping?

__1 No __2 Yes __X DK __Y N/A

Card: Column

42: 55 __ Going to parties and other social affairs?

__ 1 No __ 2 Yes __ X DK __ Y N/A

42: 56, 57 __, __ Total Expectation Score (coder only) ___ ___

42: 58 __ In general, how would you say your expectations compare to those of your wife? (or pertinent SO)

__ 1 About the same
__ 2 Spouse (or pertinent SO) expects more than pt capable or willing to do
__ 3 Spouse (or pertinent SO) expects less than pt capable or willing to do
__ X DK
__ Y N/A

42: 59 __ (If perceived discrepancy in expectations) In what specific ways do you disagree?

__ 0 No apparent discrepancy perceived
__ 1 In matters pertaining to routine household activities or chores
__ 2 In matters pertaining to the children (if any)
__ 3 In matters pertaining to work or job
__ 4 In matters pertaining to social activities
__ 5 Family budgeting or finances
__ 6 Other (specify) ______________________

Note: check the most important or the one most frequently mentioned and circle the others.

Record in detail the precise nature of the perceived discrepancy in expectations (in addition to the general categories above)

____

____

____

42: 60 __ (For hospital pts only) Do you feel that being in the hospital has helped you?

__ 1 Yes __ 2 No __ X DK __ Y N/A

Card: Column

42: 61 ___ (For hospital pts only) Do you feel that you still need treatment?

___ 1 Yes ___ 2 No ___ X DK ___ Y N/A

42: 62 ___ (For hospital pts only) What kinds of treatment do you feel you should be getting?

___ 1 Says that treatment not required
___ 2 Medicine (pills)
___ 3 Further hospitalization
___ 4 Outpatient treatment
___ 5 Other (specify) ______________________
___ X DK
___ Y N/A

42: 63 ___ (For home care pts only) Do you feel that the treatment (medicine) you have been getting has helped you?

___ 1 Yes ___ 2 No ___ X DK ___ Y N/A

42: 64 ___ (For home care pts only) Do you feel that you might be better off in the hospital?

___ 1 Yes ___ 2 No ___ X DK ___ Y N/A

42: 65 ___ (All pts) Do you feel that some time in the future you might have to go into the hospital for further treatment?

___ 1 Yes ___ 2 No ___ X DK

42: 66 ___ (All pts) All things considered, how would you feel about going to (or back to) the hospital if it were necessary?

___ 1 Yes, readily
___ 2 Doubtful
___ 3 Definitely not
___ 4 Only if I were forced
___ 5 Other (specify) ______________________
___ X DK

PROGRESS REPORT (Female Patient)

Date: ______________________

Interviewer: ______________________

Place: ______________________

Patient's Name: ______________________

Address: ______________________

Column

1, 2, 3__, __, __ITC case no.

4 __ Study group

5 __ Sex of pt ___ 1 Male ___ 2 Female

6 __ Marital status

__ 1 Married
__ 2 Single (Never Married)
__ 3 Widowed
__ 4 Divorced
__ 5 Separated
__ 6 Common-law
__ 7 Casual alliance or other
__ X DK

7 __ Place of interview

__ 1 Home of pt
__ 2 ITC
__ 3 Other (specify) ______________________

Column

8 __ Interviewer

__ 1 RN
__ 2 SW
__ 3 Other (specify) ____________

9 __ Interview at: (For HC count from time of admission to program) (For hospital group, count from time of discharge)

__ 1 Second week
__ 2 Fourth week
__ 3 Sixth week
__ 4 Two months
__ 5 Three months
__ 6 Six months
__ 7 Twelve months
__ 8 Eighteen months
__ 9 Twenty-four months
__ 0 Other (specify) ____________

10 __ Nature of report

__ 1 Progress (home care)
__ 2 Progress (hospital)
__ 3 Other (specify) ____________

11,12 __,__ Card number (this is card 43)

Card: Column

43: 13 __ In general, how much of your time is spent in homemaking activities?

__ 1 Full time (no outside employment of any kind)
__ 2 Virtually full time (minimal or sporadic employment outside the home)
__ 3 Half time (gainfully and/or nongainfully* employed outside the home)
__ 4 Minimal (works full time but has homemaking obligations)
__ 5 Not at all

Card: Column

__ X DK
__ Y N/A (specify)

*(Note: an example of nongainful employment would be aiding husband in his business or store.)

43: 14 __ (If pt works or did have a job before treatment or hospitalization) What kind of a job do (did) you have?

__ 1 Does not and did not have any job
__ 2 Clerk-typist
__ 3 Secretarial (with some administrative responsibility)
__ 4 Sales
__ 5 Professional (e.g., school teacher, nurse)
__ 6 Domestic (e.g., cook, maid, cleaning)
__ 7 Unskilled or semiskilled factory worker
__ 8 Other (specify) ________________
__ X DK

43: 15 __ Is or was this job full or part time?

__ 1 Did not work
__ 2 Full time
__ 3 Half time (20-25 hrs./week)
__ 4 Less than half time (less than 20 hrs./week)
__ 5 Minimal (less than 10 hr./week)
__ X DK

43: 16 __ How important is (or was) your income to the family?

__ 1 Did not work
__ 2 Chief breadwinner (contribution is more than 50% of total income)
__ 3 Supplementary but substantial (20-50% of total family income)
__ 4 Supplementary but minimal (10-20% of total family income)
__ 5 Supplementary but only token contribution (less than 10%)
__ X DK

Card: Column

43: 17 __ Do you do all your own housework?

__ 1 Yes
__ 2 No
__ X DK
__ Y N/A

43: 18 __ If not, who helps you with the housework?

__ 1 Family member(s)
__ 2 Neighbor(s) or friend(s)
__ 3 Paid help
__ X DK
__ Y N/A

43: 19 __ How do you feel about doing housework?

__ 1 Like it very much
__ 2 "Has to be done" attitude
__ 3 Do not like it
__ X DK
__ Y N/A

43: 20 __ If you had your choice between housework and work outside the house (a job), which would you prefer to do?

__ 1 Work outside (job)
__ 2 Both on a fifty-fifty basis
__ 3 Housework only
__ X DK
__ Y N/A

43: 21 __ How do you feel you are managing the housework?

__ 1 Easily, no difficulty
__ 2 Some difficulty
__ 3 Great difficulty
__ X DK
__ Y N/A

Card: Column

Card: Column		(1) Can not Do	(2) Need Some Help	(3) Do Alone	(9) Would not Do	(X) DK	(Y) N/A
43: 22 __	Attend to house cleaning chores						
43: 23 __	Prepare meals						
43: 24 __	Do laundry and ironing						
43: 25 __	Shop for groceries						
43: 26 __	Other shopping (e.g., clothing, etc.)						
43: 27 __	Budget for household (including writing checks and handling money)						
43: 28 __	Plan own daily activities						
43: 29 __	Solve daily problems (including children)						

43:30, 31__,__ Total (Include only 1, 2, and 3 scores)

43: 32 __ How free do you feel you are to run your household in your own way?

__ 1 Completely free
__ 2 Not as free as she would like
__ 3 Feels checked and supervised all or most of the time
__ X DK
__ Y N/A

Now, we would like to know about some other things you have been doing these past few weeks (or since the last interview)

Card: Column

43: 33 __ Have you gone to church services?

__ 1 No __ 2 Yes __ X DK __ Y N/A

43: 34 __ Have you gone to the movies?

__ 1 No __ 2 Yes __ X DK __ Y N/A

43: 35 __ Have you gone to any parties?

__ 1 No __ 2 Yes __ X DK __ Y N/A

43: 36 __ Have you visited friends? (other than parties)

__ 1 No __ 2 Yes __ X DK __ Y N/A

43: 37 __ Have you visited relatives?

__ 1 No __ 2 Yes __ X DK __ Y N/A

43: 38 __ Have you given any parties?

__ 1 No __ 2 Yes __ X DK __ Y N/A

43: 39 __ Attended any club or organization meeting?

__ 1 No __ 2 Yes __ X DK __ Y N/A

43: 40 __ Do you belong to a social club or organization?

__ 1 No __ 2 Yes __ X DK __ Y N/A

Do you belong to or take part in any of these clubs or groups?

			About How Often Do You Attend Meeting?		Are You an Officer or Committee Member?		Does the Group Meet In or Out of the Neighborhood?	
	2 No	1 Yes	Usually or Always	Only Occasionally	1 Yes	2 No	Inside 1	Outside 2
Professional organization								
Union								
Fraternal								
Religious								
Veterans								
Athletic								
PTA								
Political								
Social								
Charitable								
YM-YWCA								
Other (specify)								

Card: Column

43: 41__

__ 0 pt does not belong to any organization
__ 1 Belongs to 1 organization
__ 2 Belongs to 2 organizations
__ 3 Belongs to 3 organizations
__ 4 Belongs to more than 3 organizations
__ X DK
__ Y N/A

Card: Column

43: 42 __ How would you say your health is now (lately)?

__ 1 Excellent
__ 2 Good
__ 3 Fair
__ 4 Poor
__ X DK
__ Y N/A

43: 43 __ Do you feel you are better now than when you first started treatment (or when you went to the hospital?

__ 1 Better
__ 2 Same
__ 3 Worse
__ 4 Denies having been sick
__ X DK

43: 44 __ Generally, would you say that you are happy living here?

__ 1 Yes
__ 2 No
__ X DK

43: 45 __ If you had a choice, where and with whom would you rather live?

__ 1 Here
__ 2 Alone
__ 3 With others, relatives
__ 4 With others, friends
__ 5 Other (specify)
__ X DK

43: 46 __ Do you have any special problems or difficulties here?

__ 1 Yes __ 2 No __ X DK

43: 47 __ What kinds of difficulties are they? *

__ 0 No difficulties __ 2 Relationships
__ 1 Financial __ 3 Attitudes of others

Card: Column

__ 4 Situational (neighborhood)
__ 5 Other (specify)
__ X DK

* (Note: record the most important or the one mentioned most frequently)

43: 48 __ In general, what would you say the attitudes of the others in the house are toward you? *

__ 1 Accepting and understanding
__ 2 Wary or suspicious
__ 3 Critical
__ 4 Indifferent
__ 5 Hostile
__ 6 Rejecting
__ 7 Protective
__ 8 Other (specify)
__ X DK

* (Note: record the most important or the one mentioned most frequently)

43:49 __ In general, how would you say you get along with the others in the family (in the house or home)?

__ 1 Very well
__ 2 Pretty well
__ 3 We tolerate each other
__ 4 Not too well
__ 5 Not at all
__ X DK

43: 50 __ In general, how would you say others in the family get along with you?

__ 1 Very well
__ 2 Pretty well
__ 3 We tolerate each other
__ 4 Not too well
__ 5 Not at all
__ X DK

Next, we would like to know what you think you should be doing now; that is, what do you expect of yourself?

For instance, do you think you should:

43: 51 __ Dust, sweep, and do other usual cleaning?

__ 1 No __ 2 Yes __ X DK __ Y N/A

43: 52 __ Cook for the family?

__ 1 No __ 2 Yes __ X DK __ Y N/A

Card: Column

43: 53 __ Take care of the laundry?

__ 1 No __ 2 Yes __X DK __ Y N/A

43: 54 __ Do the grocery shopping?

__ 1 No __ 2 Yes __X DK __ Y N/A

43: 55 __ Do other shopping (household, clothing, etc.)?

__ 1 No __ 2 Yes __X DK __ Y N/A

43: 56 __ Handle and budget grocery money?

__ 1 No __ 2 Yes __X DK __ Y N/A

43: 57, 58 __, __ Subtotal (coder only)

43: 59 __ Go visit your friends or relatives?

__ 1 No __ 2 Yes __X DK __ Y N/A

43: 60 __ Entertain friends or relatives at home?

__ 1 No __ 2 Yes __X DK __ Y N/A

43: 61 __ Hold a job?

__ 1 No __ 2 Yes __X DK __ Y N/A

43: 62 __ Mix socially with the neighbors?

__ 1 No __ 2 Yes __X DK __ Y N/A

43: 63 __ Go to parties and other social activities?

__ 1 No __ 2 Yes __X DK __ Y N/A

43: 64, 65 __, __ Subtotal (coder only)

43: 66, 67 __, __ Total Expectation Score (coder only)

Card: Column

43: 68 __ In general, how would you say your expectations compare to those of your husband? (or pertinent SO)

__ 1 About the same
__ 2 Spouse or parents expect more than pt capable or willing to do (or pertinent SO)
__ 3 Spouse or parents expect less than pt capable or willing to do (or pertinent SO)
__ X DK
__ Y N/A

43: 69 __ (If perceived discrepancy in expectations) In what specific ways do you disagree?*

__ 0 No apparent discrepancy perceived
__ 1 In matters pertaining to routine household activities or chores
__ 2 In matters pertaining to the children (if any)
__ 3 In matters pertaining to social activities
__ 4 In matters pertaining to social activities
__ 5 Family budgeting or finances
__ 6 Other (specify)

*Note: check the most important or the one most frequently mentioned and circle the others.

And record in detail the precise nature of the perceived discrepancy in expectations (in addition to the general categories above)

____

____

____

43: 70 __ (For hospital pts only) Do you feel that being in the hospital has helped you?

__ 1 No __ 2 Yes __ X DK __ Y N/A

43: 71 __ (For hospital pts only) Do you feel that you still need treatment?

__ 1 No __ 2 Yes __ X DK __ Y N/A

Card: Column

43: 72 __ (For hospital pts only) What kinds of treatment do you feel you should be getting?

__ 1 Says that treatment not required
__ 2 Medicine (pills)
__ 3 Further hospitalization
__ 4 Outpatient treatment
__ 5 Other (specify) ______________________
__ X DK
__ Y N/A

43: 73 __ (For hospital pts only) Do you feel that the treatment (medicine) you have been getting has helped you?

__ 1 Yes __ 2 No __ X DK __ Y N/A

43: 74 __ (For home care pts only) Do you feel that you might be better off in the hospital?

__ 1 Yes __ 2 No __ X DK __ Y N/A

43: 75 __ (All pts) Do you feel that some time in the future you might have to go into the hospital for further treatment?

__ 1 Yes __ 2 No __ X DK

43: 76 __ (All pts) All things considered, how would you feel about going to (or back to) the hospital if it were necessary?

__ 1 Yes, readily
__ 2 Doubtful
__ 3 Definitely not
__ 4 Only if I were forced
__ 5 Other (specify)
__ X DK

MULTIDIMENSIONAL SCALE FOR RATING PSYCHIATRIC PATIENTS*

(A) Type of Patient: This scale is designed for use with psychiatric patients who can be interviewed. This scale is not to be used for the very inaccessible or mute patient.

(B) Observation Period: Ordinarily this scale can be completed following a 45 minute interview of the patient. However, some interviews are as brief as 30 minutes or as long as several hours.

(C) Behavior Rated: Only behavior observable in the interview or reported by the patient is to be rated or checked. Case records or clinical notes should not be used in making ratings.

(D) Type of Interview: Observations required to complete the scale may be obtained nondirectively or by means of a more conventional semistructured interview.

*Lorr (IMPS = MSPP).

Rating Guide

1. Base rating on your interview only	Consider only what the patient does and what he reports or admits. Disregard prior interview data of social history descriptions.
2. Compare the patient with normal individuals	The standard of comparison should be the typical behavior of a normal individual of comparable age, sex, and social class.
3. Rate what is most typical or characteristic	Behavior manifested during the interview may vary. Try to indicate what is most characteristic.

4. Consider each question independently	Make no effort to describe a consistent personality or diagnostic picture. It is well known that patients may manifest seemingly contradictory behavior for dynamic reasons.
5. Avoid dynamic interpretations	As much as possible, base your ratings on manifest behavior content and first order inferences. If, for example, a patient is overly polite and deferent, don't rate him as (unconsciously) hostile.
6. Consider the patient's reactions to you	In judging traits such as hostility, dominance, or emotional responsiveness, consider the patient's attitudes and reactions to you along with his self-reports.
7. Use extreme ratings whenever warranted	Avoid tending to rate near the bottom or middle on all scales.
8. Rate each item quickly	If you are unable to reach a decision, go on to the next item and come back later to those you skipped.
9. Rate every question	If information needed to answer a question could not be obtained, rate "Not at all."
10. Record your ratings only in the separate answer booklet	Instructions appear in the Answer Booklet.

Compared to the normal person, to what degree does the patient . . . . .

1. Manifest speech that is slowed, deliberate, or labored?

2. Give answers that are irrelevant or unrelated in any immediately conceivable way to the question asked or topic discussed?

   Cues: Do not rate here wandering or rambling conversation which veers away from the topic at issue (see item 4). Also, do not rate the coherence of the answer.

3. Give answers that are grammatically disconnected, incoherent, or scattered, i.e., not sensible or not understandable?

   Cues: Judge the grammatical structure of his speech, not the content which may or may not be bizarre.

4. Tend to ramble, wander, or drift off the subject or away from the point at issue in responding to questions or topics discussed?

   Cues: Do not rate here responses that are obviously unrelated to the question asked (see item 2).

5. Verbally express feelings of hostility, ill will, or dislike of others?

   Cues: Makes hostile comments regarding others such as attendants other patients, his family, or persons in authority. Reports conflicts on the ward.

6. Exhibit postures that are peculiar, unnatural, rigid, or bizarre?

   Cues: Head twisted to one side; or arm and hand held oddly, Judge the degree of pecularity of the posture.

7. Express or exhibit feelings and emotions openly, impulsively, or without apparent restraint or control?

   Cues: Shows temper outbursts; weeps or wrings hands in loud complaint; jokes or talks boisterously; gestures excitedly.

8. Exhibit indifference or apathy towards such matters as his treatment, his release from the hospital, or plans for the future?

   Cues: Content to stay. Willing to "leave it to the doctor." Sees no need for treatment. Seems to have no goals or expectations.

9. Manifest speech that is hurried, accelerated, or pushed?

   Cues: Pressure of speech.

10. Manifest overt signs of tension?

    Cues: Moves or shifts restlessly; body musculature appears taut, strained, or tense; fingers clothing; scratches, drums or fiddles with objects; face or neck muscles twitch; exhibits startle reactions; palms feel sweaty.

11. Express a feeling or attitude of contempt, disdain, or scorn towards other people as unworthy or beneath him?

    Cues: Derogatory or snide comments about others; sarcasm or ridicule of others; condescending.

12. Exhibit an elevation in mood, a sense of well-being or euphoria, or an optimistic and hopeful attitude towards himself and others?

    Cues: Everything is wonderful and this is the best of all possible worlds.

13. Exhibit a facial expression that is fixed, immobile, and without discernible play of feeling or expression?

14. Tend to blame, criticize, condemn, or otherwise hold himself responsible for past or present, real or fancied, thought or actions?

    Cues: Blames self for failure, difficulties, and frustrations in family relations, work, or finances.

15. Exhibit in demeanor and/or in verbalizations an attitude of self-importance, superiority, or conceit?

    Cues: Speech is pompous or stilted; boasts of his accomplishments; demands and expects special privileges.

16. Deliberately avoids talking about himself, his treatment, or his problem?

    Cues: Changes the subject; gives partial, tangential, hedging, or elusive replies; pleads loss of memory or lack of comprehension. Avoids confusion with a depressive reluctance to talk, or a schizophrenic poverty of thought.

17. Manifest movements or gestures that are slowed, deliberate, labored, or delayed?

    Cues: Acts as if he is fatigued; walking and moving seem to require special effort.

18. Dramatize or seek to attract the attention of others to himself or his symptoms?

    Cues: Seems to enjoy being observed by others; histrionic in his gestures, affected or artificial; a "show-off."

19. Manifest a hostile, sullen, or morose attitude towards others, by tone of voice, demeanor, or facial expression?

    Cues: Seems to have a chip on his shoulder; slams door or bangs chair; sarcastic tone. Try not to judge on the basis of content of remarks.

20. Exhibit a deficit in his memory for events of the last week?

    Cues: Does not know what he had for supper last night, what he did yesterday, or what treatments he received the past week.

21. Manifest speech that is loud, boisterous, and/or intense in tone?

22. Report or admit being uneasy, anxious, or agitated in anticipation of specific future difficulties or problems?

    Cues: Worried about his symptoms, his family, or his finances.

23. Manifest blocking, halting, or irregular interruptions in his speech?

    Cues: Stuttering or stammering should not be rated here.

24. Exhibit apathy, indifference, or lack of response in feeling to a discussion of his own problems, of his family, or to his surroundings?

    Cues: Doesn't laugh, smile, or react when kidded; neither sad not angry; doesn't seem to care what goes on; discusses emotional matters in a flat, detached manner.

25. Report or admit feeling anxious, apprehensive, or worried in anticipation of vague indefinable future misfortunes or outcomes?

    Cues: Feels worried about coming events but doesn't know why.

26. Manifest irritability, grouchiness, annoyance, or anger?

    Cues: Tone of voice; sharpness of response; explosiveness of retorts; use of profane or obscene language resulting from irritation.

27. Exhibit overactivity, restlessness, and/or acceleration in body movements?

    Cues: Paces or shifts about restlessly. Bearing, posture, and gestures suggest excitement or agitation.

28. Exhibit in his general demeanor or his verbalizations an attitude of self-depreciation, inadequacy, or inferiority?

    Cues: Talks about faults, failures, or his uselessness to others.

29. Tend to blame, criticize or hold other people, objects, or circumstances responsible for his difficulties, failures, or frustrations?

30. Manifest verbally or in demeanor a dejection or depression in mood and a despondent or despairing attitude?

    Cues: Says he doesn't want to talk; complains of loss of interest and enjoyment, lack of energy; discouraged about being helped; expresses lack of hope; may wish he were dead; reports crying spells or tearfulness; expects the worst. Everything seems flat and stale.

31. Exhibit a slovenly, unkempt, or disordered appearance and/or asocial manners?

32. Express feelings of guilt, sorrow or remorse for having done wrong, that are accompanied by a desire to make amends?

    Cues: Says he has been a terrible father or husband; claims sexual misdeeds; recounts past "sins"; says he hates himself for what he did; concerned with atoning for his "guilt"; has let people down.

33. Express feelings of bitterness and resentment because he feels others have wronged, cheated, injured, or slighted him?

34. Manifest speech that is low, weak, whispered, or difficult to hear?

35. Complain, criticize, gripe, or find fault with people and conditions in or out of the hospital?

    Cues: Complains about everything and anything: the medical care, the food, the aides, fellow patients, the routine, the hospital, people in general.

36. Exhibit an excess of speech?

    Cues: Difficult to stop flow of speech once started or to get a word in edgewise. Judge the amount of speech and not its rate or relevance.

37. Express suspicion of people or their motives?

    Cues: Expresses lack of trust in others; feels or suspects others are hostile towards him; questions motives of examiner; questions fidelity of wife.

38. Try to dominate, control, or direct the conduct of the interview?

    Cues: Number of times he interrupts, or "talks down" the interviewer. Tries to control or dominate the conversation.

39. Fail to respond to questions, answer in monosyllables, or give only minimal responses?

    Cues: Answers "yes" or "no"; stares blankly; has to be pushed to get an answer. Judge amount, not rate or relevance of speech.

40. Show a lack of insight regarding himself or an inability to recognize that he has problems?

    Cues: Offers physical illness as an explanation. Believes he is in a rest home or prison. Asks to be sent home immediately. Denies illness or need for treatment.

Answer the following on the basis of the patient's reports or admission. If a symptom is not present, rate "not at all."

To what extent does he appear preoccupied with or distressed by . . . .

41. Suicidal thoughts or impulses?

42. Unwanted ideas or impulses that recur persistently and which he recognizes as irrational?

43. One or more specific irrational morbid fears (phobias) of objects, persons, or situations? (Avoid confusing phobias with anxieties)

44. Compulsive acts which he regards as irrational? (Touching, counting, etc.)

45. Delusional beliefs or convictions (e.g., has ideas of persecution, ideas of sinfulness)? (note: If your response to Item 45 is "not at all" proceed directly to Item 59. If, on the other hand, your response is a positive one to any degree, you must respond to the next 13 items.)

Answer the following on the basis of evidence obtained in the interview that the patient Now has, or, during the past week had delusional beliefs.

Does the patient believe that . . . .

46. Some people talk about, refer to, or watch him?

47. He is being blocked, cheated, deprived, discriminated against, or persecuted?

48. Certain people are plotting or conspiring aginst him (e.g., secret police, criminals, international spies)?

49. Certain people are trying to or now do control his actions or thinking?

50. Certain external forces (e.g., machines, electronic devices) are influencing or controlling his behavior and thinking?

51. He has unusual or extraordinary wealth and possessions?

52. He has unusual or extraordinary abilities, powers, or knowledge (e.g., scientific or religious)?

53. He is a well-known present day or historical personality? (e.g., president, Christ?)

54. He is unworthy, sinful, evil, and/or guilty of unpardonable sins and crimes?

55. Familiar things, people, or surroundings have changed and are unreal?

56. His body is diseased, distorted, or that his internal organs are rotting or missing.

57. He has a distinct divine mission, that he received commands from God, or that he has other religious "calls"?

58. He is dead, a zombie, or similar impossible beliefs?

To what extent does he appear preoccupied with or distressed by . . . .

59. Hallucinatory voices (e.g., voices that accuse, blame, or threaten)? (Note: If your response to Item 59 is "not at all" proceed directly to Item 65. If, however, your response is a positive one to any degree, you must respond to the next 5 items.)

Answer on the basis of evidence obtained in the interview that the patient had hallucinatory experiences during the past week or during the interview.

How often did the patient . . . .

60. Hear voices that accused, blamed, or said "bad" things about him (e.g., he is a spy, homosexual, murderer)?

61. Hear voices that praised, extolled, or spoke to him about divine missions?

62. Hear voices that threatened punishment, torture, or death?

63. Hear voices that ordered him to carry out or perform certain tasks?

64. See actual visions? (Note: Check carefully as this is infrequent except in organic cases.)

65. Have other hallucinatory experiences: tactual, gustatory, olfactory (e.g., sensations of crawling on the skin, smells queer or foul odors, food or drink tastes peculiar or "bad")?

How often during the interview did the patient . . . .

66. Grin or giggle inappropriately? (Exclude reactions resulting from embarrassment.)

67. Grimace peculiarly or otherwise exhibit unusual or bizarre frowns or other facial expressions?

68. Exhibit peculiar, inappropriate, or bizarre repetitive gestures and/or manneristic body movements (e.g., rhythmic neck twisting, lip smacking, odd gestures)?

69. Use phrases or coin words not found in the ordinary language or the dictionary (neologisms)?

70. Mechanically repeat certain words or fixed phrases in a seemingly meaningless way (stereotypy)?

71. Talk, mutter, or mumble to himself without an apparent provoking stimulus?

72. Glance around at and/or appear to be startled as if hearing voices.

Does the patient know . . . .

73. Where he is?

74. The state and city in which he lives?

75. The names of the persons in the household?

76. The season of the year? (Allow for transitional periods)

77. The calendar year?

78. His own age?

SIGNIFICANT OTHER RATING SCALE

ITC Case No. __________

1. Patient's Name ______________________________

2. Male ________ Female __________

3. Born: Month ____________ Year ____________

4. Highest Grade Completed ______________________________

5. Marital Status: Married _______ Single _______ Widowed _______

   Div. _______ Sep. _______

6. Length of Hospitalization: Months __________ Days ________

7. Interviewer's Name ______________________________

8. Date of Interview ______________________________

9. Date Form Completed ______________________________

Directions: This scale is composed of questions designed to elicit important information about the behavior of psychiatric patients. Each item is preceded by the same opening words—Does the patient . . . Before each item you will see YES NO, if the patient manifests the behavior in question, you will circle YES; if the patient does not manifest the behavior in question, you will circle NO. Try to answer all questions!

[Please circle the appropriate response.]

Does the patient . . .

1. YES NO Speak in a very slow, unsure way?

4.	YES	NO	Give answers that are completely unrelated to questions asked or talk about things far off the topic being discussed?
5.	YES	NO	Answer questions in a kind of double talk – grammar is very unusual or peculiar?
7.	YES	NO	Tend to drift off the subject when in conversation?
10.	YES	NO	Make hostile or nasty remarks about the people he knows?
11.	YES	NO	Walk, sit, or stand in peculiar ways?
13.	YES	NO	Laugh or cry for no reason?
15.	YES	NO	Act as if he didn't care about getting well?
17.	YES	NO	Speak in a very quick, hurried, or "pushed" manner?
21.	YES	NO	Move around restlessly – very fidgety?
22.	YES	NO	Act as if other people were unworthy or beneath him?
27.	YES	NO	Act as if everything was wonderful and this is the best of all possible worlds?
29.	YES	NO	Fix his face so that you can't tell what he is thinking or feeling?
31.	YES	NO	Blame or condemn himself for all kinds of things that have happened either in the past or things going on right now?
33.	YES	NO	Act in a conceited way – thinks he is superior or better than those around him?
36.	YES	NO	Seem to be very tired and worn out – even walking and moving seem to require special effort?
39.	YES	NO	Want to be the center of attraction – act in a "show-off" way?
44.	YES	NO	Act as if he had a chip on his shoulder?

45. YES NO Have trouble remembering what has recently happened to him?

46. YES NO Speak in a loud, intense tone of voice?

48. YES NO Report that he is afraid or worried about such things as his illness, his family, or job?

49. YES NO Although he does not usually stutter or stammer, he has trouble like that when he talks.

50. YES NO Seem to care about any of the things going on around him?

53. YES NO Report that he is afraid or worried about things which are going to happen but he can't tell you what they are?

54. YES NO Lose his temper quickly?

55. YES NO Move around a lot when he is excited?

56. YES NO Talk as if he felt inferior or useless or no good to anyone?

59. YES NO Blame other people for his troubles and problems?

60. YES NO Always expect the worst to happen?

65. YES NO Is he sloppy in his manners and appearance?

66. YES NO Express guilt for having done wrong and say that he would like to make up for what he has done?

67. YES NO Seem bitter because he feels other people have done him wrong?

68. YES NO Speak in a low, weak voice or in whispers?

71. YES NO Complain about anything and everything?

72. YES NO Talk so much that it is hard to get a word in edgewise?

73. YES NO Act in a very suspicious way towards those around him?

74. YES NO Try to dominate or control the activities of those around him?

76. YES NO Have to be "pushed" to get an answer to a question?

77. YES NO Say that he is not sick and doesn't need any treatment?

78. YES NO Talk about taking his life?

79. YES NO Report that strange and peculiar ideas come to him?

83. YES NO Report that he is very much afraid of certain things or people?

85. YES NO Report that he has ideas of persecution or sinfulness?

88. YES NO Report that he hears voices that threaten or accuse him?

90. YES NO Grin or giggle when it is uncalled for?

91. YES NO Make peculiar expressions with his face?

92. YES NO Move his body in strange or peculiar ways?

93. YES NO Use strange words – make up words?

94. YES NO Repeat over and over certain words or sentences?

95. YES NO Talk to himself when no one else is around?

96. YES NO Act as if he is hearing voices?

97. YES NO Report that voices have said bad things about him?

98. YES NO Report that voices have said very wonderful things about him?

99. YES NO Report that voices have threatened to punish or torture him?

100. YES NO Report that voices have ordered him to do certain things?

101. YES NO Say that he actually saw things which couldn't have possibly happened?

102. YES NO Report that he has had peculiar sensations—funny smells or funny tastes?

103. YES NO Believe that some people talk about him or watch him?

104. YES NO Believe that he is being cheated by other people?

105. YES NO Believe that people are plotting against him?

106. YES NO Believe that certain people are controlling his actions?

107. YES NO Believe that things other than people are controlling him?

109. YES NO Believe that he has unusual powers?

110. YES NO Believe that he is evil or sinful?

111. YES NO Believe that familiar things or people have changed or are not real?

112. YES NO Believe that his body is diseased or rotting away?

113. YES NO Believe that he has a direct line to God?

115. YES NO Believe that he is a famous person?

116. YES NO Know where he is?

117. YES NO Know the name of the city and state in which he lives?

118. YES NO Know the names of those around him?

119. YES NO Know the season of the year?

120. YES NO Know the year?

121. YES NO Know his own age?

PSYCHIATRIC INVENTORY

This inventory is to be completed by the Interview Physician as soon as possible after the Admission Conference. It must be on file with the Treatment Center office within one week of admission.

For each of the items which follow, a number between 1 and 9 must be indicated, either by striking it off horizontally (6) or by writing it in one of the larger boxes. The number 1 usually means that the phenomenon described in the item heading is absent, 5 that it is present in moderate or medium degree, 9 that it is present to a maximum degree. (Use 0 only when you have "No Information" on a given item.) Some of these numbers are defined in detail; others are purposely not defined in order to allow the scorer more flexibility in recording.

So for each item please indicate the number which, using the definitions as a guide, you feel best describes the patient. It is important to write something (even if only 0) opposite each item. Please use pencil.

ITC Case No. ___________
(leave blank)

Patient's Name ____
(last) (first)

Male ______________ Female ________________

Born: Month ________________ Year _______________

Marital Status: Married _____ Single _____ Widowed _____ Div. or Sep. ____

Interviewer's Name ____

Conference Date ____

Inventory Completed ____

History of present illness (P. I.)

Please bear in mind that the score on the first item below, 1, will have a direct bearing on the scores of many subsequent items which refer to the present illness.

For pts transferred directly from state or other hospitals, "present hospitalization" should always be considered to date from the previous state of other hospital admission.

1. DURATION OF SYMPTOMS LEADING TO PRESENT HOSPITALIZATION: The symptoms may sometimes be an exacerbation of an underlying personality disturbance, but are clearly a decompensation which has led to the present admission. A past episode if followed by a return to a level of more or less adequate compensation should not be considered part of the P. I.

   [1] Less than 1 month
   [2] 1-3 months
   [3] 3-6 months
   [4] 6 months to 1 year
   [5] 1-2 years
   [6] 2-5 years
   [7] 5-10 years
   [8] 10-20 years
   [9] Over 20 years
   [0] No information

2. DURATION OF SIGNIFICANT UNDERLYING PERSONALITY DISTURBANCE: This refers to difficulties of adjustment that are less than an actual decompensation into a clear-cut syndome, and that either may or may not have preceded the symptoms scored in the previous item. Sometimes a previous problem may have been resolved with good recovery; this should be scored under past history.

   [1] Less than 1 month
   [2] 1-3 months
   [3] 3-6 months
   [4] 6 months to 1 year
   [5] 1-2 years
   [6] 2-5 years
   [7] 5-10 years
   [8] 10-20 years

[9] Over 20 years
[0] No information

3. PERSONS INTERVIEWED BY PSYCHIATRIST

Spouse		Mother	Father	Sibling	Child	Other : ________
[1]	Seen	[1]	[1]	[1]	[1]	[1]
[0]	Not seen	[0]	[0]	[0]	[0]	[0]

Prominent Features of Present Illness (P. I.)

4. ANXIETY: Score for the most anxiety felt over a sustained period.

[1] No anxiety
[2]
[3] Mild anxiety: Mostly of a subjective nature, or mild anxiety elicited during interviews but not at other times, or one or two brief attacks only of more severe anxiety.
[4]
[5] Moderate anxiety: The pt has definitely experienced feelings of fear in the absence of an external cause. This has caused real discomfort, such as palpitations, tremor, sweating, etc., but has not led to loss of self-control.
[6]
[7] Marked Anxiety: Disabling anxiety interfering with work and social functioning and possibly leading to loss of control.
[8]
[9] Very marked anxiety: Disabling panic with loss of self-control, shouting, screaming, etc.; or extreme discomfort from anxiety, with an obviously anxious appearance.

[0] No information

For all the following items, score as follows: 1 means not present; 3 present to a mild degree; 5 present to a moderate degree; 7 present to a marked degree; 9 present to an especially marked degree. Use intermediate numbers if necessary. 0 means No Information.

5. [ ] DIFFICULTY CONCENTRATING: Reduced capacity for mental effort and lack initiative and willingness to undertake new activities. Thought may tend to wander and is less successfully directed toward a specific goad. Express degree.

6. ☐ FATIGUE: Reduction in the amount of spontaneous movement, lassitude, bodily relaxation and some loss of tone, lack of power and of certainty and precision in movements, and possibly some retardation. "No pep," chronic tiredness.

7. ☐ HYPOCHONDRIASIS: Definite disturbing physical complaints other than in a recognized psychosomatic syndrome. Complaints usually multiple and rather vague.

8. ☐ PHOBIAS: Persistent fears of some object or situation, without apparent basis. As a symptom, or elicited on questioning as a disturbing feature of P. I.

9. ☐ WITHDRAWAL: A decreasing interest in socializing, the pt is "shy" or prefers to be alone. Score if present even if not complained of by pt.

10. ☐ CONVERSION SYMPTOMS: Somatic signs of conversion hysteria in systems under voluntary control. Express degree in terms of interference with overall function.

11. ☐ DISSOCIATIVE SYMPTOMS: A story of "twilight states," fugues, depersonalization on any basis, including feelings of unreality and bodily change associated with schizophrenia and temporal lobe epilepsy.

12. ☐ HYPERVENTILATION SYNDROME: Over-breathing which brings on tingling of hands and feet, tetany, or other symptoms, which are clearly recognized by pt as part of the P. I.

13. ☐ EVENING INSOMNIA: Difficulty in getting to sleep, whether a complaint or brought out by questioning.

14. ☐ MORNING INSOMNIA: Awakening before usual time; whether a complaint or brought out by questioning.

15. ☐ OBSESSIVE-COMPULSIVE SYMPTOMS: This includes obsessive doubting (e.g., frequent rechecking of locked doors), obsessive neatness, extreme perfectionism, rituals such as touching, avoiding, handwashing, etc.

16. ☐ OVERT DEVIANT SEXUAL BEHAVIOR IN P. I.: Story for exhibitionism, window-peeping, prostitution, sexual sadism, or other overt deviant sexual behavior, but DO NOT include homosexuality here.

17. [ ] SOCIOPATHIC BEHAVIOR IN P. I.: Story for misdemeanors of any kind, whether involved with police or not; (e.g., reckless driving, gambling, drunk and disorderly, assault and battery, etc.)

18. [ ] ANTISOCIAL BEHAVIOR IN P. I.: Whether or not he has been caught, pt has committed serious antisocial acts, felonies, etc., (e.g., car theft, robbery, hold-ups, manslaughter, etc.) Express degree.

19. [ ] EUPHORIA: Excessive or unwarranted cheerfulness.

20. [ ] PRESSURE OF SPEECH: Continued over-activity of speech with pt unable to prevent himself from pestering people.

21. DEPRESSION

[1] No depression
[2]
[3] Depression largely subjective (e.g., some feelings of worthlessness, guilt, inferiority)
[4]
[5] Depression with objective manifestations (e.g., definite indecision, guilt reactions, occasional suicidal thoughts)
[6]
[7] Marked depression (i.e., characterized by loss of interest, some agitation and/or some retardation, etc.)
[8]
[9] Depression of very marked proportions causing complete disability (e.g., retardation, nihilistic preoccupation, or severe agitation)
[0] No information

Score the remaining items as before from 1 to 9.

22. [ ] AGITATION: Hand wringing, distraught, crying, pacing the floor, etc., whether expressed as a symptom, or brought out in the history or demonstrated in the examination.

23. [ ] RETARDATION: Slowed or stuporous behavior from whatever cause.

24. [ ] SUICIDAL ATTEMPTS: History of one or more actual and definite attempts in the P. I. (If present put same score or higher in following item.) Express seriousness as a number.

25. ☐ SUICIDAL PREOCCUPATION: A real feature of P. I., but no actual attempts.

26. ☐ SOMATIC DELUSIONS: Either brought out spontaneously or by questioning.

27. ☐ DRUG CRAVING IN P. I.: Including narcotics, barbiturates, dexedrine, marijuana; include habituation where pt takes drug in amounts greater than prescribed. Proof of physiological addiction is not necessary, but score should reflect degree of dependence on drug.

28. ☐ DESTRUCTIVE OR ASSAULTIVE BEHAVIOR: Include any kind of direct physical attack on people, animals, or inanimate objects (such as smashing plates or windows). A homicidal attempt would receive a high score. Exclude indirect or symbolic attacks.

29. ☐ HEARING LOSS: 9 means totally deaf.

30. ☐ SKIN SYMPTOMS: In the P. I.; 9 means totally incapacitated.

31. ☐ CARDIAC SYMPTOMS: Whether organically or psychogenically determined in P. I.

32. ☐ RESPIRATORY SYMPTOMS: Whether organically or psychogenically determined in P. I.

33. ☐ UPPER GASTROINTESTINAL SYMPTOMS: Organic or psychogenic; include ulcer or ulcer-like symptoms, difficulty swallowing, upper abdominal pain and discomfort, anorexia nervosa, etc. Exclude obesity.

34. ☐ LOWER GASTROINTESTINAL SYMPTOMS: Organic or psychogenic; include ulcerative colitis, "irritable colon," nonspecific diarrhea, rectal or anal pain, etc.

35. ☐ OBESITY

[1] Means significantly underweight

[2] Within 10 pounds of average for height and age on admission (Norms available in inpatient office)

[3] 10 – 20 pounds over average for height and age

[4] 20 – 30 pounds over

[5] 30 - 40 pounds over
[6] 40 - 50 over
[7] 50 - 60 over
[8] 60 - 70 over
[9] More than 70 pounds over average weight for height and age

36. [ ] UNDERWEIGHT

[1] Means significantly overweight
[2] Within 10 pounds of average for height and age on admission
[3] 10 - 20 pounds under average for height and age
[4] 20 - 30 pounds under
[5] 30 - 40 pounds under
[6] 40 - 50 under
[7] 50 - 60 under
[8] 60 - 70 under
[9] More than 70 pounds under average weight for height and age

37. [ ] URINARY TRACT SYMPTOMS: Whether organically or psychogenically determined.

38. [ ] GENITAL TRACT SYMPTOMS: Organic or psychogenic; include impotence, premature ejaculation, dysmenorrhea, frigidity, etc.

39. [ ] OTHER SYMPTOMS; Describe:

Past History, Previous to P. I.

Remember that Item 1, page 1, dates the onset of the P. I. Symptoms which occurred Before that should be scored in this section.

Score each of the boxes below using the same 9 point scale as before: 1 absent; 3 present to mild degree; 5 present to moderate degree; 7 present to marked degree; 9 present to exceptionally marked degree; 0, no information.

40. [ ] NEUROTIC SYMPTOMS: This is to refer to neurotic symptoms (anxiety, depression, obsessive-compulsive, hysterical, etc.) which clearly occurred as a separate episode in the past before the onset of the symptoms which led to the present hospitalization. There should have been a period essentially free of symptoms before the P. I.

41. ☐ SCHIZOPHRENIC OR PSYCHOTIC SYMPTOMS: This is to refer to an episode of clearly psychotic symptoms (depressive, schizophrenic, etc.) which occurred in the past and followed by a remission. There should have been a perioid essentially free of symptoms before the P. I.

42. ☐ SOCIOPATHIC SYMPTOMS: Story for misdemeanors of any kind, whether involved with police or not (e.g., reckless driving, gambling, drunk and disorderly, assault and battery, etc.).

43. ☐ ANTISOCIAL SYMPTOMS: Whether or not he has been caught, pt has committed serious antisocial acts, felonies, etc. (e.g., car theft, robbery, hold-ups, manslaughter, etc.). Express degree.

44. ☐ OVERT DEVIANT SEXUAL BEHAVIOR: As defined on p. 3 – exclude homosexuality.

45. ☐ NARCOTIC, BARBITURATE, OR OTHER DRUG ADDICTION: As defined on p. 4.

46. ☐ OTHER PSYCHIATRIC PROBLEM:

47. ☐ ORGANIC C.N.S. DISEASE: Except trauma and delirium.

48. ☐ C.N.S. TRAUMA: Consider as trauma any injury in which C.N.S. involvement was objectively demonstrated, or where there was concussion with more than momentary loss of consciousness.

49. ☐ DELIRIUM: A period of delirium or confusion without head injury such as may occur in the course of another illness; or true encephalitis.

50. ☐ OTHER SIGNIFICANT PHYSICAL ILLNESS (e.g., rheumatic fever, diphtheria, tuberculosis, poliomyelitis, diabetes, etc.).

51. ☐ ACCIDENTS: From any cause.

52. ☐ PHYSICAL DISABILITY (e.g., continuing disability from poliomyelitis, amputations, kyphosis, severe facial or other scarring, blindness, etc.).

53. ☐ PETIT MAL: Clinical and/or EEG evidence.

54. ☐ GRAND MAL: Clinical and/or EEG evidence.

55. ☐ PSYCHOMOTOR SEIZURES: Clinical and/or EEG evidence.

56. [ ] OTHER SEIZURES: Include doubtful cases here.

Mental Status Examination

Strike off the number which you feel best describes the pt. Note that not all the numbers are defined. If you feel that one of the intermediate undefined numbers best describes him, strike it through and write in a few words of explanation.

57. MOTOR ACTIVITY

[1] Stuporous or Cerea Flexibilitas: Will not communicate with the physician in any meaningful way, although may obey commands like "stick out your tongue."
[2]
[3] Moderately underactive: Sits or lies quietly with little energy when left alone, but will communicate when an effort is made to speak with him.
[4]
[5] Average or ordinary: As regards motor activity; relaxed and easy.
[6] Restless: Displays tension, change of position in chair or on bed, or moist palms; but can sit for an interview.
[7]
[8] Agitated: Paces around in the room or constantly moving but can cooperate for an interview.
[9] Excited: Very overactive, in constant motion; unable to cooperate for an interview.

58. FACIAL EXPRESSION

[1] Morosely depressed: Cries or weeps a great deal of the time.
[2] Quietly depressed: Miserable, hopeless, or stiff facial expression.
[3] Anxious or tense
[4]
[5] Average or ordinary
[6]
[7] Self-satisfied: Not actually smiling or laughing, but seems more than usually pleased with himself.
[8] Smiling or laughing: Continuously cheerful expression.
[9] Ecstatic: Face expresses intense, continuous, and unrealistic pleasure.

59. SOCIALIZATION

[1] Inaccessible: To all efforts at socialization.
[2] Isolated: Completely on his own, will not mix with other patients unless constantly and continually pushed.
[3] Shut-in: Tends to remain alone for long periods; will not enter into activities unless directly encouraged.
[4] Introverted: Some tendency to remain by himself, without spontaneous interest in other patients and staff. But with a small amount of pushing soon becomes involved in activities.
[5] Average or ordinary: Neither especially extraverted nor especially introverted.
[6] Extraverted: Tends to be quite interested in staff and other patients, but not to the extent that he assumes group leadership.
[7] Outreaching: Actively involved and a leader in many activities.
[8] Meddlesome: Tends to involve himself into activities of other patients where he is not always welcome, but not to a disrupting extent. However, he is not a leader either.
[9] Disruptive: Attempts to push himself into and break up other activity on the ward.

60. AMOUNT OF SPEECH

[1] Mute: No intelligible language of any kind.
[2] Blocking: Frequent and prolonged periods of silence when someone attempts an interview or conversation with him.
[3] Retarded: Slow and diminished amount of speech.
[4] Mildly undertalkative: Appears to talk less than the average patient.
[5] Average or ordinary
[6] Voluble: Appears to talk somewhat more than the average patient.
[7]
[8] Overtalkative: Tends to pester people but can restrain himself for short periods.
[9] Incessantly overtalkative: Unable to stop talking and pestering people even when requested.

61. IDEAS OF INFLUENCE (part of Langfeldt's derealization). Exclude persecutory ideas.

[1] No ideas of influence: Has never at any time considered that his thinking or behavior was influenced by other persons or things.
[2]

[3] Mild ideas of influence: Pt considers it possible that he is being influenced by subtle, unusual, or mysterious forces outside himself (e.g., gestures, glances, beams, waves, rays, etc.). He has not felt this directly. If pt has actually felt the influence directly, score 5 or more.

[4]

[5] Moderate ideas of influence: Pt actually felt his mind being influenced on occasion, as above, but may have few doubts.

[6]

[7] Definite ideas of influence: Pt gives clear statement that he has actually felt his mind and behavior being influenced. Pt has no doubt about this.

[8]

[9] Major ideas of influence: Has definitely felt that not only his mind but various bodily functions are influenced by machines, or by the thoughts and actions of others. This is continuous or almost so.

62. DESTRUCTIVE BEHAVIOR

[1] Attempts suicide or self-mutilation during his first week in hospital.

[2] Threatens suicide or self-mutilation during the first week in hospital (i.e., this threat seems sufficiently serious so that an order for suicide precautions is written).

[3] Risk of Suicide: Thought to be a definite and serious suicide risk because of threats before admission. No attempts or threats in hospital.

[4]

[5] No destructive behavior or threats of assault.

[6]

[7] Threatens assault or destruction: But no overt destructive behavior.

[8] Destructive of property: For instance, beds, windows, sheets, flowers, etc., but is not assaultive toward personnel or patients.

[9] Actively assaultive: Actually hits or strikes patients or staff—may destroy hospital property.

Emotional Reactions

63. AMOUNT OF AFFECT SEEN IN INTERVIEW

[1] Completely flat: Essentially no expression of affect seen in interviews.

[2] Bland: Inadequate or diminished affect.
[3] Reserved: Some diminution of affect.
[4]
[5] Ordinary or average amount of affect shown
[6]
[7] Demonstrative: Affect demonstrated freely, frequently, and easily.
[8]
[9] Labile or explosive: Affect demonstrated violently or uncontrollably.

64. INAPPROPRIATENESS OF AFFECT SEEN IN INTERVIEW

[1] Affect appropriate to content of thought; no inconsistencies.
[3]
[5] Questionably appropriate affect
[7]
[9] Definitely inappropriate affect to content of thought (i.e., the pt's total attitude is not consistent with or appropriate to those words, gestures, or tones of voice which ordinarily express pain or pleasure).
[0] No information

For the following two items, if you feel that the pt shows both depression and manic tendencies, decide which is more important and rate that one.

65. MANIC TENDENCY: Refers to mood change and accompanying phenomena.

[0] Not applicable because of depression; rate following item.
[1] Normal mood
[2]
[3] Cheerful and enthusiastic to a degree which society can understand and tolerate.
[4]
[5] Euphoric: Distractible; very talkative; laughs easily; flight of ideas.
[6]
[7] Excited: Continual exhilaration with grandiose unrealistic plans or significantly expansive ideas.

[8]
[9] Manic frenzy: An uncontrollable, violent, rapidly exhausting reaction of exaltation.

66. DEPRESSION

[0] Not applicable because of Manic Tendency; rate previous item.
[1] Normal mood
[2]
[3] Depression largely subjective: e.g., some feeling of worthlessness, guilt, inferiority.
[4]
[5] Depression with objective manifestation: e.g., definite indecision, guilt reactions, occasional suicidal thoughts.
[6]
[7] Marked depression (i.e., characterized by loss of interest, some agitation and/or some retardation, etc.).
[8]
[9] Depression of severe proportions causing complete disability; (e.g., retardation, nihilistic preoccupation, or severe agitation).

Disturbances in Thinking

67. THINKING DISORDER

[1] Average thinking processes (i.e., no thinking disorder).
[3]
[5] Borderline illogical: Or questionable thinking disorder.
[7]
[8] Clear and definite thinking disorder: (paralogical, autistic, or paleological); definite abnormality demonstrated clearly during examination. This is defined as thinking in which many of the pt's ideas and concepts have no recognizable connection with external reality. Instead, concepts are connected in ways determin ed by inner thought processes. This may show itself as ideas that are haphazard, abrupt, incorrect, or bizarre.
[9] Fragmented thinking: Completely incomprehensible thought processes with many neologisms.
[0] No information

68. PARANOID TENDENCIES

[1] No suspiciousness
[2] Questionable suspiciousness: Suspiciousness as defined below questionably present.
[3] Suspiciousness without overt delusions. One or more of the following must be present: the pt is quite concerned about other people's actions, thoughts, and ideas concerning him; he may have ideas of reference, or unjustified ideas of jealousy. He may feel that other people are ganging up on him.
[4]
[5] Questionable paranoid delusions: Some doubt as to whether these are actually present.
[6]
[7] Unsystematized paranoid delusions: Delusions present as defined below without a logical structure to explain them.
[8]
[9] Systematized paranoid delusions (i.e., the pt has ideas of suspiciousness, jealousy, or persecution that have crystallized into fixed firm beliefs so that the pt has a logical explanation for what is happening).
[0] No information

TRUE HALLUCINATIONS: That is, perceptions experienced by the pt during the present illness which as far as can be determined had no physical basis. Mark all columns.

69 Aud.	70 Vis.	71 Olf.	72 Gus.	73 Other	
[1]	[1]	[1]	[1]	[1]	Absent
[2]	[2]	[2]	[2]	[2]	
[3]	[3]	[3]	[3]	[3]	Questionably present
[4]	[4]	[4]	[4]	[4]	
[5]	[5]	[5]	[5]	[5]	Mild but definitely present
[6]	[6]	[6]	[6]	[6]	
[7]	[7]	[7]	[7]	[7]	Present to moderate degree
[8]	[8]	[8]	[8]	[8]	
[9]	[9]	[9]	[9]	[9]	Present to major and disturbing degree
[0]	[0]	[0]	[0]	[0]	No information

74. SERIAL 7'S

[1] Correct and rapid
[2] Correct but hesitant
[3] 1 mistake
[4] 2 or 3 mistakes
[5]
[6] Many mistakes
[7]
[8] Unable to do although attempted
[9] No cooperation
[0] Not given

75. PHYSICIAN'S ESTIMATE OF INTELLIGENCE

[1] Genius
[2] Very superior
[3] Superior
[4] Bright normal
[5] Average
[6] Dull normal
[7] Borderline
[8] Defective
[9] No cooperation
[0] No estimate made

76. ANXIETY

[1] No anxiety
[2]
[3] Mild anxiety mostly of a subjective nature, or mild anxiety elicited during interviews but not at other times, or one or two briefs attacks only of more severe anxiety.
[4]
[5] Moderate anxiety: The pt has definitely experienced feelings of fear in the absence of an external cause. This has caused real discomfort such as palitations, tremor, sweating, etc., but has not led to loss of self-control.
[6]

[7] Marked anxiety: Disabling anxiety interfering with work and social functioning and possibly leading to loss of control.

[8]

[9] Very marked anxiety: Disabling panic with loss of self-control, shouting, screaming, etc.; or extreme discomfort from anxiety, with an obviously anxious appearance.

77. INSIGHT AT TIME OF INTERVIEW

[1] Denies existence of any problem: Pt does not consider himself sick; no insight.

[2] Pt considers himself sick but ascribes all his symptoms to physical causes; does not see any emotional component.

[3] Pt recognizes he is ill, but extraneous or irrelevant problems or persons are considered the sole cause.

[4] Pt may occasionally admit that the cause of the illness lies to some extent within himself.

[5] Pt feels that causation of his illness lies within himself, but is unconcerned.

[6] Pt feels that the cause of his illness is within himself, is concerned, but cannot give any explanation.

[7] Pt believes the cause of his illness is within himself but the explanation he gives for his problems is very incomplete.

[8] Some emotional insight: Pt has a partial understanding of the importance of emotional factors.

[9] Pt has a considerable degree of insight into the interrelationships of various emotional causative factors.

[0] No information

Initial Psychiatric Diagnoses

In the boxes below, starting from the left and keeping the decimal point in the appropriate place, write the diagnostic Code Number found at the left-hand margin of pages 78-86 of the APA Statistical Classification of Mental Disease. On the line, write the description which corresponds to that code number.

78 79 80 81

PRIMARY

[ ] [ ] [ ] [ ]

82 83 84 85
SECONDARY

☐ ☐ ☐ ☐

Comments:

86. INITIAL PROGNOSIS: Physician's best prediction of status in 1 year.

[1] Will probably recover except for one or two relatively minor complaints. Will do much better than before admission in social relationships. Illness unlikely to recur even under severe stress.
[2]
[3] Will be much improved but will still have a few minor complaints. Social relations improved but still a few difficulties. With stress symptoms may recur.
[4]
[5] Will be improved with definite improvement in symptoms and one or more areas of social adjustment, although some symptoms will persist and total adjustment will not be as good as before the illness began.
[6]
[7] Will be unchanged (i.e., condition the same as when pt entered hospital although he may manage to make a tenuous adjustment at home with support or in a sheltered environment).
[8]
[9] Will be worse
[0] No information

87. INITIAL GOAL OF TREATMENT: Check one only.

[1] Strengthen defenses only (i.e., by using repressive or somatic techniques).
[2]
[3] Social or family adjustment only: This may or may not involve retaining symptoms.
[4]
[5] Modification of symptoms only (i.e., an attempt to make the patient's symptoms more socially acceptable, or less disturbing to him).
[6]
[7] Minimal personality change

[8] Personality restructuring: An attempt to modify the patient's characterological structure in a fundamental way.

[0] Other goal: ______________________________

Comments:

Patient's Name ____________
ITC Case No. ____________
Interviewer ____________

PUBLIC HEALTH NURSE
Report and Ratings

1. In general, how much and what kind of looking after does the patient require?

2. Who in the household is available to do this?

3. Is this adequate? (In your opinion, is respondent emotionally and physically able to handle the patient?)

4. How does the respondent (and others in the household, especially children) feel about looking after the patient? Does it seem a burden? Are they sympathetic, accepting, tolerant – or hostile and rejecting?

BEHAVIOR CHART

Name ______________________ ITC Case No. _____

Weeks:	1	2	3	4	5	6	7	8	9	10	11	12	13	14	15	16	17	18	19	20	21	22	23	24	25	26
Masturbated																										
Flight of Ideas																										
Distractible																										
Impulsive																										
Hostile																										
Destructive																										
Combative																										
Angry																										
Resistive																										
Agitated																										
Irritable																										
Restless																										
Talking																										
Industrious																										
Cheerful																										
Smiling–Laughing																										
Games																										
Reading																										
Quiet																										

Name ______________________________ ITC Case No. _____

Weeks:	1	2	3	4	5	6	7	8	9	10	11	12	13	14	15	16	17	18	19	20	21	22	23	24	25	26
Lacks Initiative																										
Brooding																										
Preoccupied																										
Sad																										
Weeping																										
Picks, Rubs																										
Anxious																										
Apprehensive																										
Fearful																										
Panicky																										
Suspicious																										
Confused																										
Indifferent																										
Motionless																										
Untidy																										
Suicidal																										
Delusions																										
Hallucinations																										

PHYSICAL SIGNS

Name ______________________ ITC Case No. _____

WEEKS	1	2	3	4	5	6	7	8	9	10	11	12	13	14	15	16	17	18	19	20	21	22	23	24	25	26
Weight																										
B/P																										
Temp.																										
Pulse																										
Resps.																										
Urine																										

PRESCRIPTION

Patient's Name ______________________ ITC Case No. _____

Drug ______________________ Drug No. ______________

Milligrams ______________________

Times Per Day ______________________

______________________, M.D.
Signature

BACKGROUND INFORMATION

Interviewer: ____________

Date this Interview: ______

ITC Case No. ___________

1. Patient's Name ____
   (Last) (First) (MI)

2. Sex ____ Male ____ Female

3. Address ____
   (No.) (Street) (City) (County)

4. Age _____ 4a. Birth Date: ____________ Month ___________ Year

5. Marital Status ____
   (Admission)

6. Marital Status ____
   (Discharge)

7. Birthplace ____
   (City) (State) (If not U.S., Country)

8. Religion ______________________________

9. Race ______________________________

10. Usual Occupation ____

11. Highest Grade Completed ____

12. H.I. Score ______________________________

13. Date Admitted ______________________________

14. Date Discharged ______________________________

15. Total Days Hospitalized ______________________________

16. Type of Discharge ______________________________

17. Diagnosis (in full) ______________________________

____

18. Number of Hospital Admissions ____________________

ADMISSION NOTE

Name ______________________________ Age _____ Sex _______

Race ____________________ Marital Status _________

Type of Admission _______________________________________

Presenting Problem:

Impression:

Remarks:

______________________, M.D.
Signature

HOME VISIT REPORT

ITC Case No. ______________________________ Date ______________

Patient's Name ____

Name of Family Physician ____

Address ____

T ______________________________ P ___________________ R _______

B/P ____________________________

Weight ____________________________

Sleep Pattern ____

Appetite ____

Physical Condition ____

____

____

Comments ____

____

____

____

____

____

Signature ______________________

Appendix B

TABLES

Table I. Age Distribution of Drug, Placebo, and Hospital Control Patients

	Drug		*Placebo*		*Hospital Control*		*Total*	
	N	*%*	*N*	*%*	*N*	*%*	*N*	*Total*
Under 20	2	3.5	1	2.4	–	–	3	2.0
20-24	8	14.0	2	4.9	3	5.6	13	8.6
25-29	7	12.3	8	19.5	12	22.2	27	17.8
30-34	11	19.3	7	17.1	8	14.8	26	17.1
35-39	7	12.3	11	26.8	6	11.1	24	15.8
40-44	9	15.8	5	12.2	10	18.5	24	15.8
45-49	6	10.5	1	2.4	6	11.1	13	8.6
50-54	6	10.5	5	12.2	7	13.0	18	11.8
55-59	1	1.8	1	2.4	2	3.7	4	2.6
Total	57		41		54		152	
Mean age	35.9		36.2		37.6		36.6	

Table III. Racial Distribution of Drug, Placebo, and Hospital Control Patients

	Drug		*Placebo*		*Hospital Control*		*Total*	
	N	*%*	*N*	*%*	*N*	*%*	*N*	*%*
White	39	68.4	28	68.3	35	64.8	102	67.1
Negro	18	31.6	13	31.7	19	35.2	50	32.9
Total	57		41		54		152	

Table II . Sex Distribution of Drug, Placebo, and Hospital Control Patients

	Drug		*Placebo*		*Hospital Control*		*Total*	
Sex	*N*	*%*	*N*	*%*	*N*	*%*	*N*	*%*
Male	20	35.1	13	31.7	16	29.6	49	32.2
Female	37	64.9	28	68.3	38	70.4	103	67.8
Total	57		41		54		152	

Table IV. Educational Attainments of Drug, Placebo, and Hospital Control Patients

Education	*Drug*		*Placebo*		*Hospital Control*		*Total*	
	N	%	*N*	%	*N*	%	*N*	%
0–6th grade	7	12.5	4	10.0	10	19.2	21	14.2
Junior high (7–9th grade)	16	28.6	14	35.0	21	40.4	51	35.4
Partial high school (10–11th grade)	12	21.4	8	20.0	14	26.9	34	23.0
High school graduate	18	32.1	9	22.5	5	9.6	32	21.6
Partial college	2	3.6	4	10.0	2	3.8	8	5.4
College and postgraduate	1	1.8	1	2.5	0	–	2	1.4
	56		40		52		148	
No data	1		1		2		4	
Total	57		41		54		152	

Table V. Hollingshead Index of Social Position Scores of Drug, Placebo, and Hospital Control Patients

	Drug		*Placebo*		*Hospital Control*		*Total*	
HI Score	*N*	*%*	*N*	*%*	*N*	*%*	*N*	*%*
10-19	1	1.8	1	2.5	0	–	2	1.3
20-29	0	–	1	2.5	1	1.9	2	1.3
30-39	1	1.8	2	5.0	1	1.9	4	2.7
40-49	9	15.8	6	15.0	4	7.5	19	12.7
50-59	13	22.8	6	15.0	7	13.2	26	17.3
60-69	17	29.8	13	32.5	15	28.3	45	30.0
70-79	16	28.1	11	27.5	25	47.2	52	34.7
Total	57		40		53		150	
Mean	60.5		58.8		64.9		62.2	

Table VI. Residential Mobility Patterns of Drug, Placebo, and Hospital Control Patients in 5-Year Period Before Admission

Number of Moves in 5 Years	*Drug*		*Placebo*		*Hospital Control*		*Total*	
	N	%	*N*	%	*N*	%	*N*	%
None	20	35.1	12	29.3	10	19.2	42	28.0
1	6	10.5	3	7.3	9	17.3	18	12.0
2	13	22.8	10	24.4	15	28.8	38	25.3
3	9	15.8	7	17.1	5	9.6	21	14.0
4	3	5.3	2	4.9	7	13.5	12	8.0
5	3	5.3	3	7.3	4	7.7	10	6.7
6	1	1.8	1	2.4	1	1.9	3	2.0
7	0	–	1	2.4	0	–	1	0.7
8	0	–	0	–	1	1.9	1	0.7
9 or more	2	3.5	2	4.9	0	–	4	2.7
Total	57		41		52		150	

Table VII. Length of Residence at Current Address of Drug, Placebo, and Hospital Control Patients

Length of Residence at Present Address	*Drug*		*Placebo*		*Hospital Control*		*Total*	
	N	%	*N*	%	*N*	%	*N*	%
Under 1 year	14	25.0	15	38.5	22	41.5	51	34.5
1-3 years	10	17.8	10	25.6	11	20.8	31	20.9
4-10 years	20	35.7	4	10.3	15	28.3	39	26.4
11-19 years	7	12.5	8	20.5	3	5.7	18	12.2
20 or more years	5	8.9	2	5.1	2	3.8	9	6.1
Total	56		39		53		148	

Table VIII. Marital Status of Drug, Placebo, and Hospital Control Patients

Marital Status	*Drug*		*Placebo*		*Hospital Control*		*Total*	
	N	%	*N*	%	*N*	%	*N*	%
Married*	31	54.4	18	43.9	28	51.9	77	50.7
Single (never married)	14	24.6	11	26.8	9	16.7	34	22.4
Other	12	21.0	12	29.3	17	31.5	41	26.9
Total	57		41		54		152	

*Includes stable common law.

Table IX. Length of Last or Most Recent Marriage of Drug, Placebo, and Hospital Control Patients

Last Marriage	*Drug*		*Placebo*		*Hospital Control*		*Total*	
	N	*%*	*N*	*%*	*N*	*%*	*N*	*%*
Under 1 year	3	7.0	2	6.7	5	11.4	10	8.5
1-5 years	8	18.6	4	13.3	10	22.7	22	18.8
6-10 years	6	14.0	7	23.3	8	18.2	21	17.9
11-20 years	14	32.6	11	36.7	18	40.9	43	36.8
Over 20 years	12	27.9	6	20.0	3	6.8	21	17.9
Total	43		30		44		117	

Table X. Number of Children Born to Married Drug, Placebo, and Hospital Control Patients

Number of Children	*Drug*		*Placebo*		*Hospital Control*		*Total*	
	N	%	*N*	%	*N*	%	*N*	%
0	6	14.0	3	10.0	11	24.4	20	16.9
1	9	20.9	5	16.7	7	15.6	21	17.8
2	4	9.3	6	20.0	9	20.0	19	16.1
3	8	18.6	6	20.0	8	17.8	22	18.6
4	5	11.6	2	6.7	2	4.4	9	7.6
5	4	9.3	3	10.0	5	11.1	12	10.2
6–9	7	16.3	5	16.7	3	6.7	15	12.7
Total	43		30		45		118	
Mean	3.07		3.03		2.29		2.76	

Table XI. Number of Previous Hospitalizations of Drug, Placebo, and Hospital Control Patients

Number of Previous Hospitalizations	*Drug*		*Placebo*		*Hospital Control*		*Total*	
	N	%	*N*	%	*N*	%	*N*	%
None	11	19.3	10	24.4	8	15.1	29	19.2
1-2	31	54.4	15	36.6	25	47.2	71	47.0
3 or more	15	26.3	16	39.0	20	37.8	51	33.8
Total	57		41		53*		151*	
Mean	1.93		2.02		2.28		2.08	

*The exact number of hospitalizations of one patient is unknown.

Table XII. Number of Patients under Previous Outpatient Care in Drug, Placebo, and Control Groups

	Drug		*Placebo*		*Hospital Control*		*Total*	
	N	%	*N*	%	*N*	%	*N*	%
Outpatient care	25	43.9	16	39.0	18	33.3	59	38.8
No outpatient care	32	56.1	25	61.0	36	66.7	93	61.2
Total	57		41		54		152	

Table XIII. Mean Problems Score and Percentage of Patients in Drug, Placebo, and Hospital Control Groups Evidencing Each of 22 Behaviors

	Drug (*N*=44)	*Placebo* (*N*=33)	*Hospital Control* (*N*=43)
Mean Problems Score	33.2	32.8	32.1
Trouble at night	72.7	63.6	67.4
Nursing problem	11.3	18.1	15.2
Source of worry	51.2	48.5	50.1
Worry about safety of others	24.9	27.2	27.9
Uncooperative	47.7	39.3	60.4
Strain on others	54.5	36.3	41.9
Patient's behavior upsetting	60.0	48.4	69.0
Bodily symptoms been of concern	52.2	60.6	60.3
Sexual problem	34.0	27.2	24.6
Odd speech and ideas	71.9	72.7	69.7
Caused trouble with neighbors	15.9	18.1	16.3
Upset household work and routine	61.2	42.3	52.5
Interfere with social activities	29.4	21.1	22.2
Had to stay away from work with patient	36.1	21.7	20.6
Stay away from school because of patient	37.5	19.0	14.3
Caused you concern generally	83.9	81.8	74.4
Physical strain on significant other	56.8	63.6	51.1
Requires excessive amount of attention	54.5	36.3	37.2
Children ashamed of patient	10.7	17.4	4.3
Children afraid of patient	6.9	16.0	9.1
Significant other ashamed of patient	18.2	9.1	16.3
Significant other afraid of patient	11.4	18.3	6.9

Table XIV. Percentage of Female Drug, Placebo, and Hospital Control Patients Wholly or Partly Unable to Perform Specified Household Activities

	Drug (N=37)	*Placebo* (N=28)	*Hospital Control* (N=38)
Mean Domestic Performance Score	13.8	15.9	14.0
Attend to house cleaning chores	52.8	42.3	60.5
Prepare meals	50.0	40.7	51.4
Attend to laundry and cleaning	47.1	32.0	52.8
Shop for groceries	55.2	45.5	54.5
Other shopping (clothing, etc.)	43.8	32.0	47.2
Budget for the household	50.0	43.5	56.7
Plan daily activities	61.8	32.1	34.2
Solve daily problems	62.9	40.7	64.9

Table XV. Percentage of Drug, Placebo, and Hospital Control Patients Participating in Various Activities in Month Preceding Hospitalization

	Drug	*Placebo*	*Hospital Control*
Went to the movies	27.3	32.5	15.7
Read books	32.7	27.5	47.2
Read magazines	47.3	69.4	51.9
Worked on a hobby	20.0	10.5	25.9
Wrote letters	36.5	36.8	34.0
Read newspaper	58.9	59.5	64.8
Went to church	45.5	44.7	35.2
Watched TV or listened to radio	76.4	81.6	74.1
Visited relatives or friends	61.8	68.4	60.4
Entertained relatives or friends	48.2	47.4	42.6
Attended club or organization meetings	10.7	17.9	3.7
Went shopping	57.1	55.6	53.7
Played cards or other games	34.0	18.4	24.1
Involved in athletic activities	18.5	7.9	7.5
Watched a spectator sport	9.1	5.3	5.6

Table XVI. Point in Study Intake and Success

	Drug			Placebo			Total		
Time Period	*Number of Successes*	*Total Number of Risk*	*Percentage of Successes*	*Number of Successes*	*Total Number of Risk*	*Percentage of Successes*	*Number of Successes*	*Total Number of Risk*	*Percentage of Successes*
First 6 months	12	18	67	6	14	43	18	32	56
Second 6 months	30	30	100	10	16	63	40	46	87
Third 6 months	42	51	82	13	25	52	55	76	72
Fourth 6 months	44	49	90	14	18	78	58	67	87

Table XVII. Age Distribution of Community Drug and Placebo Cases

	Drug		*Placebo*		*Total*	
	N	%	*N*	%	*N*	%
Under 20	0	–	2	8.7	2	3.8
20-29	8	27.6	8	34.8	16	30.8
30-39	15	51.7	5	21.7	20	38.5
40-49	3	10.3	6	26.1	9	17.3
50-59	3	10.3	2	8.7	5	9.6
Total	29		23		52	
Mean	34.7		33.5		34.2	

Table XVIII. Sex Distribution of Community Drug and Placebo Patients

	Drug		*Placebo*		*Total*	
	N	%	*N*	%	*N*	%
Male	9	31.0	7	30.4	16	30.8
Female	20	69.0	16	69.6	36	69.2
Total	20		23		52	

Table XIX. Racial Distribution of Community Drug and Placebo Cases

	Drug		*Placebo*		*Total*	
	N	%	*N*	%	*N*	%
White	20	69.0	16	69.6	36	69.2
Negro	9	31.0	7	30.4	16	30.8
Total	29		23		52	

Table XX. Educational Attainments of Community Drug and Placebo Patients

	Drug		*Placebo*		*Total*	
	N	%	*N*	%	*N*	%
0-6th grade	4	13.8	1	4.3	5	9.6
Junior high or partial high school	11	37.9	12	52.2	23	44.2
High school graduate	9	31.0	8	34.8	17	32.7
Partial college	4	13.8	1	4.3	5	9.6
College and postgraduate	1	3.4	1	4.3	2	3.8
Total	29		23		52	

Table XXI. Hollingshead Index of Social Position Scores of Community Drug and Placebo Patients

HI Score	*Drug* N	%	*Placebo* N	%	*Total* N	%
10-19	0	–	1	4.3	1	1.9
20-29	4	13.8	0	–	4	7.7
30-39	1	3.4	0	–	1	1.9
40-49	6	20.7	5	21.7	11	21.2
50-59	4	13.8	3	13.0	7	13.5
60-69	6	20.7	7	30.4	13	25.0
70-79	8	27.6	7	30.4	15	28.8
Total	29		23		52	
Mean	57.2		60.2		58.5	

Table XXII. Residential Mobility Patterns of Community Patients in 5-Year Period Before ITC Admission

	Drug N	%	*Placebo* N	%	*Total* N	%
None	4	14.8	4	17.4	8	16.0
1	3	11.1	1	4.3	4	8.0
2	6	22.2	4	17.4	10	20.0
3	6	22.2	5	21.7	11	22.0
4	3	11.1	2	8.7	5	10.0
5 or more	5	18.5	7	30.5	12	24.0
Total	27		23		50	
No data	2				2	

Table XXIII. Marital Status of Community Drug and Placebo Patients

	Drug		*Placebo*		*Total*	
	N	%	*N*	%	*N*	%
Married	20	69.0	13	56.5	33	63.5
Single (never married)	5	17.2	5	21.7	10	19.2
Widowed, separated, and divorced	4	13.8	5	21.7	9	17.3
Total	29		23		52	

Table XXIV. Number of Children Born to Married Community Drug and Placebo Patients

	Drug		*Placebo*		*Total*	
	N	%	*N*	%	*N*	%
None	5	20.9	2	11.1	7	16.7
1	2	8.3	5	27.8	7	16.7
2	3	12.5	3	16.7	6	14.3
3	3	12.5	2	11.1	5	11.9
4	5	20.9	4	22.2	9	21.4
5 or more	6	25.0	2	11.1	8	19.0
Total	24		18		42	

Table XXV. Mean Problems Score and Percentage of Patients in Community Drug and Placebo Groups Evidencing Each of 22 Behaviors

	Drug (N=29)	*Placebo (N=23)*
Mean Problems Score	31.7	33.7
Trouble at night	55.6	57.2
Nursing problem	11.1	0.0
Source of worry	44.5	38.1
Worry about safety of others	18.5	38.1
Uncooperative	48.1	57.2
Strain on others	46.2	40.0
Patient's behavior upsetting	40.8	57.2
Bodily symptoms been of concern	81.5	66.7
Sexual problem	25.9	35.0
Odd speech and ideas	55.6	70.0
Caused trouble with neighbors	18.5	10.0
Upsets household work and routine	44.5	80.0
Interferes with social activities	40.9	33.3
Had to stay away from work with patient	45.5	41.2
Stay away from school because of patient	27.3	21.4
Caused you concern generally	81.5	95.2
Physical strain on significant other	55.6	76.2
Requires excessive amount of attention	51.9	52.4
Children ashamed of patient	0.0	21.4
Children afraid of patient	23.5	33.3
Significant other ashamed of patient	7.4	23.8
Significant other afraid of patient	7.4	19.1

Table XXVI. Mean Domestic Performance Score and Percentage of Females in Ambulatory Drug and Placebo Groups Wholly or Partly Unable to Perform Specified Household Tasks

	Drug (N=20)	*Placebo (N=16)*
Mean Domestic Performance Score	17.0	16.8
Attend to housecleaning chores	45.0	31.2
Prepare meals	36.8	37.5
Attend to laundry and cleaning	47.4	33.3
Shop for groceries	41.2	27.3
Other shopping	38.9	33.3
Budget for the household	53.8	37.5
Plan daily activities	33.3	33.3
Solve daily problems	45.0	31.2

Table XXVII. Percentage of Community Drug and Placebo Patients Participating in Various Activities in Month Prior to ITC Admission

	Drug (N=29)	*Placebo (N=23)*
Went to movies	27.6	26.1
Read books	58.6	56.5
Read magazines	65.5	72.7
Worked on a hobby	37.9	30.4
Wrote letters	41.4	45.5
Read newspaper	93.1	77.3
Went to church	48.3	52.2
Watched TV or listened to radio	78.6	95.4
Visited relatives or friends	79.3	72.7
Entertained relatives or friends	60.7	45.5
Attended club or organizational meetings	33.3	36.4
Went shopping	58.6	63.6
Played card or other games	35.7	52.2
Involved in athletic activities	20.7	17.4
Watched a spectator sport	13.8	9.1

INDEX